THE BIG Enid Blyton BOOK

PAUL HAMLYN · LONDON

CONTENTS

	Page
A LETTER FROM ENID BLYTON	8
HURRY, SECRET SEVEN, HURRY!	14
WHEN MOTHER LOOKS OUT OF THE WINDOW	18
MR. PINK-WHISTLE HAS SOME FUN	20
THE SPIDER'S WEB	23
JESUS AND THE CHILDREN	25
LET'S HAVE A CLUB OF OUR OWN (1)	26
A MAP OF FAIRYLAND	28
NATURE QUIZ (1): THE FOUR BIRD-WATCHERS	32
WOLVES IN THE NIGHT!	36
THINGS TO MAKE ON A RAINY AFTERNOON (1): MISS HANNAH'S WINDMILL	46
RAMBLES WITH UNCLE NAT (1) LAMBS AND LAMBS' TAILS	48
JUST A SPOT OF BOTHER!	50
THE LITTLE GOOSEBERRY MAN	54
RAMBLES WITH UNCLE NAT (2): POND DWELLERS	62
FLASH THE PONY	64
A DAY WITH LITTLE NODDY	67
THE LAND OF NURSERY RHYME: A PLAY IN TWO ACTS	69
THE RUBADUB MYSTERY	78
RAMBLES WITH UNCLE NAT (3) THE LITTLE MINER	88
THE ANIMALS' PRAYER	90
MAKING A BIRD-CAKE	91
ZERELDA'S UNFORTUNATE REHEARSAL	93
MAWKINS THE HARE	98
LET'S HAVE A CLUB OF OUR OWN (2)	102
THE LITTLE DAUGHTER OF JAIRUS	107
BRER RABBIT'S CLEVER TRICK	111
FIVE — AND A HALF-TERM ADVENTURE!	115
RAMBLES WITH UNCLE NAT (4): THE BRILLIANT LEAVES	122
THE SLEEPERS: A PUZZLE POEM	124
PLEASE HELP ME, MR. PINK-WHISTLE!	125
WALNUT SHELLS	126
THINGS TO MAKE ON A RAINY AFTERNOON (2): MISS HANNAH'S RED INDIAN HATS	130
T. P. S. O.	130
TWO LITTLE PUZZLES	131
BEWARE THE BEARS!	132
LULLABY	135
THE LAND OF FAR-BEYOND	136
RIDDLE ME REE	137
NODDY AND THE LITTLE WOODEN HORSE	140
THE GANG	142
MAGIC	145

Page

HE COULDN'T DO IT! 146
THE WHISTLER 152
RAMBLES WITH UNCLE NAT (5): TRACKS IN THE SNOW 156
THE STORY OF THE CHRISTMAS TREE 158
MR. TWIDDLE AND THE DOG 162
FIRE-EATING AND OTHER THINGS! 165
THE LUCKY DUCKS 166
THE FOUR WISE MEN AND THE SERVANT 169
THE SECRET ISLAND 170
THINGS TO MAKE ON A RAINY AFTERNOON (3): MISS HANNAH'S ROUNDABOUT 178
LOONY THE SPANIEL 180
FIVE GO OFF IN A CARAVAN 181
THE FIRST WILD ROSE 182
GOOFY ISN'T VERY CLEVER 188
RAMBLES WITH UNCLE NAT (6): A LITTLE TWIGGING 190
MAMZELLE'S "TREEK" 192
NATURE QUIZ (2): A BUNCH OF FLOWERS 196
MR. GOON IS ASTOUNDED 202
FOXGLOVE FAIRIES 207
BIRDS AND FLOWERS IN APRIL 207
A LITTLE AQUARIUM 213
BOM 214
THE HUMBUG ADVENTURE 218
MISS NAN NOCKABOUT 220
YOU'RE TOO SMART, BRER RABBIT! 222
THE BONFIRE AT NIGHT 226
ON DORSET HILLS 228
ENID BLYTON'S FOUR CLUBS FOR CHILDREN 229
A NIGHT ON THUNDER ROCK 230
THE MYSTERY OF THE VANISHED PRINCE 238
NEXT-DOOR JAMES 240
A LIST OF BOOKS BY ENID BLYTON 243

ACKNOWLEDGEMENTS

Enid Blyton would like to join the publishers of her Anthology in thanking all those publishers of her books who have kindly given permission for extracts to be reproduced: Arthur Barker Limited; Basil Blackwell Limited; The Brockhampton Press Limited; William Collins, Sons & Company Limited; Evans Brothers Limited; Hodder & Stoughton Limited; Sampson Low, Marston & Company Limited; The Lutterworth Press; Macdonald & Company Limited; Macmillan & Company Limited; Methuen & Company Limited; The National Magazine Company Limited; George Newnes Limited; The Sunday Dispatch; The Sunday Times. Details of the extracts will be found in the complete list of Enid Blyton's books on page 243.

Published by PAUL HAMLYN - Spring House - Spring Place - London N W 5

Printed in Czechoslovakia

A letter from ENID BLYTON

(Photograph by Dorothy Wilding)

Dear Boys and Girls,

Many thousands of you write to me during the year, and, alas, it is not always possible for me to send an answer to each letter. But now I have a chance to send you a personal letter in this book, and to thank you for all the interesting, amusing and loving letters you have sent me, week after week; and also I want to say that I could not possibly have done without the generous help that so many of you give me with the four great charities we help between us. Few people besides myself know of the kindly, unselfish ways in which you raise money — yes, thousands of pounds! — for children not so lucky as yourselves, and for sick or injured animals. These generous children are not only my readers, they are my friends and comrades.

Now about this book. The publishers thought that the idea of a book like this was completely their own — but it wasn't, you know! It has been the idea of many of you children throughout the last few years. It is called an Anthology, which means a collection of writing — verses, stories, anything that is written to be read. You children did not call it an Anthology when you thought of the idea — you called it various names, and one of the best names sent by a twelve-year-old girl was "A dip-into book — a book with all the characters we know, Miss Blyton, so that we can open the book anywhere and dip into it, and meet the Famous Five again, and Kiki the parrot, and Fatty and all the rest." Another of you, a teen-age boy, called it a "Reminder Book", when he spoke about the idea. "I'd like a book — a big one, please — that will remind me of so many of the books I loved." Well, here it is. I couldn't get into it *all* the characters you know so well, but I have tried to choose the ones I think you know best.

In the thousands of letters you send me, the same questions appear again and again. "How did you begin to write, Miss Blyton — and why did you choose to write for *children?*" "How do you think of your characters? Are they real?" "Where is Kirrin Island?" "Is Kiki the parrot a *real* parrot?" "Where do the Five really live? I would so like to meet George." And so on, and so on. Questions come about practically every book I have written, and the characters seem as real to you as they are to me when I write the books. Now that I have the chance I am going to answer a few of your questions.

I began to write because it was what I most loved doing, and because I had what all real story-tellers must have — imagination. I am happiest when I am telling a story — a story with plenty of life-like characters, with excitement, fun, and a really good mystery or adventure that I myself enjoy sharing with the characters. I almost feel as if I were one of them, there with them, seeing what they see, sharing their inmost feelings. All real story-tellers feel this, of course.

Born story-tellers are very fortunate. They do not have to think out or plan their stories — their characters spring into their mind, alive and real, and seem to lead a life of their own, which can be watched and listened to by the author almost as if he or she were watching them on a cinema screen. Sometimes you say to me — "How do you *begin* a story, Miss Blyton? Do you think it all out first?" No — I shut my real eyes, and look into my *mind's* eye — and almost at once I see my characters — yes, as clearly as I would see you! I hear their voices, their conversations — and very soon the whole story is being acted out in my mind's eye, and my quick fingers tap out what I see, on my little typewriter (usually on my knee!). Does one of the characters have a crooked nose? I see it clearly, and it goes into the story. Does one have a merry, infectious laugh? I hear it, and so will you, when you read the book! The story unravels itself like a skein of wool, and I myself do not know what is going to happen, any more than you do. This makes the story just as exciting for me as for you! Sometimes when I have finished writing for the day, perhaps leaving the characters in some great difficulty, I say to myself, "Good gracious! Poor things, I simply do not know how they will ever get out of this!" But next day, when the characters once more come alive in my mind's eye, hey presto, they set to work to get out of their fix in some miraculous way of their own. And I think to myself, "Well, well — I'd *never* have thought of that myself!" And I am just as much relieved at their escape as you are when you eventually read the story!

A few of my characters are not wholly imaginary, but are based on real people who have happened to make an impression on me. "George", for instance — the girl tomboy called Georgina (George) in the "Five" books, with her dog Tim-

The view through the rose pergola in Enid Blyton's garden at Green Hedges.

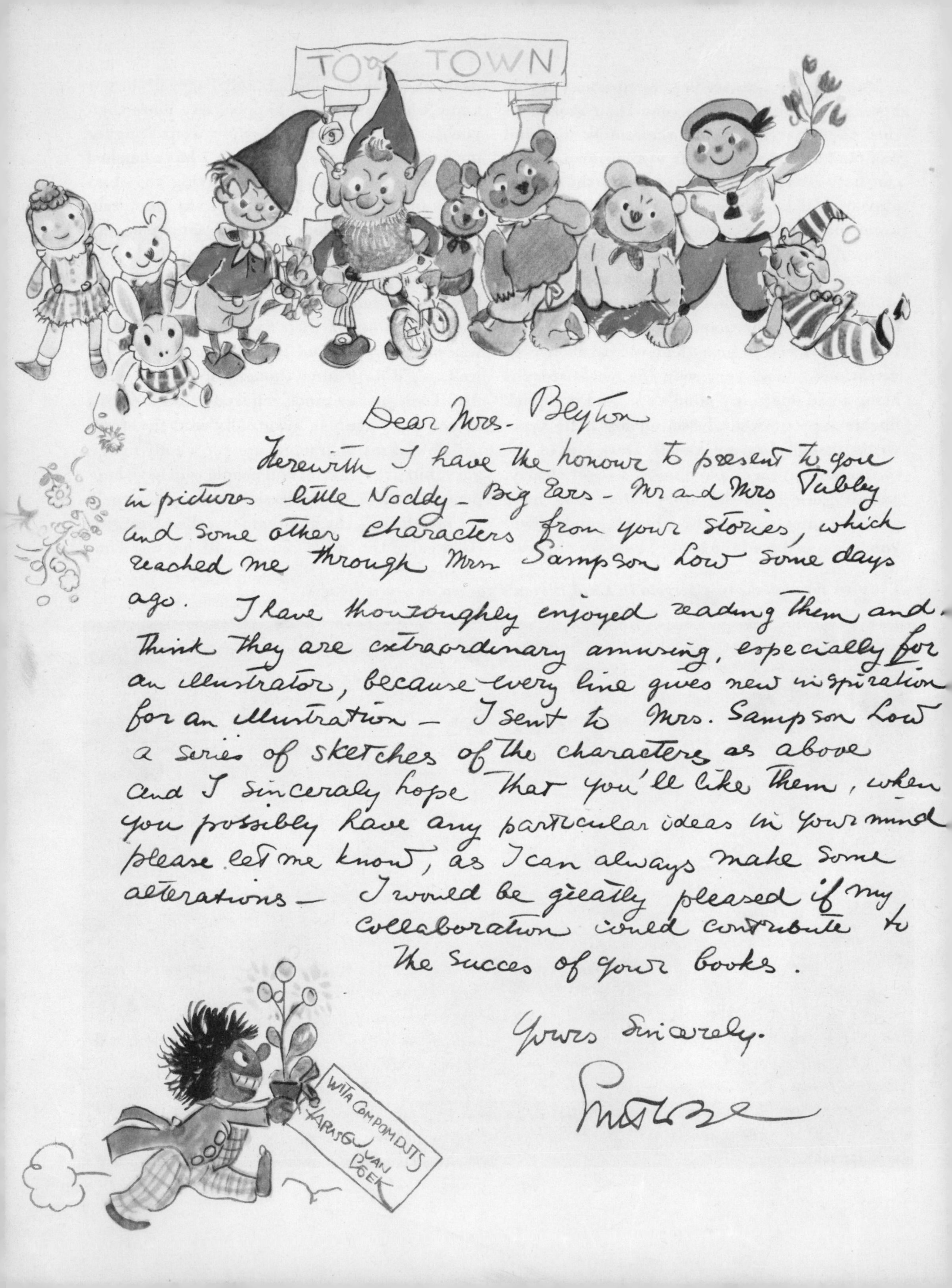

Dear Mrs. Blyton

Herewith I have the honour to present to you in pictures little Noddy - Big Ears - Mr and Mrs Tubby and some other characters from your stories, which reached me through Mrs Sampson Low some days ago. I have thoutoughely enjoyed reading them and think they are extraordinary amusing, especially for an illustrator, because every line gives new inspiration for an illustration - I sent to Mrs. Sampson Low a series of sketches of the characters as above and I sinceraly hope that you'll like them, when you possibly have any particular ideas in your mind please let me know, as I can always make some alterations - I would be greatly pleased if my collaboration could contribute to the succes of your books.

Yours sincerely.

my. She fiercely wanted to be a boy, and acted all the time as if she really were. And then one day I suddenly found her appearing in the first "Five" book! The real George had become a story-George! Fatty, in the Mystery books, is based on a plump, ingenious, very amusing boy I once knew. Kiki, the parrot in the Adventure series, was real, and said the most ridiculous things, just like the parrot in the books. Most of the animals in my tales are also based on real ones — or mixtures of real ones — that I have known and loved. I do not, however, *deliberately* put these children or animals into my stories — I do not say, "Oh — I'll put that amusing boy into my next book!" He will probably appear in some book of mine one day when I am not thinking of him at all, and I shall say — "WELL! That's the boy I watched at the seaside two years ago, sticking-out ears and all!" Or maybe a comical monkey will suddenly come into a story I am writing, and I stop and exclaim out loud, "Little monkey — you are the one I saw years ago with the man who had the barrel-organ. You sat on top, and twisted your tail lovingly round the man's neck, and whispered in his ear. And here you are again, large as life, though I'd forgotten all about you! You've been hidden deep in my mind until today!"

Another question the younger ones ask me is about little Noddy. "He *is* real, isn't he?" they say. "We'd like to go and see him, please. Where is Toyland? Can we go there in the train?"

Noddy isn't real, of course — though he is alive to me when I write about him, and I can hear his high little voice as clearly as I hear the child next door calling to his mother. I will tell you how I first thought of Noddy. It happened one day when I went to see one of my publishers. He was busy looking through a big book of pictures sent to him by a Dutch firm who wondered if any of their artists' work could be used in England.

I happened to catch sight of one page — and saw many small figures in colour there — odd, amusing, friendly, delightful — and I gazed at them, enchanted. Why, here was someone whose imagination saw the same kind of things as mine did — someone who drew characters exactly as *I* would have liked to draw them, if I had been able to! And without thinking, I said quickly to the publisher, "Look — this man is a genius! He could draw exactly the kind of pictures I want for some of my stories! If only I could do a *book* with him!"

And quick as lightning the publisher replied, "Right! You think of the book, and write it — and we'll send it to the artist. He is a Dutchman and his name is Van Beek. What sort of a book do you think you could do with him?"

And into my mind, life-like and real, came for the first time the figure of little Noddy, in Toyland — with Big-Ears his friend beside him, and a host of other amusing little characters, bobbing all about.

"We'll make a book about a little wooden man — called Noddy, because he nods his head up and down — and he can live in Toyland, and have a friend called Big-Ears," I said. "And there will be the Tubby Bears, and Micky Monkey, and the Wobbly-Man, and . . ."

"That's settled, then," said the publisher. "Just let me have the book as soon as you can."

So I wrote the first Noddy book as Toyland came alive in my mind's eye, peopled with all the folk you know so well.

Off went the book to Holland, to the Dutch artist, Van Beek, and back it came, very quickly indeed — and just as I had thought, the artist's mind's eye saw Noddy and his

WHEN I had sent the first Noddy book to Van Beek, the Dutch artist I told you about (see this page), he at once sent me a joyful letter, and at the top he painted Noddy, Big-Ears and the rest, for the very first time — exactly as I myself had imagined them to be. I was so pleased that I kept the letter and treasured it, and I thought you might like to see it too. It is seldom that a writer and an artist can work together so closely, seeing the same things in the same way.

friends, and Toyland, just as mine had seen them. It is very odd to think that I would never have pictured Noddy in my mind if I hadn't glimpsed Van Beek's drawings that day. Funny little Noddy — where in the world did you *really* come from?

In the summer time I write mostly in my garden, my typewriter on my knee. I watch the goldfish jumping in my ponds — they are so tame they will feed out of my fingers, and will even come and nuzzle against them when I have no food. My two cats come with me, and dab at the water, shaking their paws in disgust when they feel the wetness. They are with me at this moment, solemnly lying beside me, watching my busy fingers . . . ah, one has leapt down to chase a butterfly. Now they have both gone indoors, and the garden birds will soon come flying down again. We have so many here, of all kinds — even kingfishers and a long-legged heron who sometimes comes early in the dewy morning to catch my goldfish! The kingfisher catches them too, but he can only manage the tiny ones. I know when the heron is by the pond, for he wakes me by saying, "Kronk-kronk!"

The birds nest everywhere in my garden, in spite of the cats. Blackbirds, thrushes, chaffinches, blue tits in the nesting-boxes, great-tits, hedge sparrows, wrens, starlings, fly-catchers — what an array I see when I feed them in the mornings! The nuthatch comes for the nuts on the hazel-trees, and the little tree-creeper runs up and down and round and round the trunks of many a garden tree. I could write a whole book about the small visitors, feathered and furred (or prickled, like the hedgehog who comes each night) who live secretly and happily in the garden of Green Hedges.

And now I want to talk about just one more thing before I end — and that is the great pleasure I have from the help you give me with our four Clubs. These have been going for years, as you know, and perhaps the best-known one is the Famous Five Club, whose 115,000 members help me with the little Children's Home in Beaconsfield, where I live. Here we take thirty small children, all under five — those who have been ill, and need care — those whose mothers are in hospital, or, alas, have deserted them — children who have been half-starved, and so on. This Club began not only because so many children were fond of the "Five" books, and

Listening to Enid Blyton telling a story.

wanted a club and a badge — but because a great number said, "Miss Blyton, I *would* like to do something for you, because you've written so many books for me." And I said, "Then please help me with this little Children's Home!" So you set to work and soon so many thousands of you helped me by earning money in countless ways to buy cots and toys and little tables and

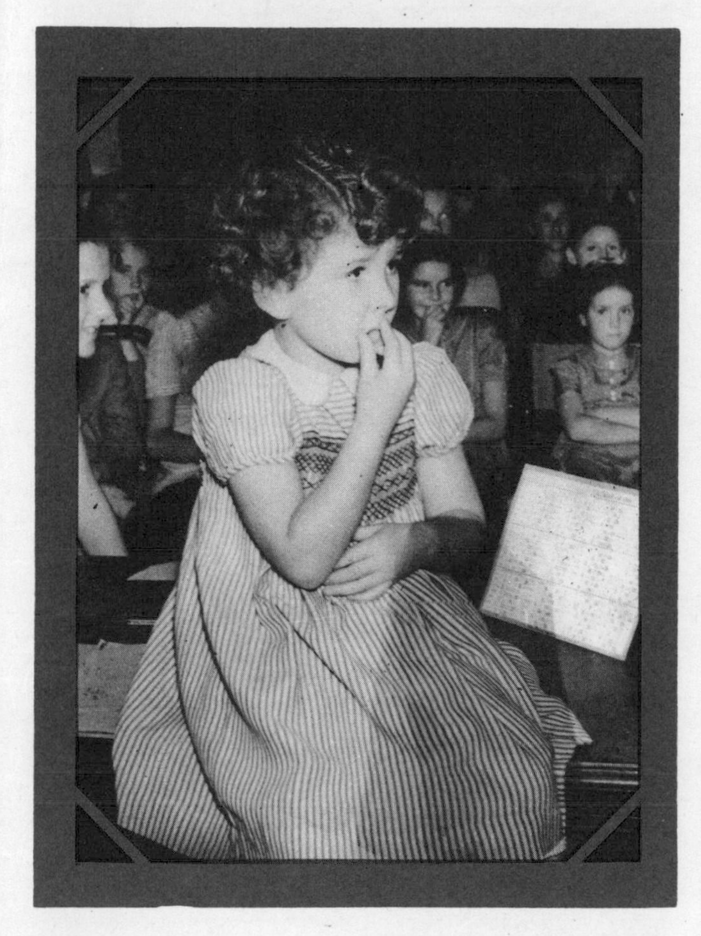

chairs, that now we have the loveliest little Home for miles around! We even have a ward called "The Famous Five Ward"! How did you earn the money? In ways too many to mention! Some of you did the washing-up for sixpence a week, or did the shopping; boys often took neighbours' dogs for walks, and earned money that way. Many prepared shows and concerts, held little sales, collected and sold old newspapers, picked wild flowers, bunched them and sold them . . . I really haven't space to list all the good work done, not only by the members of the Famous Five Club, but also by the thousands of children belonging to my Sunbeam Society, who earn money for the little ones in the Sunshine Homes for Blind Children; and by those who try to help me with the Centre for Spastic Children, in Chelsea, for which you may have heard me broadcast at times. And then there are those 200,000 children and more who are my Busy Bees, the Youth Section of the grand P.D.S.A., all animal-lovers, who in dozens and dozens of different ways earn money for our Animal Dispensaries, and for our own Busy Bees Caravan, which helps so many sick or injured animals.

I am prouder of these children than I am of anything else, and I am glad that, because of my books, I have this great army of helpers, kindly and generous, not only in this country, but all over the world. I would like to have even more, so if you have a really kind heart (and your mother will tell you at once, if you have!) look on page 227, where you will see how to join any of our fine clubs, if you would like to.

What a long letter — but I thought you would like to know something about this Anthology, and something about the author too — just as I love to know about *you*. You will recognize many of the extracts, of course, because they are taken mostly from books you know well (though a few I have specially written for you), but if you want to be certain what book the extract comes from, look up the list of my books at the end of the Anthology. I hope you will enjoy this book as much as I enjoyed writing for you all the books from which it is made — and if there is any special new book you badly want me to write — well, just let me know!

My love and best wishes to you all,

Enid Blyton

The Secret Seven, as most of you will know from the books about them, are seven children who have formed a Club of their own. Here is a story about them, and their golden spaniel, Scamper.

THE Secret Seven had been out together for a picnic. Scamper was with them, his tail wagging happily. He loved being alone with Peter and Janet — but it was even better to be with the whole of the Seven! There was always somebody fussing about him then, patting him, or talking to him.

"Well, I must say the baskets weigh a lot lighter coming *home* from a picnic than *going* to one!" said Janet, swinging hers to and fro. "Oooh, sorry, Colin — I didn't know you were just behind me."

"You'd better give that basket to Scamper to carry," said Colin. "That's three times you've banged me with it."

"Shall we go home through the fields or through the town?" said Peter.

"Through the town!" said everyone. They were all thinking the same thing — what about a call at the ice-cream shop?

So they went back through the town. It was market-day and the streets were full. People rushed about here and there, carrying parcels, calling to one another, and the cars had to go very slowly indeed because there were so many people walking in the road.

A man came down the street, cycling quickly. He rang his bell as if he were in a great hurry, and people tried to get out of the way. Peter just skipped to one side in time as the man cycled past. He turned to stare after him indignantly. "He almost knocked me over," began Peter, and then stopped. Even as he spoke, something had happened.

CRASH! The man on the bicycle had bumped into a car and had been flung off into the road. A woman gave a loud scream and people hurried up at once.

The children ran to see what had happened. The man lay there, half-dazed, his head badly

"Who was the man? Do you know?"

bruised, and his cheek cut. A policeman came up.

"He was going so *fast*," said a woman near-by. "He kept shouting to people to get out of the way. He was in an awful hurry and didn't seem to see that car."

The man tried to speak and the policeman bent town. He listened hard and looked puzzled.

"Is his name Gate?" asked Janet.

"He keeps saying 'Gate,' " he said. "Is that his name? Does anyone know?"

More people crowded up and the policeman began to send them off. "Now, now — move away," he said. "Ah, here's a doctor. *Will* you move away, you kids? Give the poor fellow a chance."

The Secret Seven moved off with all the other children who had crowded round. "I'll never again ride *my* bicycle fast," said Barbara. "I never will, now I've seen how suddenly accidents can happen."

"Who was the man? Do you know?" asked Peter.

"I've never seen him before," said Pam.

"Well, I seem to know his face," said George, puzzled. "Yes, I know I do. But I just can't think *who* he is."

"*I* think I've seen him before, too," said Jack, frowning. "I've watched him doing something. What on earth can it be?"

"Oh, never mind," said Pam. "What does it matter? He's in safe hands now, with a policeman there and a doctor."

"I just *can't* remember," said George. "It's no good. I sort of feel he's something to do with the railway. He's not one of the porters, is he?"

"No," said Jack, who knew all the porters because he so often went to meet his father at the station.“ He's not a porter — he's not the ticket-clerk either, or the station-master. All the same, I can't help thinking you're right — he *is* something to do with the railway."

"Oh, stop bothering about it," said Pam. 'I want to forget the accident. It was horrid."

They walked along, swinging their baskets and bags, Peter and Colin arguing about football,

The seven children raced down the road and there stretched the railway-line.

and the three girls listening. Suddenly George interrupted.

"I know! I've remembered who that man is!" he said. "And we're right — he *is* something to do with the railway."

"Is his name Gate?" asked Janet.

"No," said George. " 'Gate' is part of his work, though. He's the man who opens and shuts the gate at the railway-crossing! You know — we've often watched him coming out of his little cottage and swinging the big gates open, one after the other — and then shutting them over the line when the train has passed."

"Oh *yes* — of course! You're right," said Jack. "It's Williams, the level-crossing man!"

"I *say* — I hope there's someone at his cottage who will open the gates for the next train!" said Peter, stopping suddenly. "That's why he was in such a tremendous hurry, I expect. He wanted to get back in time to open the gates."

"The six-fifteen is due soon," said Colin. "My father's on it!"

"Let's go back quickly and tell the policeman!" said Janet, suddenly feeling scared at the thought of a train racing along the lines and crashing into closed crossing-gates.

"No time," said Peter, looking at his watch. Then, like a good leader, he made up his mind quickly. "This may be serious," he said. "If there's no one at Williams' cottage to open the gates for the next train, there'll certainly be a smash. Even if the train doesn't rock off the lines, those big gates will be smashed to pieces. Buck up — we'll run to the cottage and find out if anyone is there."

The seven children, with Scamper racing behind, barking excitedly, ran along the road and round the corner. Down the next road and up a little hill and down again — and there, some way in front of them, stretched the railway-line.

"Buck up!" panted Peter. "We're nearly there. We have still a few minutes before the train is due."

Peter reached the cottage first. It stood close beside the level-crossing, a pretty little place with a tiny garden of its own. Peter yelled as he ran up to it.

"Is there anyone at home! I say — is there anyone in?"

He banged at the door and then rang the bell beside it. Nobody answered. Nobody came. Then Colin ran to the window and looked inside.

"ANYONE IN?" he shouted at the top of his voice. He turned round. "The place is empty!" he said. "That's why Williams was biking so fast

Colin managed to open his gate first.

to get back. He hadn't left anyone to see to the gates!"

"And that's why he kept saying, 'Gate! Gate!' " said Janet. "What *are* we to do?"

"Open the gate ourselves, of course," said Peter, trying to be as calm as possible. He could see that the three girls were getting excited and alarmed. That would never do. Everyone must keep calm, everyone must help. Those gates were very, very heavy!

Colin looked round to see if anyone was near who could help them. A strong man would be most welcome! But not a soul was there except a small girl, who stared at them solemnly all the time.

"George, Janet! Come with me to the nearest gate and help me to open it!" shouted Peter. "Jack, you go to the other one with Pam and Barbara and Colin. And for goodness' sake make haste! The train's due in about a minute!"

"We must all look out for it!" shouted Colin. "It will be down on us at top speed before we know where we are!"

Soon all seven children were straining hard at the heavy gates. A great bolt had to be lifted from its hole in the ground first, and then an iron ring undone at the top of the post. It held the gate closed, and only when it was lifted back from the post would the gate open.

"I can hear the train!" yelled Janet, who had very sharp ears. "And the lines are beginning to tremble. Hurry, hurry!"

Colin, with three people to help him, managed to open his gate first and swing it slowly across the line and back, so that the way was clear. But Peter's bolt was stiff and took a good deal of easing up.

"The train's coming!" screamed Pam. "The train's coming! Get away, Peter, get away!"

Yes — the train was certainly coming. It whistled as it came roaring along, and when Peter looked up he could see it tearing down the line towards them.

With a last heave, he pulled the bolt out of its hole. Then, with all the others now helping, he swung the gate back as quickly as he could, only just in time. Pam screamed again as the engine raced past her, making quite a wind. A surprised fireman looked out of the engine-cab at the children on the line beside him. Then the long row of swaying carriages came rumbling past, making a truly enormous noise.

In a few moments the train was gone, racing away down the line, growing smaller and smaller every minute. Soon it would draw in at the station a mile away, and Colin's father would fold his evening paper and get out.

"I wonder if Dad saw me?" said Colin as the train rumbled away.

"I feel rather faint," said Barbara suddenly, and sat down against one of the gates. "Oh dear — how silly."

"It's just the excitement," said Peter, whose heart was thumping so hard in his chest that he found it quite difficult to speak. "My word, we didn't have much time. But we just did it!"

A shout came to their ears, and they turned. It was the policeman on a bicycle, with two or three men behind in a car.

"Hey — what are you doing on the lines, you children? Did anything happen to the gates?"

"No. We *just* managed to open them in time for the train," shouted back Peter.

"Well, I'm blessed," said the policeman, getting off his bicycle as the three men jumped out of their car.

Yes — the train was certainly coming.

It was a policeman on a bicycle.

"Did you remember the gates, when you found out who that man was who was knocked down?" asked Peter.

"Yes — the fellow managed to tell us at last," said the policeman. "I shot off at once — and these men came in their car as soon as they could. My word — when I saw the train racing by, I thought everything was up! I listened for the gates to be smashed — but no, the train just raced by as usual."

"You mean to say you kids opened them?" said one of the other men, astonished. "How did you think of such a thing?"

"We remembered who that man was — Williams, the crossing-gates man," said George. "Then we thought of the gates — and the train that was due — and we ran like hares to open them."

"We only *just* managed it," said Jack. "Whew — I'm dripping wet! They *were* heavy, those gates!"

"I'm melting, too!" said Barbara, who was still sitting down, but already looking a little better.

"Who *are* you children?" said another man, a big, burly fellow, looking at them hard. "You seem a jolly good bunch of kids, I must say! You've probably saved a nasty accident, you know!"

"We're the Secret Seven," said Peter proudly, and tapped his badge. "Ready to do any job of work, at any time!"

"So I see," said the man. "Well, I'm a railway official, so you can take it from me that you've saved us pounds and pounds of damage by opening those gates — besides possibly a horrid accident. The train *might* have swerved off the rails when it hit the gates."

"I'm jolly glad it didn't," said Colin. "My father's on that train! Wait till I tell him our tale tonight!"

"Well, before you do that, I'd like you to do

WHEN MOTHER LOOKS OUT OF THE WINDOW

When Mother looks out of the window,
She thinks she is just seeing me!
But she isn't — she's seeing a Captain
Sailing his ship on the sea!
Or maybe she's seeing a cowboy
Riding his horse all alone,

"We're the Secret Seven."

something else for me, if you will," said the big man, and winked at his two companions.

"What's that?" asked Peter, with visions of another exciting bit of work to do.

"Help me to eat a few ice-creams!" said the man. "You look so hot — you ought to cool down. And that would be a good way of doing it — don't you think so?"

"Oooh yes!" said everyone, and Barbara stood up at once. She felt quite prepared to eat three ice-creams if this man offered them!

The two men with him went to swing the gates back across the lines again, so that people might pass over on foot or in cars. The big man jumped into his car, and told the children to follow him to the ice-cream shop down the road.

Soon they were all sitting together, with such enormous ice-creams in front of them that they really couldn't believe their eyes.

"This is the biggest ice-cream I've ever had in my life," said Peter.

"You deserve it, old son," said the big man, who was eating an ice-cream, too. "How in the world did you open those gates in time? You had only a few minutes to race away from Williams, get down to the crossing, and swing back those heavy gates. I don't know *how* you did it!"

"Yes — you're right," said Peter, thinking about it. "*I* don't quite know how we did it, either. But the thing is — we *did* it!"

Well, that's really all that matters, Secret Seven. You saw what had to be done — and YOU DID IT!

"This is the biggest ice-cream I've ever had in my life!"

Or an Indian Chief in his feathers
Stalking a foe on his own.
She calls out, "Hey, Timmy, I want you!"
But Timmy (that's me) is away
I'm flying a plane, I'm a pilot,
I'm up in the clouds all day!
(It's only in bed that I'm Timmy,
Because it wouldn't be fair
For Mother to come up and kiss me
And find a Red Indian there!)

Mr. Pink-Whistle has some fun!

This is a tale of Mr. Pink-Whistle, the little man with pointed ears, who is half a brownie, and goes about the world putting wrong things right. He has a nice cat called Sooty. Here he is trying to help two children in trouble.

ONE day Mr. Pink-Whistle was sitting reading by the fire, when he heard a knock at his front door. It was rather a timid little knock — rat-a-tat-tat.

"Sooty," said Pink-Whistle to his big black cat, "see who's at the door, please."

Sooty scurried to the door and opened it. Outside stood two little girls, looking rather scared.

"Oh!" said one, when she saw Sooty, "this *must* be Mr. Pink-Whistle's house, because we know he has a cat called Sooty who looks after him. Please, are you Sooty?"

"That's my name," said Sooty. "Do come in."

The two little girls went in and wiped their feet very carefully on the mat. Sooty took them into the room where Mr. Pink-Whistle sat. He smiled at them.

"Oh, you're just *exactly* like Mr. Pink-Whistle in our stories!" said one little girl. "You are, really!"

"I'm glad," said Pink-Whistle. "As a matter of fact I always do look like myself, of course. What are your names?"

"I'm Katie and she's Jessie," said Katie. "And we've come to ask your help. We've heard so many stories about you, and how you go round the world putting wrong things right — so we thought we'd ask you to put something right for *us*. Will you, please, Mr. Pink-Whistle?"

"Of course," said Pink-Whistle. "Sooty, bring some biscuits and lemonade."

So, over biscuits and lemonade, the two little girls told kind Mr. Pink-Whistle their troubles, just as you would if you had something to tell him.

"That's my name," said Sooty. "Do come in."

"You see, it's like this," said Katie, "there are two boys in our village who are very cruel and unkind, Mr. Pink-Whistle. They throw stones at the cats and dogs, they take birds' eggs out of the nests, they hide round corners and jump out at us, and —"

"Yes, and they knock at doors and run away, and they go to the greengrocer's and take apples and oranges when he's not looking," said Jessie. "And, oh dear, lately they've been lying in wait for Katie and me and the other girls, and taking our dolls from us."

"And they *broke* my doll," said Katie, with tears in her eyes. "They dropped her on the pavement. So we've come to ask you if you could put things right for us. We are all getting so afraid of Tom and Len."

"I hope you don't think we're telling tales," said Jessie. "We just simply didn't know what to do. And now the two boys are frightening babies in their prams by booing at them when they pass. The worst of it is that their parents think they are wonderful boys and won't believe a word against them. So what are we to do?"

Mr. Pink-Whistle looked very solemn. He handed round the biscuits for the third time. "This is very serious," said. "Serious for you because you are frightened — and serious for the boys because they will grow up into just the kind of people we don't want. Hmmmmmm! I must certainly think of something."

"We knew you would," said Katie. "What will you do?"

"I don't quite know," said Pink-Whistle. "I'll think about it. I'd like it to be something that will teach the parents to be sensible about their boys, too. You know, as a rule, if children grow up bad it's the fault of the fathers and mothers."

"Yes, we've noticed that," said Katie. "If your mother is nice you're usually nice yourself. But if you've a horrid mother, you're horrid too. And a silly mother makes a boy or girl horrid, because they don't take any notice of her."

The clock struck four. Katie got up at once. "We must go," she said, "or we shall be late for tea. Mother will worry about us. Thank you, Mr. Pink-Whistle, for listening to us, and for the lemonade and biscuits."

"Yes, thank you very much," said Jessie.

"What a very nice mother you both must have!" said Pink-Whistle, shaking hands with them. "Now you needn't go red! You've just told me that nice mothers have nice children — and, as I can see you are both nice, I know what your mothers are like!"

The two little girls went away, excited and pleased. They trusted Mr. Pink-Whistle. He

The two little girls told kind Mr. Pink-Whistle their troubles.

would do something to stop those two boys and put things right.

He did! He thought and he thought, and then the next day he called Sooty. "I'm going off to that village the girls came from," he said. "I'm going to make myself invisible so that no one can see me. And I'm going to find those boys — and their parents, too — and give them a shock. I'll be back when my job is finished, Sooty."

"Very good, Master," said Sooty. "Just let me brush your hat for you. What a pity there aren't more people like you in the world, always trying to put bad things right!"

Pink-Whistle went off. Sooty couldn't see him when he got to the gate, because he had already made himself quite invisible. Ah, Pink-Whistle could see a lot of queer things going on when he was invisible —nobody knew he was there, then!

He soon found the two boys. He saw them hiding behind a wall, waiting for an old woman to come. They had water-pistols in their hands. Just as the old woman came round the wall the boys squirted their pistols.

The water went right into the old woman's face. She gasped, and dropped her basket. The eggs in it broke, and the yellow yolk dripped out on to the pavement.

"Oh! Oh! What is it? I've been shot! Oh, what has happened to me?" groaned the old woman, sitting down on the kerb with her head in her hands.

Pink- Whistle made sure that someone was coming to help her. Then he quickly followed the two boys, who had run away at once, laughing. They jumped on a bus. Pink-Whistle jumped on, too. Nobody saw him, of course, nobody at all. He sat down just behind the two boys, quite invisible.

He waited till the bus had started, then he spoke in a loud and angry voice.

"Which boys on this bus frightened an old lady just now? Who shot her with a water-pistol and made her drop her basket and break her eggs?"

There was a startled silence in the bus. All the passengers looked round to see who was speaking. The boys went red from their foreheads down to their necks, and hardly dared to breathe. Who knew all this? Was it a policeman?

"I can see those boys," said Pink-Whistle, in a loud and stern voice. "I CAN SEE THEM!"

In fright the two boys leapt off the bus. Pink-Whistle went too, though they didn't see him. "Now we've got to walk home," said one boy, crossly. "Who was that shouting at us in the bus?"

"Pooh! What does it matter?" said the other boy. "Come on, Len —let's ring a few door bells and run away!"

Pink-Whistle followed Len and Tom. They crept up to a front door and tugged at the bell. Then they ran away. They went to another door

In fright the two boys leapt off the bus.

and did the same thing. Pink-Whistle frowned. He walked behind them down the street.

When the boys came into the High Street, Pink-Whistle began to shout loudly again. "Where are those two boys who rang the bells and ran away? Where are they? Bring them here to be punished!"

Everyone was startled to hear this sudden voice coming from nowhere. As for the two boys, they were terrified! They looked all round, and people began to point at them. "They must be the two boys, look! Somebody must be after them!"

The boys fled at once. Pink-Whistle followed them, still invisible. Round the corner they met a small girl with a little puppy. Len pounced on the dog and the little girl screamed.

"Don't! Don't hurt him! He's only little!"

Tom took up an old tin lying in a nearby ditch and began to tie it to the tail of the frightened puppy. The little pup snapped at him and squealed. Len smacked it.

Pink-Whistle's voice boomed out again.

"Where are those boys? Where are those two bad boys?"

Len and Tom clutched at each other in fright. That voice again! Who was following them? They left the little girl and the scared puppy and ran at top speed down the road.

The little girl felt a kiss on her cheek, and something was pressed into her hand. "Go and buy yourself some sweets," said a kind voice in her ear — but there was nobody there — how very, very strange!

Pink-Whistle followed the boys. They both turned in at the same gate. "My mother and father are in with yours this afternoon," said Len. "We're all going to the pictures together tonight. So I can come in with you."

"Aha! Good!" thought Pink-Whistle, and he went in at the gate, too, round the back and in at the kitchen door with the two boys. They didn't see him, of course.

The boys slammed the door and clattered in without wiping their feet. Len went to the larder door and grinned at Tom. They both stuck their dirty fingers into a jar of jam and licked them. Then they took some plums out of a pie and ate those.

The SPIDER'S WEB

It hangs where daisies mauve
and white
Stand dreaming in the morning light,
A spider's web, a fairy thing
Whose threads to daisy-petals cling,
And quiver in the sunlit air;
And on the cobweb here and there
Round beads of amber dew are hung,
By elfin fingers deftly strung
Along each gleaming silver thread.
The hairy spider-witch has fled,
And crouches in a huddled heap,
Beneath a daisy, half asleep.
And for this hour of sun and dew,
The web belongs to me and you!

"Not a word!" said Tom and winked at Len. Then they went into the sitting-room. Their parents were there, talking.

"Well — have you been good boys today?" asked one of the mothers.

"Oh, yes," said Tom. "Both top of our class, and we came straight home as you said, and here we are."

"Who went into the larder just now and helped themselves to jam, and plums out of the pie?" said a loud voice suddenly. "Where are the boys who did that mean thing? Stealing, I call it."

There was a sudden silence. The parents looked at one another to see who had spoken. The boys went as red as beetroots.

"Who said that?" said a father at last. "How strange that voice sounded! I don't like it. Come on — let's go to the pictures. We all look scared! I'm sure the boys wouldn't take anything from the larder."

"But they did! Didn't you, boys?" said Pink-Whistle's stern voice. The boys stood trembling and didn't say a word.

One of the fathers stood up, looking pale. "Come along. We'll go. There's something queer going on here. Somebody calling through the window or down the chimney or something!"

They all went out. They caught a bus and so did Pink-Whistle. As soon as they were all seated on the bus, he began again.

"Where are the boys who scared that little girl and tied a can to her puppy's tail? Where are they? Bring them to me!"

Again Tom and Len went red and trembled. Everyone looked at them. A man spoke up from the corner. "Who is it that wants to know about those bad boys? There they are on that seat there, shaking in their shoes. Come and get them!"

The boys leapt off the bus in fright, and their parents followed, troubled and puzzled. They went into the cinema without a word — but each mother and father was thinking hard. Why was that voice following them? Why did their boys look so red and ashamed?

And dear me, the voice came with them into the cinema as well! Every time there was a quiet piece in the picture the voice sounded near to the boys and their parents — speaking in a loud whisper this time.

"Who scared the old woman with a water-pistol? Who rang the bells and ran away? Who frightened the little girl with the dog? Who has parents who don't know what their boys are up to? Who went into the larder and —"

"There's something queer going on here," said one of the fathers.

Len began to cry. Tom went very white this time, instead of red. The parents felt so upset that they couldn't watch the picture any more. One by one they rose and went out. Pink-Whistle followed them.

They went home to Len's house. Pink-Whistle slipped in with them, too. The parents faced the boys.

"What's all this about? Where does this voice come from? Is it true what it keeps saying?"

"No," said Len.

"No," said Tom, his head down.

"Who tells untruths to their parents?" began the voice again. "Who lies in wait for little girls and breaks their dolls? Who throws stones at dogs and cats? WHO, WHO, WHO?"

"We do, we do," sobbed Len and Tom, suddenly, almost scared out of their lives. "We do all those things. We won't any more. We won't!"

"I'll see you don't!" said Len's father, angrily. "To think you do these things behind our backs and pretend to be so good to our faces!"

"They want whipping," said Tom's father. "We've not been firm enough with them."

"Oh, Tom, oh, Len — how could you do things like that?" wailed their mothers.

"Partly your fault, partly your fault," said the voice again. "Why don't you look after your children better? *I'll* look after them! *I'll* tell the world about them! *I'll* . . ."

"No, no, no!" cried Len. "Go away, whoever you are. You frighten me. Go away!"

"I'm going," said Pink-Whistle solemnly. "I'm going. I'm going." His voice became softer and softer. Then suddenly and most frighteningly it was loud again. "But I'm coming back if you don't keep your word. Yes — I'm COMING BACK!"

He went then, back to his little cottage and to Sooty, feeling quite tired out. "I *think* I've put that right," he said to Sooty. "But you never know!"

"What's all this about?" asked the boys' parents. "Where does this voice come from?"

Good old Pink-Whistle. He certainly has put it right. Those boys — and their parents, too — are quite, quite different. Oh, dear — I do hope *I* never hear his voice booming out because I've done something wrong. I would be so ashamed, wouldn't you?

There is another story about Mr. Pink-Whistle beginning on page 125 of this book.

JESUS and the children

JESUS always loved little children, and they loved Him. They knew He would welcome them, wherever He was, and they loved the stories He told them.

One day, when Jesus was talking to the people, some mothers and fathers, who had small children, thought they would take them to Jesus for Him to bless them and put His wonderful hands on them.

So they gathered together their little ones, carrying some in their arms, with others toddling at their sides, and they went to find Jesus.

The disciples saw them coming with the children. One of the mothers spoke to them eagerly. "We have brought our children to Jesus. It will make such a difference to them if He would bless them. It would help them to grow up good and kind. He is such a wonderful man."

"He's busy," said a disciple, rather unkindly. "He can't see you just now."

"He is talking to many people," said another disciple. "He can't be bothered with children just now. Go away and come back later."

The parents were sad and disappointed. As they turned to go away Jesus saw their faces, and He called to his disciples:

"Bring the little children to me! Do not stop them coming. They belong to my kingdom just as you do — and, indeed, unless you have the open heart of a little child, you will not be able to enter my kingdom!"

So the mothers and fathers gladly brought their children to Him, and He took them into His arms one by one. He blessed them and loved them, and then He let them go.

Let's have a Club of our own - 1

(This story, which is in two parts, has been written because so very many of you continually ask me HOW to form a Club, and what to do when it is formed. Well, here in this tale you will read how six ordinary children formed a Club successfully — and you too will be able to do the same, once you have read the story from beginning to end.)

"LET'S have a Club of our own!" said Mark to his friend James. "About five or six of us. It would be fun."

"Right. But how do we set about it?" said James.

"Well — first we'd better choose the members we'd like," said Mark. "NOT Fred — he's never serious about anything. And not Jane — she giggles all the time."

"Have we *got* to have girls?" said James.

"Well — I'd like my twin sister Mollie to be in any club I started," said Mark. "She's not a giggler — she's fun. And she wouldn't mind making badges for us."

"Oh, well — that's something," said James. "That's three of us already. *I'd* like old Dick — he's good at everything, but he never boasts. And he's always ready to do a good turn. He'd be a good club member."

"Yes, I'd like Dick, too," said Mark. "And we'd better have Katie, Mollie's best friend. She's almost like a boy — she climbs trees like a monkey, and runs faster than I can. She's a jolly good sport."

"Right. That's five. Do we want anyone else?" said James. They thought hard for a minute.

"What about Eric?" said Mark. "I know he's lame, because he's had polio — so he might not be able to come for long walks with us, or climb trees — but he's so quick-brained, and so *funny*. Do let's have him."

"Of course," said James. "He's so often left out of things that I bet he'd love to join our Club. All right — that's six of us. The next thing is to ask each of them if they'd *like* to join."

So Mark asked his sister Mollie and her friend Katie, and he asked Eric too, the boy who limped. Mollie was thrilled.

"A club! Oh, I've always wanted to have a club or belong to one," she said. "And how lovely to have Katie in it, too. I wouldn't belong if you didn't ask Katie."

"I know," said Mark. "Anyway, *I* couldn't have a club without *you*, Mollie. I'm asking Eric, too — and James is asking Dick. Six of us."

"How exciting!" said Mollie. "Are we going to do it properly? Have badges, you know, and a meeting-place, and so on?"

"Rather!" said Mark. "We'd better have the first meeting soon, and decide on a name for the club, and all that kind of thing."

They went to find Katie and ask her, and she nodded her head of short curls, and grinned her wide smile. "Thanks — yes. I'd love to join," she said. "Especially as Mollie will be in the club too. When's the first meeting?"

"We thought we'd have a hurried talk in the bicycle shed after school this afternoon," said Mark. "When everyone has gone. Okay?"

"Right," said the girls. Mark went off to find James. He was with Dick and Eric, both of whom were delighted at the idea of a club.

"First meeting after school this afternoon in the bicycle shed," said Mark, and the others nodded. Eric was so proud of being asked, that he could hardly stop smiling all the afternoon. He was lame — he couldn't climb or run or play quick games — and yet the others wanted him in their club! How pleased his mother would be!

After school, the six met for the first time in the bicycle shed. It was deserted, so they were quite on their own. They grinned at one another.

"This isn't a real *meeting*," said Mark. "It's just to arrange a few important things quickly.

After school, the six met in the bicycle shed.

And away went all the six on their bicycles, their minds full of the new idea.

Mollie swept the hen-house out vigorously.

First — we must have a *proper* meeting-place — where we shall be alone and undisturbed. Anyone got any ideas?"

"Yes! What about my garage?" said Dick.

The others considered this, and then James shook his head.

"No. It would be all right if it was empty, but most of the time your father's car is there, Dick. We might scratch it or something, and get into a row. Let me see — has anyone a shed?"

Two of them had, but as one was a tool-shed that was always kept locked, and the other was so tumbledown that it let the rain in, neither was much good!

"It's a puzzle," said Mark, scratching his head to make his thoughts come quickly. "We simply MUST have somewhere to meet."

"Somewhere in the woods, under a big tree?" suggested Katie.

"No — too many people walk in the woods," said Dick. "*I* know — what about that old hen-house of yours, Mark? The one you don't use now?"

Everyone brightened up at once. "Yes! Just the thing," said Mark. "Fancy us not thinking of that, Mollie! Right. That's settled, then. The hen-house is to be our meeting-place — and now, when shall we meet?"

"Soon," said James. "Tomorrow evening! At half past five. We'll settle all the rules then. Gosh, I must go — look at the time! Well, good-bye, members! We haven't a password or anything yet — but we soon will have! So long!"

And away went all the six on their bicycles, their minds full of their new idea.

At half-past five the next evening Mark's

Here's a map of Fairyland,
Can you find the way,
And wander safely east to west
One very sunny day?
You mustn't pass a wizard's house,
Or venture near a witch,
You mustn't go through Goblin Land,
Or leap a magic ditch.
Beware of little paths that lead
To where enchanters dwell,
Don't even stop to make a wish
Beside a wishing-well!
But take the winding path that leads
Towards the End-of-Day.
It really is a lovely trip
When once you know the way!

mother was astonished to see so many children trooping down to the old hen-house. She called to Mark and Mollie. "Twins! If you are going to that dirty old hen-shed, do, for goodness' sake, sweep it out. All your clothes will be filthy!"

"Right, Mother," shouted back Mark, and grinned at the others. "I knew Mother would say that — so I've put an old broom down there already! Mollie said she'd clean it up a bit."

The hen-house was not large, and it was certainly dusty. All the members except Mollie had to stand outside while she swept it vigorously.

"Pooh!" said Eric, coughing. "I shall soon cluck like a hen if the dust gets down my throat a bit more."

Soon they were all in the shed. There was only one box there, and a perch for the hens that used to roost in the hut. "We'll bring an old rug or something," said Katie. "And a box or two."

"And put up a shelf to hold our club-things," said Mark.

"What club things?" asked Eric.

"Well — notebooks perhaps, a tin for any money we have for the club — maybe a bottle of orangeade and a tin of biscuits," grinned Mark. "You never know what our mothers will give us, they'll be so glad to be rid of us for a few hours at a time."

"This is going to be fun," said Katie. "Now, let's start properly, Mark."

"Right," said Mark. "The meeting is now begun. We have several things to settle. One is the name of our club. The second is what badge to have, and how to get one for each of us. The third is to choose a leader — or we can choose him — or her — *first*, if you like. Then we'd better have a password — and perhaps a secret signal when we meet. And it would be a good idea to choose some *aim*, as well."

"What do you mean by that?" asked Katie.

"Well — we'll discuss that matter when it comes up," said Mark. "Any other suggestions for discussion?"

"No. Let's choose our leader," said Eric. "I've brought bits of card — *and* pencils — enough for everyone. We can get straight on with it."

"Oh, good!" said Mollie. "I thought I'd be sent back to the house to get things like that! Hand round the little cards, Eric. You always think of everything!"

Eric handed round the slips of cardboard, which he had cut from two post-cards. He also handed out five short pencils.

"Now — write down the name of the one you would like best for leader," said Mark, looking rather solemn. "And remember — it's to be someone you not only like but respect enough to obey and to follow. That's what my father says about leaders. They *must* be liked and they *must* be respected and obeyed. Of course, no one must vote for himself — that's understood!"

Soon each of the six was scribbling on his or her bit of card. They folded them in half and handed them to Eric, with their pencils. "Shall I open them and tell you what they say?" said Eric, looking round, and everyone nodded. He opened the first one, and read out loud the name on it.

"This one says *Mark*," he said, and Mark went red with pleasure. Thank goodness *someone* had voted for him." He thought it must be Mollie. Eric unfolded another card, and read out Mark's name again! "*Mark*! Ha — two votes already for you, Mark!"

He opened the third folded card. "This card says *Dick*," he said. "That's two for Mark, one for Dick." He unfolded the other three — and each held the same name!

"Mark! Mark! Mark! Five for you, Mark, and one for Dick," said Eric, smiling all over his face. "Well, it's what I expected. Congratulations!"

"And thanks for voting for *me*, Mark old boy," said Dick, pleased.

"How do you know *Mark* voted for you? It might have been any of us," said Katie.

"No. Mark couldn't vote for himself, so he naturally voted for Dick," said Eric. "Everyone else voted for Mark — so it *had* to be Mark who voted for Dick. Am I right, Mark?"

"Quite right!" said Mark, his face red with pleasure. "Well, thanks awfully for voting me leader. I'll do my best to be a decent one. Now then — let's choose the name for our club. The 'something' Six — what shall it be?"

Ideas came quickly, and were shouted out eagerly. "The Strong Six! The Striking Six! The Shocking Six! The Trusty Six! The Secret Six!"

"Not the Secret Six. Too much like the well-known Secret Seven," said Mark. "Let's have a definite name of our own."

"The Stalwart Six! The Sturdy Six!" cried Eric. "The . . ."

"Wait! What about the *Sturdy* Six?" said Mark. "Seems a good, strong sort of name to me. To be sturdy is to be trustable and straight and

"Now — write down the name of the one you'd like best for leader."

dependable and strong — 'The Sturdy Six' — yes, that seems a good name to me for our club. Hands up those who like it best of all the names."

Every hand went up. Mark nodded. "Right — I hereby proclaim that we six are now formed into a club which has the name of The Sturdy Six."

Mollie grinned round in delight. "Mark's a good leader already!" she remarked. "I hereby proclaim that he is a . . ."

"Shut up, please, Mollie," said Mark. "Now about badges. We shall need to have S.S. on them, for Sturdy Six. Er — any suggestions?"

The four boys gazed hard at the two girls, and they at once responded! "All right — we know what those looks mean!" said Mollie. "You want us to make the badges for us all. Right, we will!"

"How will you make them?" asked James.

"Easy!" said Katie. "We'll get six buttons all the same size. We'll cut out bits of cloth, and embroider S.S. on them for Sturdy Six. Then we'll sew each bit over the button, so that the S.S. is on the front — and sew a little safety-pin on the back to pin the badge on to our coats. S.S. for the Sturdy Six — shan't we be proud to wear them?"

"Thanks awfully," said Mark. "Now for a password. Any suggestions?"

There were plenty! "Hen-house!" said Eric, looking round at the perches.

"New laid eggs," said Katie, and everyone chuckled.

"Sturdy!" said Mark.

"Cluck-cluck!" said Mollie. That made everyone laugh so much that it was chosen at once for the password.

"Whatever will people think when they hear us murmuring 'cluck-cluck' to each other when we meet?" said Katie.

"Well, it's really only a password to gain entrance to our meeting-place," said Mark. "In future, no one can enter any of our meetings, wherever they are, unless he or she first says the password. So don't forget it, please."

"Shall we discuss a secret signal now?" asked Dick, but Mark was looking at his watch. He shook his head.

"Sorry — the meeting's over. Meet here on Friday evening at half past five again. We'll then discuss what our aim should be, what things we can do together, and a secret signal if we think it's necessary. Buck up — it's time to go if we're going to get any homework done this evening!"

They all trooped out of the hen-house, feeling thrilled and pleased. "I'm glad you're leader, Mark," said Eric. "You can direct everything well, that's quite plain. Well — the Sturdy Six are now a club — and I'm jolly glad to belong to it!"

(Later on in this book I will tell you what the club did at their second meeting, so that if any of you have formed a club meanwhile, in the way that the Six did, you too will know what to do next!)

"The Stalwart Six! The Sturdy Six!" cried Eric.

Nature Quiz 1

THE FOUR BIRD-WATCHERS

JACK and Alice lived in Hazel Cottage, and next door were Joan and Richard. They were great friends and loved going out together.

Now it was winter-time, and each family had put up a bird-table. Jack's mother said that that was the quickest way to get to know all the common garden birds. "Until you know at least twelve you can't call yourselves bird-lovers," she said. "Because if you don't know twelve or so, you haven't loved the birds enough to learn which one is which."

"All right, Mother — we'll be bird-watchers from now on!" said Jack. "And if we don't soon know our twelve commonest winter birds, the ones that come to our bird-tables, you can take down the tables!"

"Right!" said Mother. "I'll give you a quiz in a month's time. So you'll have to do quite a spot of bird-watching, if you're going to get top marks."

The four bird-watchers glued their faces to the window pane to see which birds came to the table and exactly what they were like. Robins, sparrows, tits, starlings, thrushes ... which were which, what did they say, and how did they behave? "I *think* I know all the birds now," said Richard, at last. "Let's get your mother to give us that quiz. And, by the way, *I've* got a small quiz for your mother too, Jack!"

"Good," said Jack, and went to find his mother. "Tell the others to come in to tea this afternoon and I'll give you your quiz," she said. So, after tea, when they were all sitting round expectantly, Mother gave them her quiz. (See if you can win top marks too!)

"Now," said Mother, "I'm thinking of a little brown bird. He . . ."

"Sparrow!" said Jack at once.

"Wait," said Mother. "I'm thinking of a little brown bird, with a thin beak like a robin's, who has a quaint little habit of shuffling his wings, and he calls peep-peep and has a cheery little song . . ."

"Hedge-sparrow!" shouted Joan and Richard together.

"Right," said Mother. "Now I'm thinking of a bigger bird, also brownish in colour, and he wears dark-brown freckles on his breast, and . . ."

"Thrush!" yelled everyone, at the mention of freckles.

"Gracious! You'll be guessing the answers before I've asked the questions soon," said Mother. "Now — let me see — I'm thinking of a rather noisy bird, who has no real song, but makes all kinds of peculiar whistles and gurgles and splutters. He's about the size of a thrush, but has a short tail, and he wears feathers of all colours — purple, green, violet, blue . . ."

"It's the starling!" said Alice, suddenly.

"Right!" said Mother. "Now, I'm thinking of a tiny bird, very pretty, with a bright blue head, white cheeks and a dark line through his eyes and round his neck. He has green and yellow feathers, too, and he is a marvellous . . ."

"Acrobat!" yelled Richard. "It's the blue-tit. I know him well, because he comes to our bird-

SKYLARK
CHAFFINCH
BLUE TIT
PIED WAGTAIL
WREN
GREAT TIT
HEDGE SPARROW
ROBIN
HOUSE SPARROW
STARLING
SONG THRUSH
BLACKBIRD
MANSELL

SWALLOW
HOUSE-MARTIN
SWIFT
SPOTTED
FLYCATCH
CUCKOO
NIGHTINGALE
KINGFISHER
YELLOW HAMMER
TAWNY OW
E. MANSELL
PEEWIT
WILLOW WARBLER
ROOK

table and swings upside down on the string of nuts. He keeps saying 'pim-im-im-im-im.' "

"You're too clever," said Mother. "Well, this time I'm thinking of a little friendly bird, with a beautiful red breast, and . . ."

"Robin!" shouted everyone, and Mother didn't even finish what she was saying!

"You'll deafen me!" she said. "I'd better give you a difficult one. Now — I'm thinking of a neat little bird, dressed in black and white, with a long tail that . . ."

"Magpie!" said Joan, but the others looked at her scornfully.

"Magpies don't come to the bird-table! And Mother said a little bird, not a big one."

Mother went on. "He has a long tail that keeps wagging up and down, and he runs quickly over . . ."

"Pied Wagtail!" said everyone together.

"Of course!" said Mother. "I *was* surprised at your magpie, Joan!"

"Yes, that was silly," said Joan. "Go on, please!"

"This time I'm thinking of another little bird who has an extraordinarily loud song," said Mother. "To see him creeping about the undergrowth you would think him to be a little red-brown mouse. He has a funny little cocked-up stump of a tail . . ."

"Wren, wren, wren!" shouted Jack, and he was right.

"Well, I must say you're really very good," said Mother. "Now, what about this one — I see a neat, handsome little bird, who calls 'Pink-pink!' loudly, and has a merry rattle of a song, as well. He wears a bright chestnut-pink breast, and when he flies you see white bars flashing on his wings . . ."

There was a silence. "The great-tit says 'pink-pink' but he hasn't a pink breast," said Richard. "Let me see — oh, I know, I know — the chaffinch, of course!"

"Right!" said Mother. "Now, a little noisy brown bird we see everywhere, and hear calling 'chirrup-chirrup' and . . ."

"House-sparrow!" cried everyone. "That's easy!"

"And now, a bird wearing a glossy black dress, with a bright golden beak, whose song is . . ."

"Very, very beautiful!" chimed in everyone. "Blackbird, of course. You can't beat *us*!"

"Two more and the quiz is ended," said Mother. "I'm thinking of a little bird, about the size of a sparrow — oh, a handsome fellow in a glossy black waistcoat, with a black head and collar, a grey tail, yellow breast and beautiful green back. He loves nuts and fat. He calls 'Pee-ter, pee-ter, pee-terpee' or 'pink-pink' and . . ."

"Great-tit, great-tit!" cried Joan and Alice together. "He's an acrobat too, like the blue-tit."

"Quite right," said Mother. "And now just one more — a bird which doesn't come down to your bird-table, but sometimes comes down on the lawn in the early morning. He's a big bird, brown, with a little crest of feathers he can raise up and down."

Nobody answered. It couldn't be a thrush. Oh dear — they simply *must* guess the last one.

"A bit more description, please," said Richard.

"Usually," went on Mother, "he is only a tiny speck high in the sky, and it's his song we know better than the bird himself . . ."

"Sky-lark!" cried everyone. "Of course! Well, we've guessed them all!"

"Very good indeed," said Mother. "Go to the top of the class!"

"Mrs. Robins," said Richard, solemnly, "I've thought of just a small quiz for *you*. I'm thinking of a bird. It's small, very small. It has a red back . . ."

"A red back?" said everyone, puzzled.

"Yes, a red back, with black spots," went on Richard, "and six legs, and . . ."

"Don't be silly, Richard. What is it?" said Joan.

"A *lady*bird!" said Richard, and everyone fell on him at once, pummelling him hard.

"Now, now," said Mother, "let the poor fellow breathe. Well, look out for the next quiz, and see how much you know!"

WOLVES IN THE NIGHT!

This extract is from one of the eight books in the Adventure series — THE MOUNTAIN OF ADVENTURE. The four children — Jack, Philip, Dinah and Lucy-Ann — are together for a summer holiday in the mountains of Wales. They set out to camp with David, an old Welsh shepherd, taking donkeys; Kiki, Jack's talkative parrot, goes too, and also Snowy, a tiny kid who will not leave Philip. This extract from THE MOUNTAIN OF ADVENTURE gives the events that lead up to one of the strangest adventures the children have ever had.

THE sun was shining brightly when the camp awoke next day. It made them all feel cheerful and lively. Snowy, the kid, who had resented the shepherd David sleeping with Philip and Jack the night before, and had butted him continually, bounded about lightly everywhere, rushing at David whenever he met him.

"What happened to you last night, David?" asked Jack, when they were all having a meal. "Why were you so frightened?"

"Noises," said David.

"What sort?" asked Philip curiously. "*We* didn't hear any."

David immediately made some surprising noises that sent Kiki, the parrot, sailing into the air and Snowy bounding away in fright. The children stared at David in astonishment.

By means of odd words and gestures David managed to convey to the children that he had gone to see if the donkeys were all right in the night, and had heard these noises near where they were tethered.

"That explains why *we* didn't hear them, I suppose," said Jack. "David makes them sound like animal noises — fierce and savage!"

Lucy-Ann looked scared. "Oh! You don't think

there are wild animals anywhere about here, do you, Jack? I mean, *fierce* wild animals?"

Jack grinned. "Well, if you are thinking of lions and tigers and panthers and bears, I think I can say you needn't be afraid of finding *those* here. But if, like Dinah, you include snakes, foxes, hedgehogs and so on in your list of fierce wild animals, then I should say, look out!"

"Don't be silly, Jack. Of course I don't mean those," said Lucy-Ann. "I don't quite know what I *did* mean. I just felt scared — and wondered what animal had made the noises David heard."

"Probably his own imagination," said Philip. "Or a bad dream. It wouldn't take much to scare him."

David did not seem to want to go any further. He kept pointing back over the way they had come. But the children were not going to let their trip come to such a disappointing end. They meant to go and find the Butterfly Valley, if it took them all week! They went to a lot of trouble to make David understand this.

He turned sulky, but mounted his donkey to go with them. Jack now had the map, and examined it very carefully. It was annoying that the Butterfly Valley wasn't marked. Perhaps very few people knew about it.

They all set off across the valley and up into the mountains again. Perhaps the next valley would be the one they wanted, or the one after that. But although they travelled hopefully all the day, they did not find any valley full of butterflies. The children began to think it was all a fairy tale.

There was no track to follow now, though the boys kept a keen look-out in case they should come across one again. When they camped that night, they discussed what they had better do next.

"If we go on any further we shan't know our way back," said Jack. "David would, perhaps, because he was born and bred among mountains, and, like a dog, could follow his own trail well enough, if we had to go back. But he's so brainless that I don't like to trust to him too much. I wouldn't be surprised if he lost the way going back, if we take him much further!"

"Had we better go back then?" asked Lucy-Ann in disappointment.

"Or camp here for a few days," said Jack, looking round. "It's quite a good place."

They were halfway up a steep mountain that rose very sharply from where they were, and looked quite unclimbable.

"What a queer mountain!" said Dinah, gazing up. "I shouldn't think anyone ever climbed all the way to the top. It's all crags and rocks and jutting-out bits."

"We'll camp here," decided Philip. "The weather looks quite settled. There's a spring near by. We can mess about with our cameras and field-glasses."

They told David. He did not seem pleased, but went off to tether the donkeys for the night. They were all tired that evening, children and donkeys both, for they had had a very long day. They cut the big ham that Mrs. Evans had provided for them, afraid that it might go bad if they didn't eat it soon.

David looked as if he thought he would sleep in the tent again that night, for he cast various longing glances in that direction. However, the night was hot, and he felt he couldn't bear to be

David shot into the boys' tent and gave them a terrible shock.

under cover. So he arranged himself under his rug in the open, fairly near to the two tents. The donkeys were some way away, tethered to trees by long ropes.

That night there was a loud snuffling around the camp. Lucy-Ann awoke suddenly and heard it. She went right down to the bottom of her sleeping-bag, frightened. What could it be? Was it the wild animal that David had heard?

Then she heard a howl! The boys heard it too, and awoke. David, outside, was already awake, having heard both the noises. He was shivering with fright, all kinds of fears coming into his simple, peasant mind.

The moon was up and everywhere was silvery bright. David sat up and looked down the hill. What he saw made his hair rise straight up on his head.

Wolves! A pack of wolves! No, no, it couldn't be wolves! He was dreaming! Wolves had not been known in the mountains for hundreds of years. But if those creatures were not wolves, what were they? And that noise of snuffling he had heard. That must have been a wolf, too! No, not a *wolf*. It *couldn't* have been such a thing.

David sat there, hugging his knees, his mind going round and round — wolves or not? Wolves or not? What were they doing near the donkeys?

Another howl came — half a howl, half a bark, a horrible noise. The shepherd shot into the boys' tent and gave them a terrible shock.

He stammered something in Welsh, and then in English, "Wolves!"

"Don't be silly," said Jack at once, seeing that the man was scared to death. "You've had a bad dream."

David dragged him to the tent opening and pointed with a trembling finger to where the pack of snuffling animals stood, not far from the donkeys.

The boys stared as if they could not believe their eyes. They certainly *looked* like wolves! Jack felt a cold shiver down his back. Good gracious! Was he dreaming? Those creatures were more like wolves than anything else!

Kiki flew above the animals.

Snowy the kid was trembling as much as David was. The trembling somehow made the boys feel scared too. The only person who was not in the least scared was Kiki, the parrot.

She too had caught sight of the wolves. She sailed out of the tent at top speed to go and investigate. Anything unusual always interested Kiki. She flew above the animals, whose eyes gleamed green as they turned at her coming.

"Wipe your feet!" screamed Kiki, and made a noise like a mowing-machine cutting long grass. It sounded really terrible in the still night air of the mountain-side.

The wolves started in fright. Then with one accord they all galloped away down the hillside into the night. The parrot shouted rude remarks after them.

"They've gone," said Jack. "Gosh, were they real? I can't understand it!"

When it was dawn, David got up to see if the donkeys were all right. Neither he nor the boys had slept again that night. David had been too scared to, and the boys had been too puzzled.

It was almost daylight on the mountain. David crept down quietly to the donkeys. They were all there, safe and sound but uneasy. David untethered them to take them to the stream to drink.

The boys were looking out of their tent, down the hillside, on watch. There was no sign of any wolf now.

Suddenly something happened. David, who was taking the donkeys in a line to the stream, gave a terrified scream, and fell to the ground, covering his face. The boys, holding their breath, thought they saw something moving in the bushes, but they couldn't see what.

David gave another scream and got to his feet. He mounted a donkey and rode at top speed up to the tent.

"Come!" he cried in Welsh, and then in English. "Black, black, black!"

The boys had no idea at all what he meant.

David galloped off at breakneck speed.

They stared at him in amazement, thinking he must have gone mad. He made a violent gesture to them, pointed to the following donkeys as if to tell the boys to mount and follow him, and then galloped off at breakneck speed.

They heard the hooves of his donkey echoing on the mountain-side for some time. The other donkeys looked doubtfully at one another, and then, to the boys' dismay, trotted after David!

"Hi! Come back, you!" yelled Jack, scrambling out of the tent. "Hi! Hi!"

One donkey turned and made as if to come back, but he was pushed on by the others behind. In a trice they had all disappeared, and the sound of their hooves grew fainter and fainter as they galloped away after David and his mount.

The two boys sat down suddenly. They felt faint. Jack turned pale. He looked at Philip and bit his lip. Now they were in a terrible fix.

They said nothing for a moment or two, and then the girls' two scared faces looked out from their tent.

"What's happened? What's all the yelling? Was that David galloping away? We didn't dare to look!"

"Yes — it was David — running away from us — and all the donkeys have gone after him," said Philip bitterly. "We're in a pretty fix now!"

Nobody said anything. Lucy-Ann looked really alarmed. No David! No donkeys! What were they going to do?

Jack put his arm round her as she came and sat by his side. "It's all right! We've been in worse fixes than this! At the worst it only means a few days here, because as soon as David gets back to the farm, Bill will come and look for us."

"Good thing we unloaded the donkeys and have plenty of food," said Philip. "And our tents and sleeping-bags. Blow David! He's a coward."

"I wonder what he saw to make him gallop off like that," said Jack. "All I could make out were his shout of 'Black, black, black'!"

"Black what?" asked Dinah.

"Black nothing. Just black," said Jack. "Let's

go down to the place where he got his fright and see if we can spot anything."

"Oh *no*!" said the girls at once.

"Well, I'll go, and Philip can stay here with you," said Jack, and off he went. The others watched him, holding their breath. He peered all round and then turned and shook his head and shouted.

"Nothing here! Not a thing to see! David must have been imagining things! His bad night upset him."

He came back. "But what about those animals in the night?" said Philip, after a pause. "Those wolves. We both saw those. *They* seemed real enough!"

It wasn't long before Dinah suggested having something to eat, and went to the big panniers that had been unloaded from the donkeys the night before. She pulled out some tins, thinking that it would be a change to have sardines, and tinned peaches, or something like that. Anything to take their minds off the shepherd's flight, and the disappearance of the donkeys!

They sat down rather silently. Lucy-Ann kept very close to the boys. What with wolves and David's fright she felt very scared, herself!

"I hope this won't turn into one of our adventures," she kept saying to herself. "They always happen so suddenly."

Snowy the kid bounded up to Philip and knocked a tin flying from his hand. He nuzzled affectionately against him and then butted him. Philip rubbed the furry little nose and then pushed the kid away.

"I'm glad *you* didn't go off with the donkeys, too!" he said. "I've got used to having you around now, you funny aggravating little thing. Take your nose out of that tin! Lucy-Ann, push him off — he'll eat everything we've got!"

Kiki suddenly flew at Snowy, screaming with rage. She had had her eye on that tin of sliced peaches, and to see Snowy nosing round it was too much for her. She gave him a sharp peck on his nose, and he ran to Philip, bleating. Everyone laughed and felt better.

Kiki suddenly flew at Snowy, screaming with rage.

They sat there, eating by the tents, occasionally glancing up at the mountain that towered so steeply above them. It had no gentle slope up to the summit, as most of the mountains around had, but was steep and forbidding.

"I don't much like this mountain," said Lucy-Ann.

"Why?" asked Dinah.

"I don't know. I just don't like it," said Lucy-Ann. "I've got one of my 'feelings' about it."

The others laughed. Lucy-Ann often had 'feelings' about things, and really believed in them. It was just like her to start having 'feelings' about the mountain, when everyone was also having uncomfortable ideas about wolves and other things.

"Well, you needn't have any 'feelings' about mountains," said Philip. "Mountains are all the same — just tops, middles and bottoms, sometimes with sheep on and sometimes without!"

"But not many have *wolves*," said Lucy-Ann seriously, and that made the others feel uncomfortable again.

"What are we going to do today?" asked Jack, when they had finished their meal. "I suppose we *must* stay here till Bill comes to find us. We can't try to walk back home, because for one thing we don't know the way, and for another we'd never be able to carry enough food to get there without starving."

"We'd far better stay here," said Philip at once.

"Yes — it does seem the most sensible thing to do," said Jack. "We've got our camp here — tents set up and everything — so we might as well make the best of it, and enjoy the camping. I wish there was somewhere to bathe though. It's so jolly hot. That little stream's too small to do anything but paddle in."

"Let's all keep together," said Lucy-Ann. "I mean — we could frighten those wolves away perhaps if we screamed at them — but one of us alone might be — might be . . ."

"Gobbled up!" said Jack, and laughed. "What big *eyes* you've got, Granny! And, oh, what big TEETH you've got! Do you feel like Red Riding Hood, Lucy Ann?"

"Don't tease her," said Philip, seeing Lucy-Ann's alarmed face. "It's all right, Lucy-Ann.

The children went to splash in the little stream.

Wolves are only really hungry in the winter-time and it's summer now."

Lucy-Ann looked relieved. "Well — I suppose if they'd been really hungry they would have attacked the donkeys, wouldn't they?" she said.

They got up, cleared away the meal and went to splash in the little stream. The wind suddenly began to blow rather chilly, and, looking up, the children saw that big clouds were coming up from the south-west.

"Looks like rain," said Jack. "I hope the wind doesn't get up much more, or it will blow our tents away. Do you remember how they were blown clean away from over us on our last adventure — on the Island of Birds? That was an awful feeling."

"Well," said Philip, "if you really think the tents might blow away, Jack, we ought to find a better place to camp than this — somewhere not too far, though, because we don't want to miss seeing Bill and David when they come for us. A copse of trees or a cave or somewhere like that — right out of the wind."

"Let's look now," said Dinah, pulling on her coat. It was extraordinary how cold it got as soon as the sun went in and the wind blew up the mountain. "We'd better take Snowy with us, or he'll eat everything we've left!"

Snowy had every intention of coming with them. He capered along by Philip and Jack, as mad as ever. He was now very annoyed with Kiki, and leapt at her whenever she came within reach, wanting to pay her back for nipping his nose.

When the girls had been left a little way behind, Philip spoke in a low voice to Jack. "We'd better find a cave, I think, Jack — I don't like the idea of those animals prowling around us at night — wolves, or whatever they are. If we were in a cave we could light a fire at the entrance and that would keep any animal off."

"Yes. That's quite a good idea," agreed Jack.

They hunted about for some kind of rocky shelter or cave, but there seemed none to be found. The mountain was so steep that it really was difficult to climb, and Lucy-Ann was afraid of slipping and falling.

Snowy leapt ahead of them, as sure-footed as ever. The boys wished heartily that it was as easy for them to leap about the mountain as it was for the kid.

"Look at him up there standing on that rock!" said Jack, feeling exasperated and far too hot with his climbing. "Hey, Snowy, come and give us a leg up! If only we had four springy legs like yours!"

Snowy stood there, whisking his little tail, and then ran back and disappeared. "Where's he gone?" said Jack. "Oh, there he comes again. Philip, there must be a cave or overhanging rock up where he is — he keeps going back and disappearing into it, whatever it is!"

They climbed up to where Snowy was, and sure enough, just at the back of the overhanging rock was a long low cave, its roof formed by another overhanging rock, its opening fringed with ferns of all kinds.

"This would do awfully well for us," said Jack, going down on hands and knees and looking in. "We could light a fire on the rock outside — the one Snowy stood on — and feel quite safe tonight. Clever little Snowy! You found us just what we wanted!"

"But how in the world are we going to get everything up here?" said Philip.

This was certainly a problem. The boys hailed the girls and helped them up on to the rock where Snowy stood. "Look," said Jack, "here's a good place to sleep in tonight. We can see quite well from here if Bill and David come — see what a good view we have from this rock — and we'd be safe from the wolves if we lighted a fire at the entrance to the cave."

"Oh, *yes!*" said Lucy-Ann, pleased. She went into the cave. She had to bend her head at the opening, but inside the roof grew higher. "It's not *really* a cave!" she said. "It's just a space under that big jutting-out rock — but it will do awfully well."

They all sat down on the rock, wishing the sun would come out. Snowy lay down beside them and Kiki sat on Jack's shoulder.

But suddenly she rose up into the air and screeched loudly. Snowy leapt up and stood looking downwards. What was the matter?

"Is it the wolves again?" asked Lucy-Ann in alarm. They listened. They could hear a noise of some animal or animals down below in the thick bushes, under the birch-trees.

Just at the back of the overhanging rock was a long low cave.

"Get back into the cave," said Jack to the girls. "And keep quiet."

The two girls went silently back into the darkness of the cave. The boys listened and watched. What animal was it down there? It must be big, by the noise it made!

Snowy suddenly bleated loudly and took a flying leap off the rock before Philip could stop him. He disappeared into the bushes below — and then a loud and welcome sound filled the air.

"Ee-ore! Ee-ore! Ee-ore!"

"Goodness! It's a donkey!" cried Jack and scrambled down to see. "Have they come back? Is David with them?"

They soon found what they were looking for. Dapple the donkey was in the bushes, nuzzling Snowy, evidently full of delight at seeing him again. But there was no sign at all of the other donkeys or of David.

"Dapple! You darling!" said Lucy-Ann, running up to him in joy. "You've come back to us."

"Come back to *Snowy*, you mean!" said Philip. "He was always fond of Snowy, weren't you, Dapple? So you came back to find him. Well, we're very glad to see you, because you will solve a very knotty problem for us — how to get all our goods into that cave!"

"Here, Dapple!" called Philip. "Come and help us with these things, there's a good fellow."

Dapple stood obediently whilst the boys strapped things on to his back. He took all the bedding up to the cave first, scrambling up the steep bits with difficulty, but managing very well indeed. Then he carried up the panniers of food.

"Thanks, Dapple," said Jack, giving him a pat. "Now come and have a drink!"

They all went to the stream and drank and splashed. The sun had come out again and immediately it was very hot. The children flung off their coats and lay about, basking.

"We must collect wood for the fire tonight," said Jack. "We shall need a good lot if we're going to keep the fire going all night long. We'll stack it in the big panniers and get Dapple to take it up for us."

"Good old Dapple," said Dinah.

They collected as much wood as they could, and soon it was all piled up on the rock outside the cave. The boys made a fire but did not light it. There was no need to do that till night.

The day soon went, and the sun sank behind the mountains in a blaze of crimson. As soon as darkness fell on the mountain-side, the children retired into the cave. The thought of wolves kept coming into their mind, and they kept remembering David's scream of terror when he had seen something in the bushes. "Black, black, black!" What *could* he have seen?

The children hadn't thought much of these things during the bright daylight, but they came back vividly into their minds now it was dark. They debated whether or not to have Dapple in the cave with them.

But Dapple settled that idea by firmly refusing to go under the overhanging rock.

"All right, Dapple," said Jack crossly. "Stay outside and be eaten by wolves if you want to!"

"Oh, *don't* say things like that," said Lucy-Ann. "Dapple, do come inside! Please!"

Dapple lay down firmly outside, and the children gave it up. There would be no difficulty about Snowy or Kiki. One would want to be with Philip, the other with Jack.

"Now we'll light the fire," said Jack, as stars began to glimmer in the sky. "It's getting very dark. Got the matches, Philip?"

The fire soon burnt up, for the twigs and branches were very dry. The cheerful flames leapt and flickered, and the fire crackled merrily.

"That's very very nice," said Lucy-Ann, pleased. "I feel safe tucked away in this cave with a fire at the entrance. Philip, make Snowy go the other side of you. He's sticking his hooves into me. I wish he'd wear bedroom slippers at night!"

Everybody laughed. They all felt safe and comfortable, tucked up in their sleeping-bags, with the fire lighting up the cave, filling it with jumping shadows. Snowy was pressed against Philip, Kiki was on Jack's middle. Somewhere outside was Dapple. Lucy-Ann wished he was in with them, then the whole family would be safe.

They all watched the flames for a while and then fell asleep. The fire flickered down as the wood was burnt up, and soon only the embers glowed.

Philip woke up with a start a few hours later. He saw that the fire had died down, and he crawled out of his sleeping-bag to put on more wood. It would never do to let it go out!

Dapple was still outside, lying quietly. Philip saw him when the flames leapt up to burn the wood he piled on the embers. The boy went back to his sleeping-bag. He found that Snowy had crept inside it whilst he was piling wood on the fire.

There was quite a scuffle as he tried to get Snowy out of the bag. Fortunately the others were so very sound asleep that they didn't wake. Philip got Snowy out at last and slid in himself. He hastily laced up the neck of the bag before Snowy could try to squeeze in again. Snowy gave a sigh and lay down heavily right on Philip's middle.

Philip lay awake, watching the fire. The wind sometimes blew the smoke towards the cave, and for a moment or two the smell made Philip want to cough.

Then he heard Dapple stir outside, and he sat up on one elbow to see why. His heart began to beat very fast.

Silent dark figures were slinking up to the cave! They did not pass beyond the fire, but they did not seem to be afraid of it. Philip felt breathless, and his heart beat even faster, as if he had been running.

What were those figures? Were they the wolves? The boy caught sight of two gleaming eyes, shining like the headlights of a distant car — but green as grass! He sat up quietly.

The wolves were back! They had smelt out the little company. What would they do? They had not attacked Dapple, thank goodness — and the donkey did not seem to be unduly frightened. He was only moving uneasily.

The slinking figures moved to and fro behind the fire. Philip couldn't think what in the world to do! He could only hope that the fire would frighten them enough to keep them out of the cave.

After a while all the animals disappeared. Philip breathed again! Gosh, what a horrible fright he had had! What a blessing they had thought of that fire! Philip made up his mind that he wasn't going to sleep again that night, in case the fire went out. At all costs he must keep that up.

So the boy lay wide-eyed, thinking of wolves, rumblings, earthquakes and "Black, black, black." There was something queer about all these things. Did they fit together, or didn't they? *Was* there something peculiar about this mountain?

The fire was dying down again. Philip got up cautiously to put on more wood. The moon was up now and he could see for miles. He piled wood on the fire and the flames shot up. He slipped out of the cave to Dapple, the donkey.

Then the boy heard a sound. He looked up — and to his horror he saw a wolf between him and the cave! He had gone to pat Dapple — and in that moment the wolf had slunk in between the fire and cave. Would he go in?

The wolf stood still, looking at Philip in the moonlight. Philip gazed back, wondering what to do if the creature attacked him — and as he looked, a very peculiar thing happened.

The wolf wagged its long tail! To and fro it went, to and fro, like a big dog's! Philip's heart leapt. The animal wanted to be friendly! All animals were attracted to Philip — but a wolf! That was extraordinary.

The boy held out his hand, half afraid, but bold and daring. The wolf trotted round the fire and licked Philip's hand. It gave a little whine.

The moon shone down brightly on the animal's dark coat, pointed ears and long muzzle. *Was* it a wolf? Now that he was close to it Philip began to doubt.

And then quite suddenly he knew what this friendly animal was!

"Why, you're an Alsatian *dog*!" he cried. "Aren't you? Why didn't I think of it before? I *knew* there weren't wolves in this country! Where are the others? You're all Alsatians! Good dog! Fine dog! I'd like to be friends with you!"

The big Alsatian put his paws up on Philip's shoulder and licked his face. Then he lifted his head and howled. It was a wolf-like noise, but Philip no longer minded that!

It was a call to the other dogs, the rest of the pack. There came the sound of feet in the bushes below, and a crowd of dogs leapt up on to the rock. They clustered round Philip, and, seeing that their leader was so friendly with the boy, they pawed him and licked him.

The howl awakened all the three children in the cave, and they sat up in fright. To their unspeakable horror they saw, outside the cave, what looked like Philip being attacked by wolves!

"Look! They've got Philip! Quick!" yelled Jack.

All three children slid out of their sleeping-bags and rushed to Philip's aid. The dogs growled at the sudden commotion.

"Philip! We're coming! Are you hurt?" cried valiant little Lucy-Ann, picking up a stick.

"It's all right, it's all right!" yelled Philip. "They're not attacking me. They're friendly. They're not wolves, but Alsatians! *Dogs*, you know!"

"Goodness gracious!" said Dinah, and came

A crowd of dogs leapt up on to the rock.

out into the moonlight, so glad that the dogs were not wolves that she didn't even feel afraid of so many big ones!

"Oh, Philip!" said Lucy-Ann, almost in tears with the shock of delight at knowing the wolves were only dogs. "Oh, Philip! I thought you were being attacked."

"You were a darling to come to my rescue then," said Philip, smiling when he saw the little stick with which Lucy-Ann had meant to attack the wolves. "The leader of the dogs made friends with me — so all the others are doing the same!"

The dogs had apparently made up their minds to stay for the night. Philip debated what to do. "We can't possibly go back into the cave," he said. "The whole pack will come crowding in, and it would be impossible to breathe."

"Quite impossible," said Dinah, filled with horror at the thought of so many dogs sleeping with them.

"So we'll bring our sleeping-bags out here on the rock beside Dapple, and sleep there," said Philip. "The dogs can stay if they want to — they'll be good guards! And if they don't want to, they can go. There are about ten of them! I wonder how it is they're wandering about here wild. Ten of them! It's extraordinary."

They dragged out their sleeping-bags, and slid into them. The dogs sniffed round in wonder. The leader sat majestically down by Philip, as if to say, "This boy is my property. Keep off!" The others lay about among the children. Snowy was afraid of the big leader-dog and dare not even go near his beloved Philip. He went to Jack instead. Kiki stayed up in a tree. There were altogether too many dogs for her!

It was a curious sight the moon looked down on that night: four children, one goat, one parrot, one donkey — and ten dogs!

But what had frightened David? And what were ten Alsatian dogs doing in the mountains? You can read the rest of the story in the complete book:

THE MOUNTAIN OF ADVENTURE.

1
Miss Hannah's Windmill

It was a horrid, windy, rainy afternoon. The three children looked gloomily out of the playroom window.

"No good going out to play," said twelve-year-old Jack.

"We've already been for a walk and it was horrid," said ten-year-old Jane.

"I want to do something exciting," said eight-year-old Lucy.

"There's nothing exciting to do," said Jane. "And don't ask us to play snakes and ladders with you, because we don't want to. Or snap, or beggar-my-neighbour. Silly baby games."

"Let's go and ask Mother to come and play with us," said Jack. So they went downstairs and found their mother. She was very busy, and Miss Hannah, who had once been her governess, was with her. She was staying for some time to help in the house.

"Mother, come and play with us," said Lucy.

"Oh, my dears, I can't possibly," said Mother. "I've about twenty letters to write. Surely you can play by yourselves?"

"Shall *I* go and do something with them?" said Miss Hannah. "I'd like to."

The three children looked at Miss Hannah doubtfully. She seemed rather old to them. They didn't think she would be able to do anything exciting at all.

Miss Hannah smiled at them. She had a nice smile, and though it put even more wrinkles into her face it made her look younger and very cheerful.

"Well, Miss Hannah — if it wouldn't be bothering you too much," said Mother, "I'd be very glad if you would go to the playroom with them and see if you can think of something for them to do."

"Come along then," said Miss Hannah, and went upstairs with the children. "Now," she said, "shall we make something? I'm very good at making things."

"What sort of things?" asked Jack.

"Anything! I don't mind what it is!" said Miss Hannah, surprisingly. "You just say what you want and I'll show you how to make it."

"No — *you* make something for us," said Lucy, who wasn't very good with her hands.

"Good gracious — it's much more fun to make things yourselves," said Miss Hannah. "Now quick — tell me what you want to make?"

Jack was standing by the window. He looked out and saw a child running down the street. She held a windmill in her hand — a gaily-coloured paper windmill set on a stick, that whirled round and round in the wind as she ran.

"I know — let's make windmills!" he said. "Lucy would like that — you like those windmills that blow round and round, don't you, Lucy?"

"Oh yes," said Lucy. "Miss Hannah, can you make windmills?"

"Easily," said Miss Hannah. "Now — let me see — what shall we want? We shall want nice stiff paper — crayons — and drawing-pins — and some sticks."

"I'll get the sticks," said Jack. "I know where there are some — in the garden shed. I'll pop on my Wellingtons and mac and go and get them."

"And I'll find some stiff paper," said Jane. "There's plenty in our desks. Lucy, get the crayons, and find some drawing-pins."

Soon all the things were ready on the table. "Now, we only have a little while before tea-time," said Miss Hannah. "So you must all pay attention carefully." She gave them each a sheet of the stiff paper.

"It's just about the right size," she said. "About twelve inches square. Now, is everybody ready? Fold your paper into sixteen squares."

"Oh dear — how?" asked Lucy.

"Baby!" said Jack. "Like this. First you fold your paper into half. Then you fold it in half again. See?"

"Yes," said Lucy, and copied Jack. Jane was doing the same.

"Now fold it in half, and then in half again the *other* way round," said Jack. "That's right. Now open the paper and you'll have sixteen squares. *(See Fig. 1.)* What next, Miss Hannah?"

"Now make a diagonal fold across from corner to corner," said Miss Hannah. "And another one from the other corners. Good! Now — open the paper again." *(See Fig. 2.)*

They all opened their paper squares and looked at Miss Hannah. What next?

"Fold down the top row of squares," said Miss Hannah. They all did that. "Now fold over your *right* hand row of squares," she said, and they did that too.

"Now comes the only tricky bit," said Miss Hannah. "I want you to pull out the top square to a point, and flatten it — like this, look — that's the first point of our windmill."

It *was* a bit tricky pulling out the point, but you can see how it was done in Fig. 3.

"Now turn your paper round and pull out another point in the same way," said Miss Hannah, "first folding over the side squares, of course. That's right. Now do the third point — and now the fourth. Flatten all the points down well."

Jack managed easily. Jane found it easy after the first one, but Lucy made a muddle. Miss Hannah had to help her. "*This* is the way to pull out the points," she said. "Just pull them up like this — and flatten them down."

"My word — it makes a very good windmill," said Jack. "And quite simple too. I often wondered how those men who sold the windmills made them. Now I know! I suppose all we have to do now is to colour them and pin them on to the sticks with the drawing-pins."

"Quite right!" said Miss Hannah. "Make them as bright a colour as possible."

Jack and Jane used their paints and painted the windmill arms bright red, blue and yellow. Lucy coloured hers with crayons. Then they each pinned the gay windmills on to the sticks.

"Let's put on our coats and rush round the garden in the wind with our windmills," said Jane, who wanted to see if hers really worked. "There's just time. Thank you awfully, Miss Hannah."

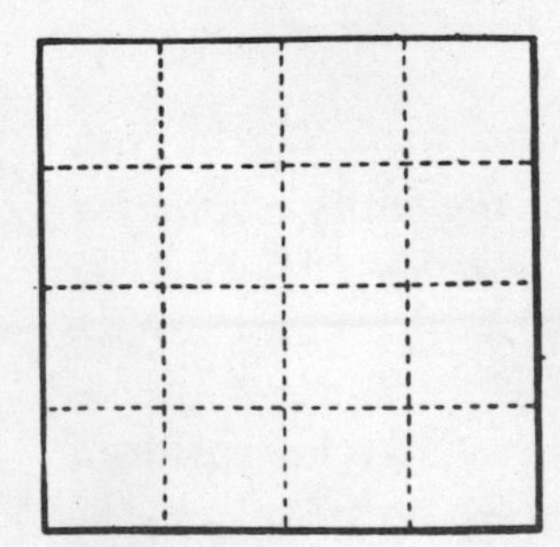

Figure 1

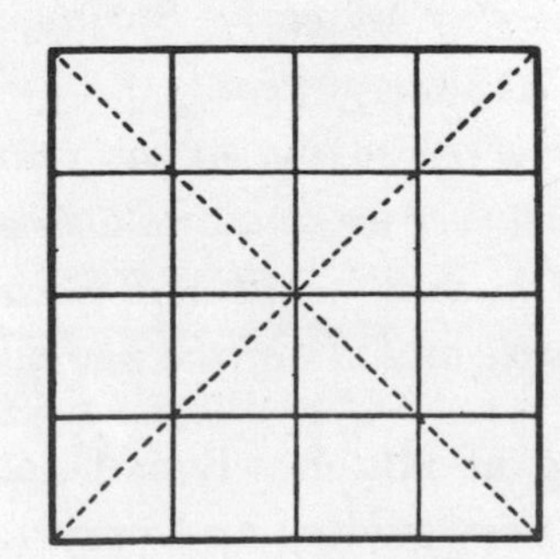

Figure 2

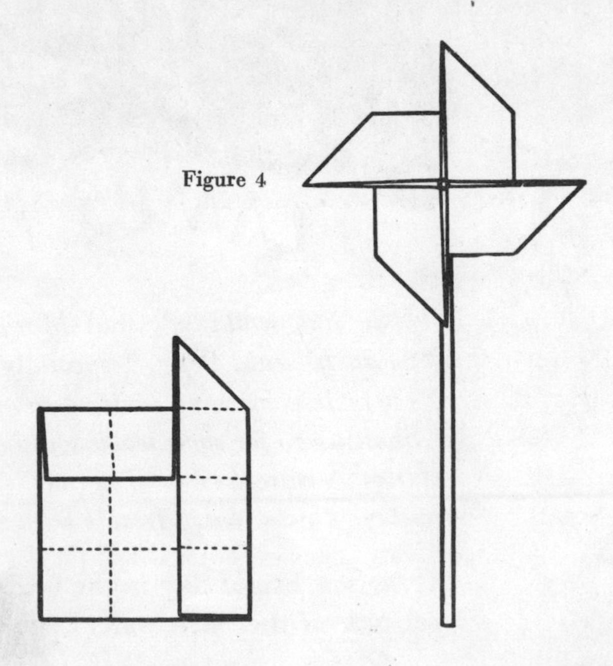

Figure 3

Figure 4

"I do like walking," said Mary, one day in early Spring.
"So do I," said Peter, "especially at this time of year."
"There is something exciting to see at every season of the year," said their Uncle Nat. "Shall we go for some walks together whenever we can, and look out for the many wonderful things Nature has to show us?" "Oh, yes!" said both children together. "Let's start to-day, Uncle Nat." In this book you will find six of the many rambles they had together.

It was a bright day in the beginning of March when Uncle Nat and the children set out on their first walk. Peter was very excited and very talkative.

"I say, there are baby lambs in the big field by the farm," said Peter. "I've seen them — tiny little things, all legs and wriggling tails."

"Yes, and there are lambs' tails all over the hedges," said Uncle Nat.

The children stared at him. Mary pictured little wriggling tails all over the hawthorn hedge. She laughed. "You do say funny things, Uncle Nat. Are you talking about Little Bo-peep's Sheep who left their tails behind them?"

"No, I'm talking about the hazel catkins," said Uncle Nat. "Haven't you ever heard them called lambs' tails before? I think it is such a good name for the long dangling catkin tails. Shall we go and see the little skipping lambs this morning and hunt for some lambs' tails to bring home?"

They set off to the big field. There were about six or seven little lambs there, with black faces, long skippetty legs, and wriggling tails.

"And here are some hazel catkins," said Mary, picking a twig with some green lambs' tails dangling down. "I like them, Uncle Nat. They will look lovely in a vase. Let's pick some more."

They had a pleasant time watching the lambs and picking the lambs' tails. Then they went home and stood the hazel twigs in water. In a day or two the catkins had lengthened out and were turning yellow. Every time Mary touched them they sent out clouds of yellow powder.

"What is the yellow powder for, Uncle Nat?" she asked. "Is it pollen? There are no bees about to take it, are there?"

"The hazel tree doesn't bother about bees," said Uncle Nat. "It uses the *wind* to blow its pollen everywhere. The pollen helps the hazel tree to make its seeds — which are the nuts we gathered in the autumn."

"But – what do the nuts grow from?" asked Peter in surprise. "There are no flowers on the hazel – unless you call the catkins flowers."

"They are flowers – the male flowers," said Uncle Nat. "But there are other flowers on the hazel too – female flowers – the ones that make the nuts. Look carefully along those little twigs you have and see if you can find them."

The children looked. At first it seemed as if there was nothing there but little brown leafbuds — but then Mary spied a bud that had a few tiny red spikes hanging out of it. "Oh, look," she said, "is that what you mean, Uncle Nat? Is this funny bud with red spikes a hazel flower too?"

"Yes," said Uncle Nat. "It is waiting for the yellow catkin pollen to fall on it – then it can begin to make nuts for the autumn. The wind blows the pollen about and some is bound to fall on the little red spikes."

"What a clever idea!" said Mary. "I never knew *that* before. I'm sure not many people know that the hazel tree has two different flowers, Uncle Nat – the long dangling catkin, and the tiny red-spiked bud."

"Well, they only need to look, and they'll see them both!" said Peter.

Just a spot of bother!

Fatty, Larry, Daisy, Pip and Bets — and, of course, Buster the Scottie — are all friends, and delight in solving any mystery that comes their way. Mr. Goon, the village policeman, dislikes them very much, and wishes they wouldn't interfere. There are many books about them — and here is a short story to bring you just a small mystery!

1. MR. GOON IS A NUISANCE.

"LET'S go down to Fatty's house and see if he'll come for a walk," said Larry to Daisy. "It's a gorgeous day — much too good to spend indoors!"

"All right," said Daisy, putting down her book. "Shall we get Pip and Bets too?"

"We'll call for them on the way," said Larry, and went to find his mother. "Mother — we're going for a walk. We'll be back for dinner."

They went to Pip's house and found him and Bets cleaning out the garden shed. "We're off to Fatty's," said Larry. "Things seem a bit boring today — perhaps Fatty will liven them up! Something usually happens when he's around."

Fatty opened the door, grinning. "Hullo! I thought it must be you four".

"Oh, good — we'll come too!" said Bets. "I'm tired of this dirty old shed. Mother told us to clean it out, but we can easily finish it when we come back. Do I look too dirty to come out for a walk?"

"You do rather," said Daisy, and brushed down her dress. The dust flew out in a cloud! "There — that's better. There's a black mark on your cheek, too. Got a hanky? Here, use mine."

They set off together, the four of them, and soon arrived at Fatty's house. They whistled, but there was no reply.

"Must be down in his shed," said Larry, and they made their way down to the bottom of the garden, where Fatty's shed was hidden among the close-growing shrubs and trees. Buster the Scottie was in the shed with Fatty, and he barked loudly and joyfully as he heard their footsteps.

"Wuff! Wuff-wuff-wuff!"

Fatty opened the door, grinning. "Hallo! I thought it must be you four, judging by Buster's delighted yaps. What's up? Anything exciting?"

"Not a thing, Fatty," said Larry. "These holidays are pretty boring. It's a super day — what about a walk? We can take old Buster too; he looks as if he wants some of his fat taken off!"

"Wuff," said Buster, quite agreeing. He was always ready for a walk!

"Well, let's go then," said Fatty, shutting his shed door and locking it. "I feel bored, too. Nothing exciting has happened these hols, and we've only a week left. I haven't even seen our enemy!"

"Who? Oh, that fat policeman, Mr. Goon!" said Bets. "He's been *very* busy, Mother says, going round and warning people about their dogs."

"Their *dogs*? Why, what's the matter with our dogs, all of a sudden?" said Fatty, surprised. "Buster, do you hear that? You'd better be careful!"

The van braked suddenly, and Goon fell off his bicycle in fright. Buster leapt on him in delight.

"Well, the farmers have been complaining that dogs are chasing their sheep, and worrying the lambs," said Bets. "So Goon's been warning everyone not to let their dogs wander."

"Well, Buster's far too scared of big old mother sheep to chase them," said Fatty. "He tried it once, and the sheep ran after him, baaing like mad. I never saw Buster run so fast in my life!"

They went down the road, Buster running in front, his tail wagging fast. A large figure in dark blue suddenly swung round the corner on a bicycle, ringing the bell violently. Buster gave a joyful bark, and leapt at the front wheel.

"Clear orf, you!" said a familiar voice, and a foot kicked out at Buster. The bicycle wobbled, and Fatty called to Buster.

"Heel, Buster! Heel, I say! Sorry, Mr. Goon. You came round the corner so quickly that you startled old Buster."

"That pest of a dog!" said the big policeman, and jumped off his bicycle. "I was just coming to warn you to keep him locked up. The farmers are complaining of dogs worrying their sheep — and I warn you, if I see a loose dog I'm going to have a few words with the owner!"

"Buster's not loose, he's with *us*," said Fatty. "Anyway, he doesn't wander about by himself."

"You just put him on a lead," commanded Mr. Goon.

"I haven't one with me," said Fatty, and walked on with the others. Buster ran back and growled, and Goon hastily mounted his bicycle again, kicking out at the little dog. That was too much for Buster and he sprang at Goon's ankles in delight. The big policeman rode a few feet down the road, still kicking out at Buster, and didn't see a small van coming out of the drive of a house. Fatty gave a loud yell.

"Look out! Mind that van!"

The van braked suddenly, and Goon fell off his bicycle in fright. Buster leapt on him in delight, and Fatty had to rush to pull him off. The van drove round Goon and went off in a hurry. Goon was much too angry with Buster to take any notice of it!

Bets picked Buster up and ran down the road with him, scared that Goon might arrest him and take him away! The others helped poor Goon to his feet, and Fatty dusted him down well.

"That van almost ran over you," he said, trying to distract Goon's anger from Buster to the van. "Coming out of the drive at top speed like that! Not even slowing down or hooting! Might have killed you, Mr. Goon! Did you take his number?"

"No. No, I didn't," said Goon, putting his helmet straight. "Where's that dog? I'll — I'll . . ."

But the others walked on quickly, and left Goon to mount his bicycle again, muttering angrily to himself. It was only when Fatty and the others had turned the corner that something struck Fatty as strange, and he stopped.

"I say — what was that van doing coming out of that drive? The people belonging to the house there are all away — and the house is locked up!"

"Oh, well — it was probably some delivery van — they wouldn't be able to make anyone hear, anyway," said Pip. "Come on, for goodness' sake, or Goon will catch us up!"

2. COME ON, PUSS!

The five children dodged down a little side-turning, and waited till they saw Goon sailing by, purple in the face. "Thank goodness he's gone," said Bets, who was scared of the big, loud-voiced policeman. "Let's go down this lane, then we shan't meet him again."

"Right," said Fatty. "It leads down to the river. We'll walk along by the water."

So down to the river they went, and sauntered by the rippling water, which was very blue that sunny morning. Buster ran along happily until he came to the boat-house, and then went to find his friend, Tom the boatman.

"Hallo, Buster," said Tom. "Where's your master? Oh, there you are, Master Frederick — do you want a boat this morning?"

"Well — it might be fun to pull across the river and go to the primrose woods on the other side," said Fatty. "I bet there are millions there this lovely spring day."

"Well, you can take the Saucy Belle," said Tom. The five children got in with Buster, who at once ran to the prow, and stood there like a small figure-head. He loved a boat!

They rowed across the river, and landed on the opposite side. They tied up the boat and then made their way to the woods upon the hill. On the way up they passed a big empty house, called 'River-View', with a 'To Be Sold' notice-board beside the gate.

"I say — look at all the daffodils in the front garden here," said Daisy, standing at the gate. "Did you ever see such a sight!"

"Let's go down the path and look at them," said Bets. "My word — if this house was in a town, people would be sure to pick these daffies if they saw the house was empty and to be sold!"

But no one had touched the hundreds of yellow, dancing daffodils, and the five children stood and admired them. Buster couldn't think why they stood and stared at such boring things

They rode across the river, and landed on the opposite side.

as flowers! He ran off to explore the garden by himself. He disturbed a cat asleep on a window-sill in the sun, and it yowled in fright when it saw Buster barking below the sill.

Buster leapt at it, and the cat sprang right over his head, and ran to a tree. It was up it in a trice, Buster barking madly at the foot, clawing at the trunk in excitement.

The five children ran to see what was the matter. "Buster! You *know* you're forbidden to chase cats!" cried Bets. "Oh, look, Fatty, the poor thing's gone right up to the top of the tree!"

"Well — I hope to goodness it can get down," said Fatty. "Let's go — and perhaps it will come down by itself when it sees that we've gone and have taken Buster with us."

So they all trooped out of the front gate, taking one last look at the hundreds of yellow daffodils lining the drive under the trees. Bets turned to watch for the cat to come down the tree, but she couldn't see a sign of it.

"Can we come and see if it's still up the tree, on our way back?" she asked Fatty. "It wasn't a very big cat — not much more than a kitten. It might not know how to climb down a great tree like that."

"Yes. We'll come back and have a look, Bets," said Fatty, smiling. "Buster's a fathead. He knows quite well that he can't catch cats or rabbits, but he always *will* chase them! Come on — we'll go primrosing in the woods now."

There were millions of primroses in the woods on the hill, and the five of them gathered enormous bunches to take home. Then they turned to go back to the river.

"Don't forget, we must look up the tree to see if the cat is still there," said Bets, and Fatty nodded. They went in at the drive gates of the big, empty house again, past the 'To Be Sold' notice, and walked by the daffodils. They came to the big tree up which the cat had gone.

They all peered up it, Buster too. "Not a sign of the cat," said Fatty. "It must have come down, Bets. Come on — we'd better go."

The cat was up in the tree in a trice.

But just as they turned to go a sound reached their ears. "Mee-ow! Mee-ow!"

"That's the cat!" said Daisy. "Where is it? That was a frightened meeow, I know it was."

They looked up the tree once more — and then, quite suddenly, Pip caught sight of the cat.

"Look! There it is! Up on the roof of the house, by that chimney!" he said. "See where that tree-branch reaches out to the roof? It must have run along that, and jumped on to the roof. Now it's scared and can't get down."

"I'd better go up and get it," said Fatty, at once. But Larry leapt up to the lowest bough, and swung himself into the tree before anyone else. He was a fine climber, and was soon at the top. He called coaxingly to the cat.

"Puss! Come on, Puss! Come here to me and I'll take you down. Puss, puss!"

"Mee-ow," said the cat, and didn't move. It sat on the roof beside a skylight, near to a chimney, and looked as if it meant to stay there all day!

Larry slid along the branch to the roof, and

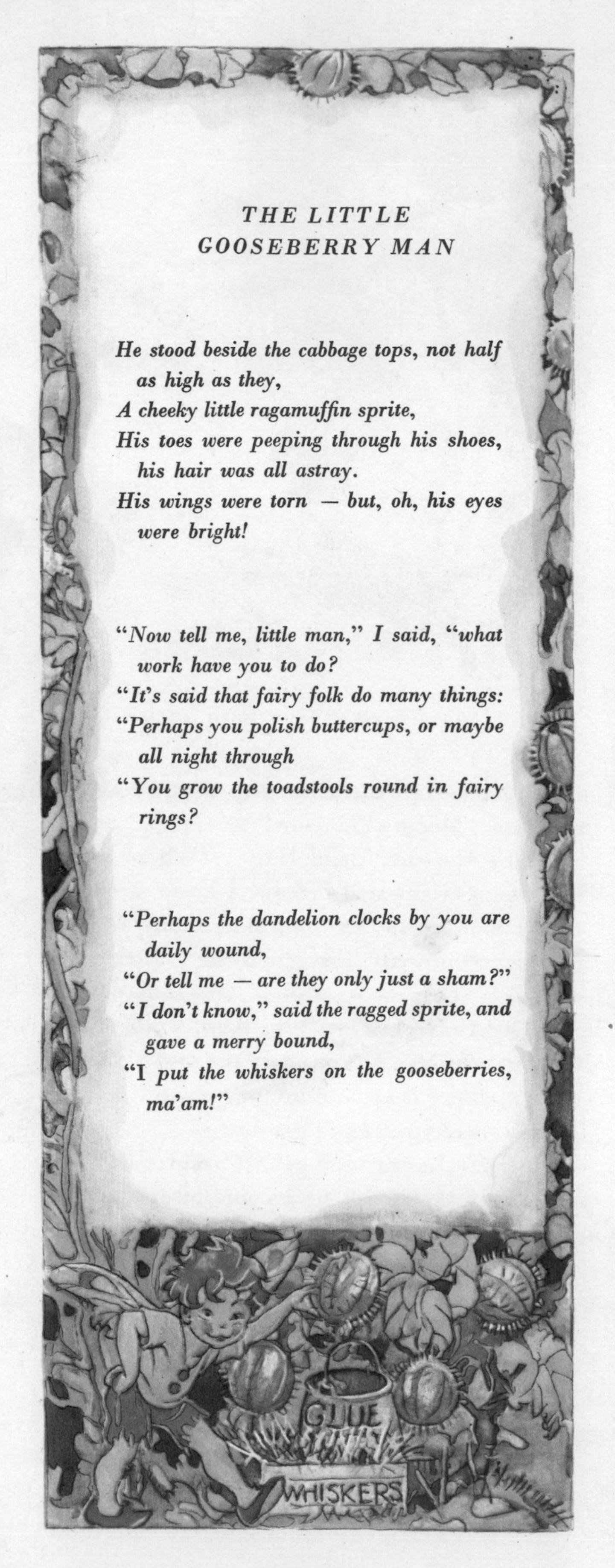

THE LITTLE
GOOSEBERRY MAN

He stood beside the cabbage tops, not half as high as they,
A cheeky little ragamuffin sprite,
His toes were peeping through his shoes, his hair was all astray.
His wings were torn — but, oh, his eyes were bright!

"Now tell me, little man," I said, "what work have you to do?
"It's said that fairy folk do many things:
"Perhaps you polish buttercups, or maybe all night through
"You grow the toadstools round in fairy rings?

"Perhaps the dandelion clocks by you are daily wound,
"Or tell me — are they only just a sham?"
"I don't know," said the ragged sprite, and gave a merry bound,
"I put the whiskers on the gooseberries, ma'am!"

Bets held her breath as she saw him climb from the branch to the tiled roof itself.

"Be careful, Larry, old thing," called Fatty, worried. But Larry was used to climbing, and was not at all afraid. He was on the roof now,

Larry was used to climbing and was not at all afraid.

climbing slowly towards the cat. "Puss!" he said. "Come on, then!" He was now beside the skylight, and the cat only three feet away. He stretched out his arm — and the cat, scared, leapt down the roof, ran to the tree-branch, and half-climbed, half-fell down the tree! It leapt on to a wall and disappeared.

But Larry didn't come down! He sat beside the skylight, peering down into the attic below, looking astonished.

"What's up, Larry? Come on down!" called Fatty impatiently. "Do buck up!"

3. CARPETS! HOW PECULIAR!

Larry gave a shout. "All right! I'm coming! Blow that cat — making me climb all the way up like this. It simply shot down the tree, didn't it?"

He slid down the roof and climbed quickly down the tree. Daisy and Bets were most relieved to see him standing safely beside them. "I was awfully afraid for you," said Bets. "You looked so high up on that roof."

"I saw something a bit queer when I looked down through the skylight there, into a sort of attic below," said Larry. "It was full of rolls of carpets! Do you suppose the people forgot to take them with them?"

"*Carpets!*" said Fatty, astonished. "What do you mean? Wasn't there any old furniture there as well — or boxes — the sort of rubbish you find in an attic?"

"No, *nothing* but carpets," said Larry. "Good-looking ones, too — the kind they call *Persian* carpets. My Granny has one in her hall, and she says it's very valuable."

"I expect the people who are selling the house have stored them there till they sell it," said Daisy. "It would save them storage fees. It costs a lot to pay storage on valuable things, you know."

"Well — if they take long to sell the house, the moths will certainly get at the carpets!" said Larry. "Fatty, do you think we'd better tell the house-agents about those carpets? I mean — if they *have* been left behind by mistake, when the people left the house, it would be a shame for them to be ruined by moths."

"Right. We'll call at the house-agent's this afternoon," said Fatty. "We shan't have time now. We'll have to buck up, because we're all pretty late. Buster, it's *your* fault! Chasing a cat like that!"

"Woof," said Buster, mournfully, afraid that Fatty was cross with him. They hurried down to to the boat, and rowed across the river at top speed. Soon they were running home, all but

"Carpets!" said Fatty, astonished. "What do you mean?"

Fatty completely forgetting about the curious sight that Larry had seen through the skylight.

Fatty thought about it as he ate his lunch, sitting opposite his mother. "Whatever are you thinking about so deeply?" asked his mother, at last, tired of sitting in silence.

"Persian carpets," said Fatty.

"Good gracious! But why think so deeply about *them?*" asked his mother, astonished.

'They're very valuable, aren't they?" said Fatty. "They oughtn't to be left in an empty house, ought they?"

"Of course not," said his mother, even more astonished. "Nobody in their senses would do such a thing. Moths could completely ruin them in no time. What carpets are you thinking of?"

"Oh — just some that Larry was telling me about," said Fatty hastily, afraid that his mother would ask him questions he would find awkward to answer.

"Dear me — I didn't know Larry was so interested in carpets," said his mother. "What carpets are these?"

Fatty changed the subject. "That reminds me," he said. "Have you an old bit of carpet I could have to put down in my shed, mother?"

His mother at once forgot about Fatty's interest in Persian carpets, and for the rest of the meal talked at great length about the old rugs she could spare. Fatty was most astonished to hear of so many!

After the meal he remembered that he and the others were to go to the house-agent's to find out about the house on the hill across the river. Once he could discover who the owners were he could write to them — or telephone — and solve the mystery of the carpets. But probably it wasn't a mystery at all!

He was just going to get his bicycle when Buster began barking loudly, as someone came cycling in at the front gate. "It's Goon!" said

Buster began barking loudly, as someone came cycling in at the front gate.

Fatty, surprised. "Now what does *he* want? Surely he hasn't come about Buster's behaviour this morning. Blow him!"

He went out to meet Goon, anxious that his mother should not hear the big policeman complaining. Goon dismounted from his bicycle and roared at Buster.

"Now you clear orf, you pest of a dog! You wait till I catch *you* after the sheep! That'll be the end of you!"

Fatty felt angry. Why did Goon always have to shout and make himself so unpleasant? He called Buster to him, and made him sit down at his feet.

"What is it now, Mr. Goon?" he said, coldly. "Please don't shout. My mother may be having a rest."

"I've a good mind to send you in a bill for having my suit cleaned," said Mr. Goon. "Look what I did when that dog made me fall off my bike this morning." He showed Fatty a dirty mark all down his coat-sleeve.

"It was that van driving out so suddenly that made you fall," said Fatty. "Not Buster."

"Yes — and I want to ask you something about that too," said Goon, still blustering. "Did you notice the car's number?"

"No. Did you?" asked Fatty. "I saw the name on the side though. But what's all the fuss about? What's wrong with the van? Do you want to prosecute the driver for rushing out of the gate like that?"

"Ha — so you saw the name on the van, did you?" said Mr. Goon. "You just tell me what it was, then!"

"You tell me why, first," said Fatty.

"Well, I want to arrest that driver," said Goon importantly. "He and his pal went to that house, knowing its owners are away, forced the door — and went off with all the carpets! And what's more, it's the third time they've done such a thing! So you tell me the name on that van, see?"

Fatty gave a sudden laugh. "It was the baker's van," he said. "I'm afraid you're on the wrong track, Mr. Goon. Our baker wouldn't steal *carpets*. Carpets! Well, that's very, very interesting!"

4. A NICE BIT OF DETECTIVE WORK

The big policeman stared at Fatty in disbelief. "It wasn't the baker's van!" he said. "That wasn't the baker driving it. I saw the driver, and it *wasn't* the baker!"

"I agree with you," said Fatty. "The thief probably just took the van. I expect he borrows a different one each time he steals carpets, when he hears that people are away for the day, or longer!"

"Yesterday, he went to Lady Burnet's," said Goon. "She'd left two maids there — and the driver told them he was from the cleaner's and had come to take the carpets for cleaning — and they let him have them! He used the *cleaner's* van that time — took it from in front of the shop, bold as you please — and it was found down by the river! Empty!"

Fatty was thinking very, very fast. Should he tell Goon what he knew, or not? Should he tell him of the carpets hidden in the attic of the house across the river? Perhaps he had better . . .

But he changed his mind when he heard the policeman's next words. "If that dog of yours hadn't gone for me this morning, I'd have been able to challenge the driver of that van, and arrest him, and get back the carpets, and . . ." he began.

"You wouldn't," said Fatty. "You didn't even know that the van had been borrowed by the thief."

"I'd have guessed it all, if that dog of yours hadn't gone for me!" said Goon. "That dog's as bad as you are, always interfering with the law!"

"That's enough, Mr. Goon," said Fatty. "I might have told you a few useful things if you'd been polite — but as it is, I'll get in touch with Superintendent Jenks as soon as I can put him on to the carpet thief. I know where the carpets are — and I *think* I know how to get

"That dog's as bad as you are, always interfering with the law!"

hold of the thief. Good afternoon, Mr. Goon!"

And with that Fatty turned his back, and walked down to his shed with Buster pattering at his heels. Mr. Goon stared after him in rage.

"I don't believe a word of it!" he shouted. "Not a word! Why, you didn't even know about the carpets till I told you!"

Fatty didn't answer. He was wondering whether to get hold of his friend, the Superintendent of Police, at once. No — perhaps not. He would look pretty foolish if those carpets that Larry had seen up in that attic were *not* the stolen ones! He would do as he had planned and go to see the house-agent. He rode off on his bicycle within the next ten minutes, and met the others as he had arranged.

"Daisy, you come with me into the agent's," he said. "I'm not going to ask for the keys or anything — only for the address of the people who want to sell the house."

So in they went, and Fatty said "Good afternoon" politely to the young girl there, sitting at a desk. "Could you please tell me the address of the people who want to sell 'River-View' up on the hill over the river?" he asked.

"Oh, I'm sorry," she said. "But someone is buying it, I think. They have had the keys for a week, and they telephoned today to say they would like them for one more day, as they had *almost* made up their minds to buy the place. So it's not much use my giving you the address of the owners."

"Thank you," said Fatty, and walked out with Daisy, thinking very hard. "They've already had the keys for a week!" he said, "and want them for one more day. That means they are probably going to clear out those carpets tonight. What a nerve they've got! Borrowing other people's vans — walking into houses when they know the owners are away, and taking all the carpets — and then storing them up where no one would ever *dream* of looking for them — in an empty house that's up for sale, and to which they've even got the keys!"

"How do they get the carpets there?" asked Daisy. "Would they go across the river by boat — or take them by car over the bridge?"

"That's a point!" said Fatty, thinking about it. "*Not* by the bridge, I think, in case the borrowed vans were seen. So that only leaves the river. They must have a boat somewhere in a creek — a covered punt, probably — and punt across at night. Look, shall we take a stroll by the river and see if we can spot some likely boat?"

Everyone agreed that it would be a very good idea, so away by the river they all went, Buster too. It wasn't long before they found what they were looking for!

"Look — there's a house-boat!" said Pip, pointing down to a little, hidden creek. "And a small boat beside it! Do you think the thieves would choose a house-boat for stuffing the stolen carpets into, and then use the little row-boat at night to ferry them all across?"

"Yes — I believe you're right, Pip!" said Fatty. "If you *are* right, then we ought to find some carpets in this house-boat, waiting for tonight's removal by boat!"

They slid down into the creek, and tried to peer in at the windows of the house-boat. It was called Rockabye, and was a very small one. Its windows had curtains pulled tightly across. Not a thing could be seen inside the boat, which, of course, was strongly padlocked.

They tried to peer in at the windows of the houseboat.

"No go," said Pip, disappointed. "Can't see a thing!"

"Wait a bit!" said Larry suddenly. "Look — what do you reckon this is?"

He was pointing down to the railings that ran round the house-boat's small deck. Everyone looked, and Daisy gave a little cry. "Carpet threads! They must have dragged the carpets over the railings, and one got caught on that nail, and left that little tuft of threads. That *proves* we're right!"

They climbed up to the river-bank again, excited. Pip pointed to the field behind. "Car-wheel marks!" he said. "Look, they must have come down that lane yonder, through that gate, and over the field to the river. It's so deserted here that it would be a hundred to one chance if anyone saw them!"

"We'd better get on to the Superintendent at once," said Fatty, delighted. "Come on — we'll rush back home, and I'll phone. My word — this is just about the quickest mystery we've ever solved!"

5. QUITE A LOT HAPPENS!

The five, with Buster at their heels, just as excited as they were, cycled back quickly to the town. Fatty went to telephone from the post-office — but to his bitter disappointment the Superintendent was not in.

"He won't be back till tonight, sir," said the clerk who answered. "If it's anything important I suggest that you report it to Mr. Goon."

That idea didn't appeal to Fatty and the others at all. They debated what to do. "There's not much time to be lost," said Fatty, considering the matter. "I believe the thieves will probably clear off after stealing this last lot of carpets. They said they wanted the keys only till tomorrow, you remember! They'll take today's haul of carpets out of that house-boat tonight and ferry them across the river in that little row-boat, collect the whole lot out of that attic Larry saw, and probably load them into a removal van — another 'borrowed' one — and that will be the last anyone ever hears of them!"

"Well, we certainly can't stop them by ourselves," said Larry soberly. "We'll simply *have* to tell Goon."

So, very much against their will, the five of them cycled down to the police station after tea that evening, with Buster running beside them. Goon was extremely surprised to see them.

"We've come to put our cards on the table," said Fatty.

"What do you want?" he said roughly. "Come to tell me a cock-and-bull story again about where the stolen carpets are? Well, I warn you, you won't bamboozle *me!*"

"We don't want to bamboozle you," said Fatty, in the polite voice that irritated the policeman so much. "We've come to put our cards on the table. We know where the stolen carpets are — we know how they're taken there — and we know that unless you go there this evening, you'll probably be too late!"

"I'm surprised you don't tell all this to the Superintendent instead of me," said Goon, suspiciously. "It's not like you to come to *me!* I'll take a pinch of salt with all you say, see?"

"Very well," said Fatty, annoyed. "Here is our information. Take it or leave it. The last lot of carpets are hidden in the house-boat called Rockabye, away up the river. They will be rowed across the water tonight, and taken up the hill to a house called 'River-View'. There are dozens more stolen carpets there, probably all valuable, stuffed into the attic. They will probably all be removed tonight, or at the latest, tomorrow."

"I don't believe a word of it!" said Goon. "Not a word! Nobody could know all that! You want to send me on a wild goose chase, just like you've done before! AND I happen to know something that proves you're wrong!"

"What's that?" asked Fatty, surprised.

"*There's nobody living at 'River-View'* " said Goon, triumphantly. "You chose the wrong house to send me to, Mr. Clever — an empty one. Now just you clear out, all of you — and I'll be reporting this silly nonsense to the Superintendent tonight. My word, you'll get a proper ticking-off, you see if you don't."

Bets looked scared. Fatty hustled them all out, afraid that he was going to lose his temper. Well — he had done his best. Now he must wait and telephone to the Superintendent later on, and hope that it would not be too late!

But Mr. Goon managed to get in first, and the Superintendent listened to him in amazement. "But why should that boy, Frederick, pull your leg?" he asked Goon. "It seems to me there may be something in his tale. I'll ring him myself."

And he did — and listened with very much interest to what Fatty had to say! "Goon didn't believe a word, sir," said Fatty. "But I'm sure we're right! Can you send some men up to 'River-View' before it's too late? I wouldn't be surprised if they're going to remove everything tonight."

"I'll send my men up there, don't you worry," promised the Superintendent. "But you keep out of it tonight, Frederick."

Fatty grinned and put back the receiver. *He* wasn't going to keep out of it — or Larry or Pip either! He wouldn't let the girls go, but he and the others would.

And so, about eight o'clock that night, when it was getting dark, the three boys rowed across the river, and then made their way up to 'River-View'. Aha! What was this in the drive, close to the side-door? A small removal

To his horror, a strong hand gripped his arm.

van! Fatty pushed Larry and Pip into the bushes, and hoped that the Superintendent's men would come in time.

To his horror, a strong hand gripped his arm from out of the bush behind him. Fatty froze into stillness. Were the thieves hiding there, then?

A voice hissed in his ear. "I told you to keep out of it!"

Gosh! It was the Superintendent himself, waiting in hiding with six other men! Fatty grinned in delight. And now, who on earth was this, coming down the drive, clomping along on heavy feet?

"It's Goon!" whispered Larry in his ear. "He

thought he'd better come along, after all, to make sure you were *wrong*, Fatty! Hallo — *now* what's happening?"

Plenty seemed to happen all at once! Three men suddenly appeared at the side-door, carrying bundles of carpets, standing in the light of a lamp in the passage behind them. Goon challenged them with a shout.

"Hey, you! What are you doing?"

In a trice the men had dropped their bundles, and leapt at Goon. He went down with a yell, and was promptly heaved into the removal van, with carpets loaded on top of him. Fatty could hear his smothered, furious shouts. A chuckle came from behind him. It was the Superintendent, highly amused.

"Goon has found out that you spoke the truth to him, Frederick," he whispered. "Now, keep back here in the bushes, please. We're going out after the men!"

He blew his whistle sharply, and Fatty jumped. Then, in a crowd, the Superintendent and his men bore swiftly down on the amazed thieves. There were shouts and blows — but it was all over very quickly indeed — far too quickly for the three boys! In no time at all, the three men were locked inside their own removal van, and driven swiftly away to the police station. The Superintendent clapped Fatty on the back.

"A neat little job, Frederick, wasn't it?" he said. "Thanks to you! Another hour and we'd have been too late. Can I give you a lift home? Our police car is under some trees, a little way down the road."

"Well — perhaps you'd better take poor Mr. Goon instead," said Fatty, generously. "He can't feel too good after being shoved into that van and having carpets thrown all over him. He's sitting down on the gravel path over there, groaning like anything."

"His feelings are hurt more than his body," said the Superintendent, hard-heartedly. "If he really didn't believe what you so kindly told him, he shouldn't have come along here tonight. Well — perhaps I'd better give him a lift. Goon — get up. We'll take you back in our car."

"No, thanks, sir," said Goon, staggering up. He had no wish to talk to the Superintendent just then. Why, oh why, hadn't he believed the fat boy when he had told him that very peculiar-sounding story? "I've got this house to go through and lock up, sir," he said, "and then

Three men suddenly appeared at the side-door.

I must get in touch with the owners. There's plenty to do! You take those boys instead."

So, very gleefully, Fatty, Larry and Pip rode proudly back in the big, black police car. "Another mystery solved, eh, Frederick?" said the Superintendent.

"Oh, this really wasn't much of a mystery, sir," said Fatty, modestly. "Let's call it Just a Spot of Bother!"

You will find another story about the Five Find-Outers — "Mr. Goon is Astounded" — on pages 202-205 of this book.

POND DWELLERS

UNCLE Nat's pond was a lovely place. It was an old pond set behind a hedge in a field. The children had gone there with their nets.

"It's a good thing for us there are no ducks," said Uncle Nat. "They wouldn't leave us much

to see. Now, dip in your nets."

Peter and Mary dipped in their nets. Mary brought hers up and gave a squeal. "I've caught two funny little things. Tadpoles, Uncle."

"They *were*," said Uncle Nat, "but now they are little half-frogs. You remember that tadpoles grow into frogs, don't you?"

Water
Beetle

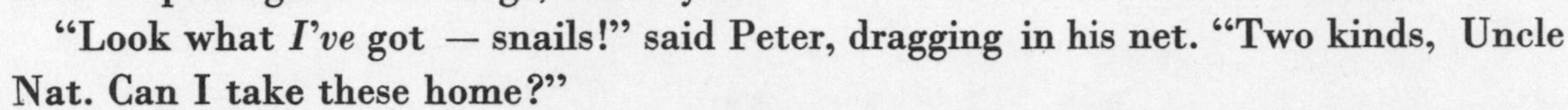

"Look what *I've* got — snails!" said Peter, dragging in his net. "Two kinds, Uncle Nat. Can I take these home?"

"Yes, they will live in a friendly manner with the tadpoles," said Uncle Nat. "Aha, Mary has a beetle. There are two kinds of large water-beetles, Mary: a fierce one that quite likes a feast of tadpoles, and a peaceful one that eats water-weed. You have caught the fierce one."

"Oh then I'd better not put him with my tadpoles, had I?" said Mary. "I don't want them to be eaten."

The beetle went back into the pond, very pleased. Then Uncle Nat put *his* net in, and pushed it about in the mud at the bottom of the pond. He let the water drain out of it and then held it up.

"Caddis-grubs! Just what I hoped. Look, children, these queer little grubs have such a soft body that they make themselves cases to live in."

The children stared at the curious grubs in their tube-like homes. They had stuck together odd bits of pond-stuff and made themselves hard little cases.

"They stick their heads out of their front doors," said Peter in delight.

"They will live at peace with our tadpoles and snails," said Uncle Nat, putting them in the jar. "I should like to take some of those little darting fish back too. Do you see them? They might build one of their dear hard little nests!"

"Nests!" said Mary, "I didn't know that fish ever built nests!"

"Well, sticklebacks do," said Uncle Nat. "We must keep a pair one day and watch them building. Now come along home or we shall be late!"

Flash the Pony

This is a chapter from a book called THE CHILDREN AT GREEN MEADOWS, which tells the story of three children who love animals, and have all kinds of pets. They have always longed for a pony, and in this extract you will read how Francis managed to rescue one.

ONE night something happened. Francis woke up to see a curious light in the sky. What could it be? He jumped out of bed to find out. He looked through the window and saw that there was a fire blazing somewhere.

"I must dress," he thought. "I'm a Scout, and I ought to go and see if I can help. I can at least fill pails of water till the fire-brigade comes."

He was soon out of doors. He didn't wake anyone else. It would only worry Mother and Granny to see the fire and Daddy couldn't possibly go and help. Rex whined to go with him, but Francis shut his ears to Rex for once, as he passed near the kennel.

The fire was at the back of the greengrocer's shop. People were milling about there in a crowd, shouting, and trying to help. The fire-engine hadn't arrived.

"The sheds that the greengrocer uses for his stores and for his delivery boys' bicycles are on fire," said a man. "Goodness knows how it happened, this fire. The greengrocer was taken to hospital today, and his wife's spending the night there with him, he's so bad."

"Nobody's in the shop part at all then?" said a woman. "Well, we must try and save it from burning down — it's bad enough that old Miller's sheds should be burnt down, and him in hospital too!"

A man went by dragging a garden hose. Francis ran to help him. Pails of water were being passed up by a chain of helpers, and the sizzling of water on flames was very loud. A horrible smell of smoke was blown around Francis, and he choked.

He ran out of the smoke, coughing. And then he heard a noise that went right through his heart.

It was the sound of a horse, whinnying in terror! A horse! Where was it? Not in the sheds, surely?

Francis ran to the chain of helpers. "I heard a horse whinnying. Is there one anywhere? Quick, tell me?"

"Why, that would be little Flash the pony,"

said the man. "We forgot all about him. I reckon old Miller kept him in one of these sheds. Poor little thing!"

Francis flew off at once, his heart beating fast. He heard the whinnying again, and ran in the direction it came from. It seemed to come from the last shed of all, where hungry flames were just licking the roof, reaching out from another shed near by.

Francis went to the shed. Yes, the pony must be inside. He heard the frantic sound of hooves as the animal ran round and round the shed, banging into the sides. It whinnied in panic.

The boy had his Scout's staff with him. When he found that the pony's door was locked, he began to rain blows on the old wooden door with his staff. Some of the strips of wood broke, and Francis tore them out. The flames came nearer, and the boy panted as he struck the door again and again.

A man came up to help. He was big and strong, and he soon broke the door down. Francis pushed himself inside while the man went on making the hole bigger. He found the pony very quickly, because the frightened creature ran right into him, almost knocking him over.

Francis caught its mane and held on tightly. He called soothingly to the little thing. "It's all right. You're safe with me. Come along!"

Somehow, he never quite knew how, he got the pony out of the broken-down doorway. He held on tightly to its mane, for the little creature was frantic, and it was only its fear of leaving this boy that stopped it from bolting.

Francis led the pony right away from the fire, and made it stand still. It was trembling from head to foot. Francis couldn't see what the little creature was like in the dark, he only knew that it was small and had a long, thick mane.

He stroked and patted the velvety nose, and spoke in his low, calm voice, saying all sorts of nonsense — but nonsense or not, the pony seemed to understand, and quietened down. It suddenly thrust its head against the boy's shoulder and left it there. Francis was too thrilled for words. It was just as if the little horse had said, "All right. You're my friend. I'll trust you and do what you say!"

The man who had helped to break down the door came to find Francis. "Hallo, Scout!" he said. "You did a jolly good deed in rescuing that terrified little creature. Is he all right now?"

"I think so," said Francis. "What is to happen to him?"

"Goodness knows!" said the man. "All the sheds are gone now — even the one the pony was in. We've saved the shop and the rooms over it, though. Bad luck, for poor old Miller."

"Yes. Awfully bad luck," said Francis. "But what about the pony, sir? I'm afraid he'll bolt if I leave him."

"Where can he go, now?" wondered the man. "He ought to be stabled for the night — but it's so late."

A brilliant idea suddenly flashed into Francis's mind. The old stables at Green Meadows!

"I think I know what to do," he told the man. "I come from Green Meadows — that big old house, you know, not far from the new blocks of flats. Well, we have some old stables there. I could take him there for the night."

A man came up to help break the door down.

"Good idea! Splendid!" said the man. "That will be one good thing done. I'll tell the police you're doing that — they've been asking about the pony. They can come and see you about him tomorrow morning."

So by the light of a rather small moon, Francis led the little pony back to Green Meadows. It went with him willingly. It liked this boy and trusted him. Its little hooves clip-clopped along the road, and in at the back gate, and up to the stables.

"In you go, Flash," said Francis. "That's right. What a good little thing you are. Now, just stand there while I tie you to the post. Can't have you wandering about, you know. I'll get you some straw to lie on. And would you like some water to drink?"

Flash would! Flash was very thirsty indeed, and drank a lot of water from the pail Francis brought. The boy couldn't think what to give him to eat, but he remembered the apples up in the stable loft — getting rather flabby and uneatable now, for it was April. Still, Flash didn't seem to mind at all. He munched four apples with pleasure, and gave little 'hrrr-rrumphs' of thanks. He wasn't really hungry — but the apples were an unexpected treat in the middle of the night.

It was cold in the stables, because the doors were always left open. Francis fetched an old rug and threw it over the pony. "There!" he said. "You can stand up and sleep or lie down and sleep, just as you like. I don't know enough about horses to know which you do!"

He shut the stable doors and went creeping back to the house. Nobody had awakened, nobody at all! Francis was just taking off his clothes when he heard a loud whinny from the distant stables.

It was Flash. He didn't like being alone. He had remembered the flames and the noise and the heat. He felt lonely and strange in these stables. He wanted that boy.

"Well! I can't have him whinnying all night and waking everyone up," thought Francis. "I'd better spend the night in the stables. But I'll want a good supply of rugs."

He had taken off his scout uniform. He pulled on some shorts, two jerseys, and put his long thick dressing-gown over the top. He pulled his eiderdown off his bed and then fetched two rugs from the hall cupboard. Surely he would be warm enough now!

Rex heard him creeping down the path and began to bark from his kennel. Goodness! Now *he* would wake everyone up! Francis stole down to the dog.

"Be quiet, you silly! It's only me. Do you want to come with me? All right — but don't frighten Flash!"

They came to the stables. Flash was lying down in the straw, wide awake. He gave a little whinny when he heard Francis and smelt him.

Francis made himself a pile of straw beside Flash and burrowed into it, on top of a rug. He wrapped himself up in the eiderdown, and pulled the second rug on top of him. Rex flopped down on his legs, and made a nice warm spot there. Flash made another on his left side! In fact, Flash was so very warm that Francis soon threw off the rug.

The pony was happy and at peace. That boy was here with him. He was safe. There was a dog too, but if he was the boy's friend, well, that was all right!

(You will be glad to know that little Flash lived in the children's orchard after the adventure, and was loved and looked after by Francis and his brother and sister.)

The pony was happy and at peace.

A day with little Noddy

Time to get up, Noddy! Wash yourself well, and don't be long!

"Now I'll boil an egg for breakfast!" says Noddy, "and drink a cup of cocoa."

Out he goes to get his little car. He opens the garage and shouts "Good morning, little Car!"

Here's his first passenger. "To the station please!" says Mr. Monkey. Off they go.

"Hurry – the train is in!" shouts a porter. Look, here it is – a toy train in all colours.

And now Jumbo wants a ride to the shops. Oh, what a squash there will be in Noddy's car!

At teatime Noddy goes to Mrs. Tubby Bear's. What a lovely tea he has!

Now he's home again, at the end of the day. Wash your car well, Noddy!

"Oh I'm so tired," says Noddy. "I think I'll go to bed!"

He lights his little candle, and says his prayers by his tiny bed.

Then he jumps into bed and thinks he will read his favourite book just for a little while.

Then down he snuggles and shuts his eyes. Good-night, little Noddy – you do look nice in bed!

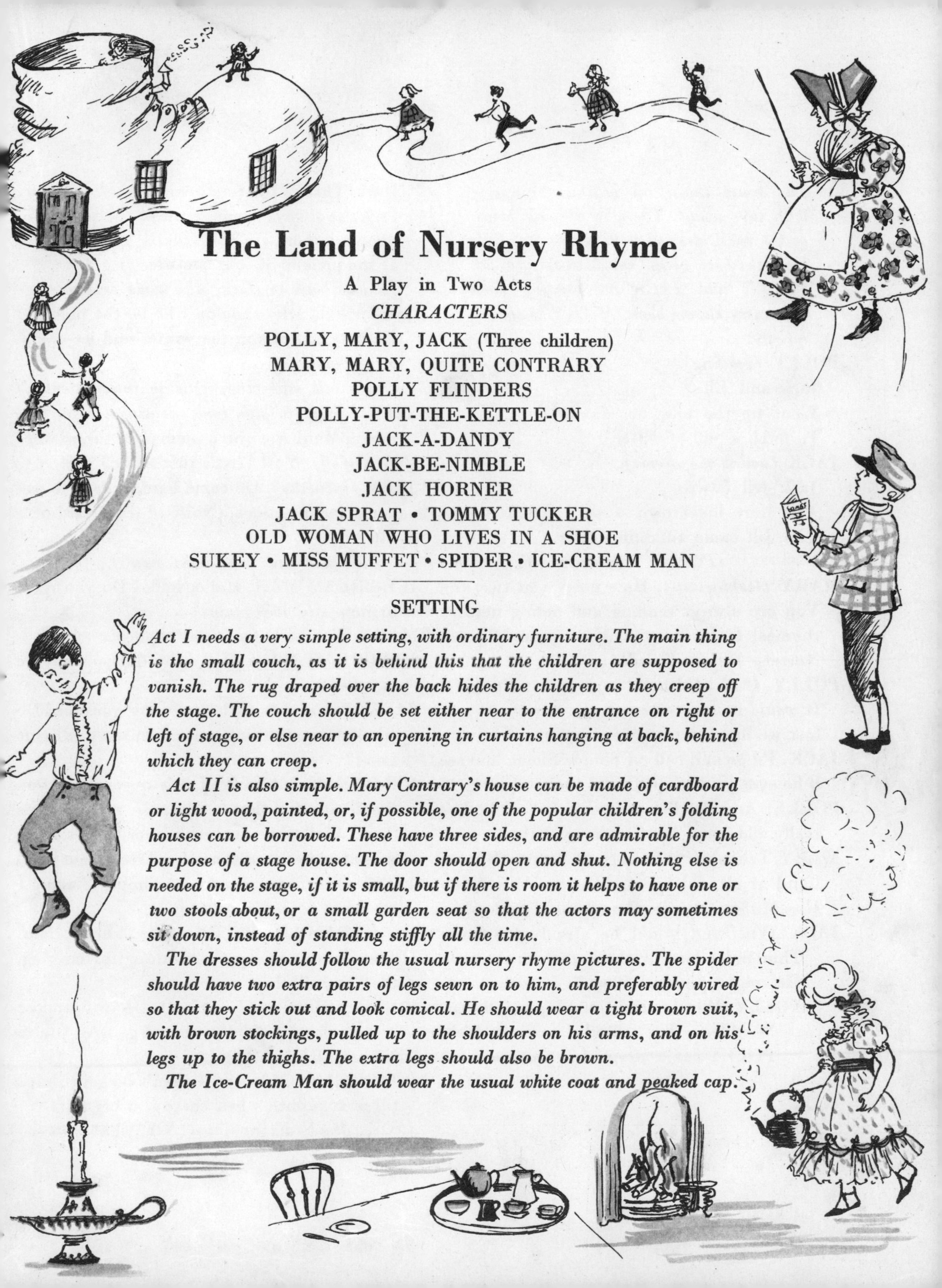

The Land of Nursery Rhyme

A Play in Two Acts

CHARACTERS

POLLY, MARY, JACK (Three children)
MARY, MARY, QUITE CONTRARY
POLLY FLINDERS
POLLY-PUT-THE-KETTLE-ON
JACK-A-DANDY
JACK-BE-NIMBLE
JACK HORNER
JACK SPRAT • TOMMY TUCKER
OLD WOMAN WHO LIVES IN A SHOE
SUKEY • MISS MUFFET • SPIDER • ICE-CREAM MAN

SETTING

Act I needs a very simple setting, with ordinary furniture. The main thing is the small couch, as it is behind this that the children are supposed to vanish. The rug draped over the back hides the children as they creep off the stage. The couch should be set either near to the entrance on right or left of stage, or else near to an opening in curtains hanging at back, behind which they can creep.

Act II is also simple. Mary Contrary's house can be made of cardboard or light wood, painted, or, if possible, one of the popular children's folding houses can be borrowed. These have three sides, and are admirable for the purpose of a stage house. The door should open and shut. Nothing else is needed on the stage, if it is small, but if there is room it helps to have one or two stools about, or a small garden seat so that the actors may sometimes sit down, instead of standing stiffly all the time.

The dresses should follow the usual nursery rhyme pictures. The spider should have two extra pairs of legs sewn on to him, and preferably wired so that they stick out and look comical. He should wear a tight brown suit, with brown stockings, pulled up to the shoulders on his arms, and on his legs up to the thighs. The extra legs should also be brown.

The Ice-Cream Man should wear the usual white coat and peaked cap.

ACT 1

The scene shows an ordinary nursery, with toys about. There is a small couch at the back, draped with a rug that falls from the back of the couch to the ground. POLLY and JACK are reading from a nursery rhyme book. MARY is sewing quietly.

POLLY *(reading).*

Jack and Jill
Went up the hill,
To fetch a pail of water.

JACK *(acting the rhyme).*

Jack fell down *(Falls.)*
And hurt his crown *(Rubs head.)*
And Jill came tumbling after.

(POLLY falls down with a crash.)

MARY *(looking up).* How noisy you two are! You are always reading and acting nursery rhymes! I wonder you don't go and live in Nursery Rhyme Land!

POLLY. Oooh! I'd love to go on a visit there! It *would* be fun to see all the nursery rhyme folk we have so often read about.

JACK. I'd go and call on Simple Simon and see if he ever paid his penny to the pieman!

POLLY. And I'd like to see if Polly Flinders really did burn her nice new clothes.

MARY. I shouldn't like to go to Nursery Rhyme Land at all. I'd be afraid of meeting Little Miss Muffet's spider. I'm afraid of spiders!

JACK. Yes, and you'd be afraid of Johnny Thin too, who put the cat down the well. He might put *you* down!

POLLY. Mary's afraid of heaps of things. We'd leave her behind if we went, Jack!

POLLY *(as a bicycle bell rings outside).* Hark! There's the Ice-Cream Man. You know, Jack, he always reminds me of the pieman in Simple Simon. He has exactly the same face as the pieman in our picture.

(Shows book to Jack, who nods excitedly.)

JACK. Well, why shouldn't he be the pieman? He may sell pies in the winter and ice-cream in the summer.

(Bicycle bell still rings outside intermittently.)

JACK *(going to side and shouting).* Hie, Ice-Cream Man! Are you a pieman in the winter?

VOICE *(off).* Yes! That's just what I am!

JACK *(excitedly).* Do come here. I want to ask you some questions. (Noise of feet heard outside.)

(Enter the Ice-Cream man.)

ICE-CREAM MAN. Hallo, hallo! Do you want to buy any ice-creams?

MARY. No, we haven't any money.

ICE-CREAM MAN. Well, why did you call me in, then?

JACK. To ask you rather a funny question! Do you know anything about Nursery Rhyme Land?

ICE-CREAM MAN. Well, it's queer that you should ask me that — because my home is there! I sell pies there whenever there's a fair on, but in between times I sell ice-cream here!

JACK. Oh! Then you know Simple Simon, I suppose?

ICE-CREAM MAN. Everyone knows *him*! Always trying to get something for nothing, the little silly!

POLLY *(tremendously excited).* Do you suppose — do you suppose — *we* could go with you to Nursery Rhyme Land?

ICE-CREAM MAN. Oh, I shan't be going back till next month when there is a big fair.

JACK *(deeply disappointed).* Oh, what a pity!

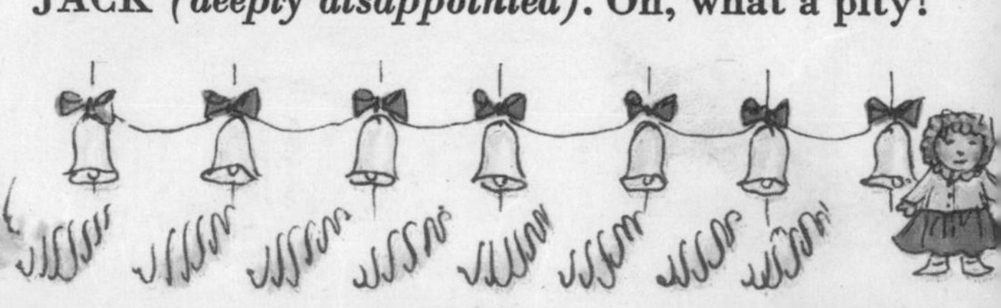

ICE-CREAM MAN. Well, there's no reason why you shouldn't go without me. I can tell you the way!

CHILDREN *(thrilled)*. Tell us, tell us!

ICE-CREAM MAN *(looking round nursery)*. There's a way to Nursery Rhyme Land in every nursery, you know. Let me see! Yes — that couch is the way!

POLLY *(puzzled)*. Whatever do you mean?

ICE-CREAM MAN. Just what I say! If you take your nursery rhyme book in your hand, say a nursery rhyme quietly to yourself over and over again, and go behind that couch, you will suddenly see the way to Nursery Rhyme Land.

JACK *(rubbing hands together in excitement)*. We'll go there! Where's the book? Come on, Polly, come on, Mary!

MARY. I don't want to come. I'm afraid.

POLLY. Pooh! Coward! Don't come then — we'll go without you!

JACK. Here's the book. Now, Polly, say a nursery rhyme over and over again to yourself, quite quietly, and I'll do the same. We will go behind the couch as we say our rhymes.

(Chanting two different rhymes quietly, they take the book and go behind the couch. They crouch down behind, still murmuring. MARY watches in astonishment.)

JACK. Oh! Look! There's the way, Polly! A shining pathway! Hurry down it!

(Sound of running feet, gradually getting softer and softer.)

MARY *(half-frightened)*. Jack! Polly! Don't play tricks on me! Come out from behind the couch!

(There is no answer.)

ICE-CREAM MAN *(with a laugh)*. They've gone, Missie. Look here!

(Swings out couch and shows empty space behind it.)

MARY *(with a squeal of fright and surprise)*. Oh! Oh! They really *have* gone! Get them back, quickly!

ICE-CREAM MAN. Oh, I can't do that. It's a pity I didn't warn them about the Old Woman, though.

MARY. What Old Woman?

ICE-CREAM MAN. The Old Woman Who Lives in a Shoe, of course. She'll think they are two of her children, if she finds them, and she'll take them off to her shoe, and whip them and put them to bed.

MARY. Oh, they'll hate that! Call them back, Ice-Cream Man.

ICE-CREAM MAN. I tell you, I can't do that. I must be off and sell my ice-creams. Good-bye! *(Goes out. Ringing of bicycle bell heard as he rides off.)*

MARY. Oh, dear, oh dear! I do hope Jack and Polly won't get caught by the Old Woman. If only I could warn them! Shall I go to Nursery Rhyme Land too? I daren't! I really daren't! *(Takes up sewing, puts it down again, wanders round room.)* But I can't leave them to be caught by that Old Woman. Why, they might never come back again! I'll go! Yes, I'll go! I can be brave if it's for the sake of other people! I must find another nursery rhyme book, and go behind the couch. How strange it all is! *(Mary finds book, and begins to murmur a nursery rhyme as she goes slowly behind couch. She crouches down. Murmuring still goes on — then she cries out loudly.)*

MARY. Oh! There's the shining path! I'll run all the way down it!

(Pattering of feet, at first loudly then softly till sound ceases altogether.)

END OF ACT 1

ACT II

In Nursery Rhyme Land. There is the front of a small house at the back of stage. Set upright against the bottom of the wall of the house is a row of cockle shells, two or three small silver bells, and half a dozen dolls, who are sitting together. There is a little front door to the house, with a knocker on it. Somebody is humming a song as the scene opens. It is MARY QUITE CONTRARY inside her house.

(Enter POLLY and JACK, excited and pleased.)

POLLY. This must be Nursery Rhyme Land, Jack. Isn't it fun! Oh, look at that dear little house! Whose is it, I wonder?

JACK. Well, I should have thought you could guess, Polly! It must be Mary Mary Quite Contrary's! See — there are the cockle shells, the silver bells, and the pretty maids all in a row!

POLLY *(laughing)*. The pretty maids are dolls! Listen! Can you hear someone humming, Jack?

JACK. Yes. It's somebody inside the house. Let's knock — and see if Mary Quite Contrary comes to the door!

(He knocks loudly. The singing stops. The door opens, MARY QUITE CONTRARY looks out.)

MARY Q. C. Hallo! I thought you were the postman.

JACK. We're not. We're visitors!

MARY Q. C. Oh, you are, are you? Well, I guess you are two of the Old Woman in the Shoe's children! You've come to see if you can have some of my cakes!

POLLY. No, we're not the Old Woman's children. We're just visiting this land.

MARY Q. C. Well, it's a long time since I've had visitors. What have you come to see?

POLLY. Everybody! Humpty-Dumpty, Little Jack Horner, Lucy Locket, Little Tommy Tucker —

JACK. Jack and Jill, Polly Flinders, Simple Simon, Little Boy Blue —

MARY Q. C. *(with hands over ears)*. Oh stop! What a list of people! Well, here's one of them, look!

(Enter TOMMY TUCKER, singing loudly.)

TOMMY T. Half a pound of tuppenny rice,
Half a pound of treacle,
Stir it up and make it nice,
Pop goes the weasel!

MARY Q. C. Tommy Tucker! Do stop that noise.

TOMMY T. *(sulkily)*. I'm only singing for my supper. Can't I sing?

JACK. Oh, are you really Tommy Tucker? I've always wanted to meet you!

(Shakes hands. TOMMY looks rather bewildered.)

TOMMY. Who are you?

JACK. I'm Jack. And this is Polly.

TOMMY T. Jack who? Polly who?

POLLY. Oh, you wouldn't know our names, Tommy Tucker. We're just children.

TOMMY T. *(wagging finger at them)*. Yes — the Shoe-Woman's children, I expect! Oh, I know you naughty children, always running away from the Old Woman, and making her cross! You'll be whipped and put to bed before long, you mark my words!

ACK. Don't be silly. We're not the Shoe-Woman's children. Now do please tell me something I've always wanted to know. Why do you sing for your supper? Doesn't your mother give you any?

OMMY T. No, she doesn't. She says I eat such a big tea that I don't need any supper. So I go out and sing.

ARY Q. C. And people get so tired of his voice that they give him bread and butter or something just to make him quiet!

OMMY T. You always were a horrid girl, Mary Quite Contrary. I don't like you a bit. I hope the Old Woman catches you one day and gives you broth without any bread.

ARY Q. C. *(giving TOMMY T. a push)*. Go away! You're tiresome and rude.

OMMY T. *(pushing her back)*. And you're spiteful and mean. *(Footsteps heard off. All look round.)*

ACK. Who's that?

OLLY. It's a cross-looking old woman!

OMMY T. Help! It's the Old Woman Who Lives in a Shoe! Mary, hide me in your house, quick!

ARY Q. C. Shan't! So there! *(She runs into house and shuts door. Enter the OLD WOMAN, looking round with sharp eyes. She sees TOMMY TUCKER first, and catches him firmly by shoulder.)*

LD WOMAN. So here is one of my naughty children! I *thought* I'd catch you somewhere near Mary Quite Contrary's house! Come to see if you can get one of her new buns, I suppose?

OMMY T. *(trying to wriggle away)*. No! I'm Tommy Tucker! Let me go, Old Woman. Let me go!

OLD WOMAN. You are coming home with me! I've some broth without any bread for you, and —

TOMMY T. I tell you, I'm *not* one of your children! Look over there! Those are your children. They don't belong here anyway, so they must live in your Shoe!

OLD WOMAN *(Letting go TOMMY T. and going over to JACK and POLLY)*. Ah, They *do* look like two of my children.

POLLY. We're not! We're not. You'd know us if we were!

OLD WOMAN. Ah, but I've so many children, I don't know what to do! I certainly don't know them all! Come along, you two rascals. Come along! Your beds are waiting for you in the Shoe!

(She takes off POLLY and JACK, both protesting and wriggling. TOMMY TUCKER skips off quietly the other way. Soon his voice can be heard singing, off. Then it stops. Footsteps heard, and MARY enters, still holding nursery rhyme book in her hand.)

MARY *(looking round in wonder)*. Well, I suppose this is Nursery Rhyme Land! It is really rather exciting. I do wonder where Jack and Polly have gone.

(MARY Q. C. opens her door a crack and peeps out. MARY sees her and smiles.)

MARY. Hallo! I can see you peeping! Are you Bo-Peep?

MARY Q. C. Of course not! I'm Mary Quite Contrary. Haven't you noticed my silver bells, cockle shells and pretty maids all in a row?

MARY. Oh, yes. Very nice indeed, though it seems a funny sort of garden to have, really. I prefer flowers!

MARY Q. C. Flowers are so ordinary to have in a garden! I like something unusual. *Everybody* has flowers!

MARY. I'm looking for somebody. I suppose you haven't seen them?

MARY Q. C. It depends who you are looking for. I've seen quite a lot of people this morning — Jack Horner, Bo-Peep, the Old Woman, Tommy Tucker, Jack and Jill —

MARY. Have you really? Well, *I'm* looking for Polly and Jack.

MARY Q. C. Ohhhhhhh! *(long drawn out)*. Polly and Jack! Well, here comes Polly, look! Pollee! Pol-lee! (Calls.)

(Enter POLLY FLINDERS, sobbing and crying.)

MARY. Whatever is the matter?

POLLY F. I've spoilt my nice new clothes. Look! *(Shows black scorched dress.)* And my mother was very cross with me and slapped me hard.

MARY Q. C. Well, it served you right, Polly Flinders. You always were a careless little girl! Only last week you tried to climb through a blackberry bush and tore your new coat! And who sat down on some wet paint yesterday? Why, *you* did! If I were your mother I'd let you wear a bathing-suit and nothing else, instead of dressing you up in nice new clothes.

POLLY. You're a horrid girl, Mary Quite Contrary. Always finding fault with somebody! I shall tell my mother of you.

MARY Q. C. If you tell your mother of me, I'll tell the Old Woman Who Lives in a Shoe about *you*. And she'll catch you and —

MARY. Oh, please don't quarrel. I thought Nursery Rhyme Land would be *much* nicer than my own land, but so far it isn't!

MARY Q. C. *(offended)*. Well, if that's what you think, I'll go indoors. Polly, this little girl was looking for you. Good-bye!

(She is about to go in, but stops as MARY speaks.)

MARY. I wasn't looking for Polly Flinders, but for another Polly. But I'm very pleased to meet *this* Polly.

POLLY F. Weren't you looking for me then? Well, there's another Polly somewhere about. Polly! Polly!

(Enter POLLY-PUT-THE-KETTLE-ON, carrying a large kettle.)

POLLY 2. Hallo! Who wants me? I was just going to put the kettle on, for us all to have tea.

POLLY F. This little girl wants you.

MARY. Well, I'm afraid I don't really. You're not the right Polly, you see. You're Polly-Put-the-Kettle-On, aren't you?

POLLY 2. Yes. Mary Contrary, just put the kettle on your fire for me, will you? It will soon boil and we'll all have tea.

MARY Q. C. Very well.

(Takes kettle and goes indoors. Reappears later without kettle.)

MARY. I'm looking for *my* Polly and *my* Jack. I suppose you haven't seen either of them?

POLLY F. There aren't any other Pollies here except myself and Polly-put-the-Kettle-On. But there are plenty of Jacks. Look! There

is one coming now! You know which Jack *he* is!

(Enter JACK-BE-NIMBLE, carrying candlestick. He sings as he comes, sets down candlestick, and jumps right over it.)

JACK-BE-NIMBLE.

Jack-be-Nimble,
Jack-be-quick,
Jack jump over the candlestick!

(Everybody claps. JACK looks pleased. Sticks hands in pockets and beams round.)

JACK-BE-NIMBLE. Thanks, folks, thanks. I'm glad you like my little trick. Hallo, who's this? *(Sees MARY.)*

POLLY 2. It's a little girl looking for someone called Jack. We thought it might be you she meant.

MARY. Well, it isn't. It's another Jack. Oh — who's this?

(Enter SUKEY, POLLY 2's sister, looking bothered.)

SUKEY. Polly, I must take the kettle off. They've all gone away!

(All sing "Polly put the kettle on," chanting last line very sadly as SUKEY comes out of MARY Q. C.'s door with the kettle.)

SUKEY. Just boiling too. It's too bad, Polly. We have no end of visitors, and we put the kettle on for tea — then they all go off suddenly, and we don't have tea after all. Bother!

MARY. So it really *does* happen then! I often wondered when I heard your nursery rhyme if you really did put the kettle on and take it off.

POLLY 2 *(gloomily)*. Oh, it happens all right. It happens a dozen times a day. And, you know, the only time anybody *did* stay to tea was when we hadn't put the kettle on! So, although they stayed to tea, they didn't have any! Most upsetting!

JACK-BE-NIMBLE *(jumping over the candlestick again)*. Which Jack does this little girl want if she doesn't want me? Perhaps she wants my cousin? I'll call him.

(Goes to side of stage and whistles loudly.)

VOICE *(off)*. Coming! Co-ming!

(Sound of hopping footsteps heard and JACK-A-DANDY enters, hopping, carrying piece of plum-cake in one hand and stick of sugar candy in the other.)

JACK-A-DANDY. Hallo, everybody! Hallo, Cousin Jack! Are you being very nimble today? Why did you whistle for me?

JACK-BE-NIMBLE. This little girl is looking for someone called Jack. I thought it might be you she was wanting.

MARY. Well, no, I'm afraid he isn't my Jack. Which Jack did you say he was?

JACK-A-DANDY.

I'm Handy-Spandy, Jack-a-Dandy,
I love plum-cake and sugar-candy,
I go into a grocer's shop,
And then I come out, hop — hop — hop!

(Does three hops and grins at MARY. Offers her his plum-cake.)

Have a bit! It's good.

MARY. Oh, no, thank you. All I want is to find m-m-my P-polly and J-j-j-jack!

(Almost in tears.)

POLLY FLINDERS. Good gracious! She's crying! Where's a handkerchief! Quick!

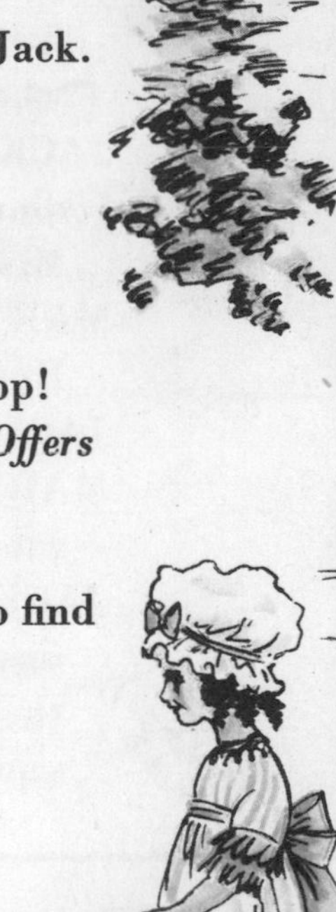

(All produce hankies and try to wipe MARY'S eyes. She can't help laughing.)

MARY. Oh, I don't need *quite* so many hankies, thank you!

POLLY-PUT-THE-KETTLE-ON. Poor child! Don't worry, we'll find your Jack for you all right. Sukey, go and tell the two Jacks who live next door to us to come along at once. It must be one of them.

(SUKEY runs off.)

MARY. I don't think somehow they can be the ones, because my Jack and Polly don't *live* here — they've only just come on a visit.

JACK-A-DANDY. Here they come with Sukey.

(Noise of footsteps heard off. Enter SUKEY with JACK SPRAT and JACK HORNER. JACK SPRAT carries plate with meat on, JACK HORNER carries a pie.)

JACK HORNER. What's the matter? I was just sitting in a corner going to eat my pie, when Sukey came up and dragged me here!

JACK SPRAT. And I was just finishing *my* dinner when I was dragged off too. I've left Mrs. Sprat to eat all the fat though!

MARY. Oh, it's Jack Sprat and Little Jack Horner — and you really do have a pie, Jack!

JACK H. Of course I have! I eat one every day.

MARY. And do you really sit in a corner to eat it?

JACK H. Only when I've been naughty at meals and my mother sends me away from the table. And then, just to be tiresome, I stick in my thumb, — like this — and pull out a plum — like this — and say, very loudly, "WHAT A GOOD BOY AM I!"

POLLY F. Well, if you had *my* mother, you'd be smacked.

MARY. These are not my Jacks, please. My Jack and Polly don't belong here, really. They aren't nursery rhyme folk.

(Enter TOMMY TUCKER. Is astonished to see crowd.)

TOMMY T. Hallo! What's all this? A mother's meeting or boy scouts, or something?

JACK SPRAT. Don't be funny. We're just trying to think how to help this little girl. She wants to find two people called Polly and Jack — and we've tried most of the Pollies and Jacks there are in Nursery Rhyme Land, but none of them will do!

TOMMY T. Well — those two children we saw this morning must be the ones, Mary Quite Contrary. Don't you remember?

MARY Q. C. Of course! But the Old Woman Who Lives in a Shoe has taken them away, Tommy Tucker!

MARY *(with a scream)*. Oh! Oh! That's just what I was afraid of! How can I rescue them?

TOMMY T. *(with a grin)*. We could do what we once did when little Bo-Peep was taken away by the Old Woman.

MARY. What was that?

TOMMY T. We sent Little Miss Muffet's spider after the Old Woman, and she ran away in fright — and Bo-Peep took her chance and escaped! Sukey, go and fetch Miss Muffet's spider.

MARY *(frightened)*. But — but I don't very much like spiders myself, please!

MARY Q. C. *(severely)*. Don't be silly! It's unkind to be frightened of spiders and wasps and moths and beetles. They can't help being what they are, poor things. How would *you*

like it if you were a spider and everyone shrieked at you and said you were nasty?

MARY. I shouldn't like it at all. I suppose it *is* rather silly of me. Well, I won't be frightened of the spider, when it comes.

(Suddenly catches sight of spider coming and screams and runs behind all the others. Enter SPIDER and grins all round. LITTLE MISS MUFFET runs behind.)

MISS MUFFET. Oh, don't be frightened of my spider, little girl. He won't hurt you. He frightened me once, but he said he was sorry and he's behaved like a perfect gentleman ever since.

SPIDER. It's not good manners to scream at me.

MARY *(nervously, coming forward a little)*. No, it's not. I'm sorry. Please, spider, would you go and frighten the Old Woman Who Lives in a Shoe, so that my brother and sister can escape from her?

SPIDER. Certainly, certainly. Always willing to oblige a lady!

(Goes out, waving all his legs.)

MARY. He does look very fierce indeed — almost as if he would eat me.

POLLY FLINDERS. He only eats flies. You needn't be afraid. He lives in a most beautiful parlour in Miss Muffet's house. Doesn't he, Miss Muffet?

MISS MUFFET. Oh, yes — and he talks to the flies in such a gentlemanly manner, and says, "Will you walk into my parlour?" in the sweetest voice.

TOMMY T. Listen! The spider's doing a nice bit of frightening, I should think!

(Shrieks and screams heard off, and sound of running feet. Enter the OLD WOMAN, running and panting. She tears across stage and off the other side, yelling "The spider! The spider! Oh, save me, save me!" *Enter the SPIDER, with POLLY and JACK behind him. MARY rushes to them with a scream of joy and hugs them.)*

MARY. You're safe! You're safe! Oh, thank you, spider!

SPIDER. I could do with a hug too.

MARY. Well — you should make friends with a bear then They love hugging!

POLLY. We didn't think *you'd* be here, Mary!

JACK. Clever girl, to send the spider to save us. You should have seen the Old Woman run!

MARY. I did! Oh, don't you think we'd better go back home before she comes again? Jack Horner, how can we get back? I can't see the shining path I ran down.

JACK H. Why not stay and have tea with Polly-Put-the-Kettle-On? You've no idea how pleased she would be.

POLLY P.K.O. Oh yes — do! I'll go and put the kettle on! *(Disappears into MARY Q. C.'s house with kettle. Comes out again at once.)* It's boiling already! Isn't that good!

TOMMY T. And I'll take you back home again later on, children. I know a short way.

MARY. Oh thank you. Everything's come right again! I'm glad I came to Nursery Rhyme Land — it *has* been an adventure!

POLLY FLINDERS. Well, come again another time.

ALL THREE CHILDREN. We will! We will!

CURTAIN

THE RUBADUB MYSTERY

The following extract (there is another later in the book) comes from one of the six "Barney" Mystery books, THE RUBADUB MYSTERY, published by Collins, in which appear Barney the Circus Boy and his wicked little monkey, Miranda; Diana and Roger, and their cheeky, irresponsible cousin Snubby — and, of course, Loony, Snubby's completely crazy spaniel. In this seaside story the three cousins and Loony the spaniel, and also Barney and his monkey, are all staying at Rub-a-Dub Inn, with Miss Pepper, a friend of the family. The children have just gone to a show on the pier . . . and afterwards some of the Mystery begins to creep in!

IRIS stepped forward to make an announcement.

"Now comes the end of our programme and perhaps the best part," she said with her engaging smile. "The Children's Competition. As usual we have two prizes of five shillings, one for the cleverest boy, and one for the cleverest girl."

A jingling noise from the Funny Man proclaimed that the money was ready and waiting. "Can I go in for it, please, Miss?" said the Funny Man pathetically. "I'm not nearly as rich as all these children here. I can sing 'Three Blind Mice' well, I can, really."

Iris went on with her little speech. "We don't mind what you do — sing, dance, recite, play our piano, tell us a funny story — or even do a bit of conjuring that will put Mr. Marvel into the shade. Now come along — who'll begin?"

Two small girls and a boy pushed their way eagerly to the stage. Another girl followed, and two more boys. Roger gave Snubby a nudge. "Go on! Do your stuff too, Snubby."

But Snubby was unaccountably overcome with nerves, and he glowered at Roger. "I'm not going to make a fool of myself, so shut up."

The children proved very ordinary indeed. Two of the girls played the piano, thumping very loudly. One boy sang a comic song, of which nobody could hear a single word.

Another small girl did a competent little step dance, but was obviously so conceited that nobody clapped very much except her fond and admiring Mamma, who must nearly have worn the skin off her hands.

Then a boy about Snubby's age gave a recitation at such a speed that nobody could follow it at all. He then retired from the platform, also at top speed, quite overcome by his effort.

The third boy refused to perform at all. He stood up on the platform the picture of misery.

"I've forgot me words," he kept saying. "I've forgot me words. Mum, what's me words?"

Mum had apparently forgotten them, too, so the small boy left the platform in tears.

"Now now, children!" said Iris reprovingly. "I'm *sure* there's somebody else who can try for the five shillings. We do badly want another boy."

"Let *me* try, Miss, do let *me* try," urged the Funny Man, putting on a little-boy voice. "I can do things lovely! Oh yes, I can! I'm top of my form, I am, for singing and whistling." He pursed up his mouth to whistle, but hard as he blew, no sound came. So he produced a big whistle from his pocket and blew on that, making Iris jump violently. Every one laughed, he was so idiotic.

"One more boy!" urged Iris. "Just one. Then we shall have had three girls performing and three boys."

The Funny Man came to stand beside Iris. He looked straight at Snubby. Then he pointed at him. "Look, Iris," he said, "there's the World's Wonder down there. See him? Chap with red hair, turned-up nose and freckles! Finest banjo player the world has ever seen. Pays a hundred pounds for each of his banjos. Whew!"

Snubby solemnly tuned up the strings of his banjo.

Every one craned necks to look at Snubby. He went scarlet to the roots of his red hair. "Come on, son!" cried the Funny Man. "Shy as a girl, are you? Not you! Come on up and play us your banjo. Tell us your tune and the pianist will accompany you."

"Go on, Snubby," said Roger, "You've got to, now. Those other boys were frightful."

Snubby went up to the platform, pretending to carry an imaginary banjo, half annoyed, half pleased at the Funny Man's patter. He stood facing the audience. The Funny Man solemnly placed a chair beside him. "To put your leg up on," he informed him. "That's a heavy banjo you have there. Rest it on your leg, mate. Now — what's your tune?"

Snubby suddenly entered into the fun of it. He laughed. "I'll play you 'What's the time when it's twelve o'clock'," he announced, and put his leg up on the chair. The song he had chosen was very popular just then, a silly jigging tune that was admirable for the banjo. The pianist nodded. He knew the tune well.

"I must just tune up," said Snubby, and he solemnly tuned up the strings of his imaginary banjo, imitating twanging noises as if he really were screwing the wires to their correct pitch. People began to laugh.

"Right. Ready?" said Snubby to the pianist. "Not too loud, please. Tune all through, the chorus twice."

He brought his hand down on imaginary strings and made a startling twanging noise. Then off he went, twanging away with his right hand, making a most remarkable banjo-like noise that followed the tune absolutely correctly. Snubby could make his noises very loudly, and the pianist did not drown him at all, but followed him perfectly. They made an excellent pair.

"Twang-a-twang-twang-twang, twang-twang-twang," went Snubby, and ended off with what sounded like a marvellous chord. He put down the leg that was supposed to be holding up the imaginary banjo and bowed solemnly.

He got more applause than any other member of the show had been given, even more than Mr. Marvel! He looked such an odd, cheeky, amusing fellow with his red hair and wide grin. Every one yelled for more.

"One more — can you manage it?" asked the Funny Man, delighted. "Any other instrument?"

"I've happened to bring my zither," said Snubby solemnly, and put down his imaginary banjo and took up his imaginary zither. "I'll have to sit down for this, please."

He sat down, and once more he and the pianist gave an extraordinary performance together. Snubby reproduced the harp-like sounds of a zither perfectly, and instead of a jiggy song, he chose a romantic tune, "If I could only give you the moon." He didn't sing it, of course, but made the sound of a zither playing the tune. It was most remarkable. Every one listened intently, Miss Pepper feeling more surprised than she had ever felt in her life.

Fancy *Snubby*, the crazy idiotic *Snubby* holding a big audience like this with just a little make-believe! Roger and Diana felt very proud to think they had such a clever cousin!

The tune ended. The Funny Man bowed to Snubby. "Quite a maestro!" he said, and Snubby wondered whether he was being rude or complimentary. He had never heard the word before, and didn't know that it meant first-class. But the Funny Man was delighted with him. He turned to the audience. "And now to give out the prizes," he said. "We award the girl's prize to little Lorna Jones for her step dancing."

There was very slight applause. Certainly Lorna had been good, but nobody had liked the little show-off.

"The boy's prize goes — of course — to our young friend here, for . . ."

Snubby walked home in a whirl of excitement.

But the rest of his words were drowned in claps and stamps and cheers. Evidently everyone approved of that award. Snubby, redder than ever, bowed and took the five shillings. What an evening! Whoever would have thought that his crazy habit of strumming imaginary musical instruments would have brought Snubby such tumultuous applause?

Snubby walked home in a whirl of excitement. "Now don't let all this go to your head," said Roger, afraid that Snubby might become quite unbearable. "After all, you can't *really* play the banjo or the zither — and you can only pick out 'chop-sticks' on the piano. You're no musician, really."

"And for goodness' sake don't play banjos and things all over the hotel," begged Diana. "They won't like it a bit if you do."

Snubby took not the slightest notice. "I've been wondering if I could imitate an organ," he said. "Or a drum."

"*No*, Snubby," said Miss Pepper firmly. "Oh dear, here comes Miss Twitt. Hurry!"

But Miss Twitt was determined to pile praises on Snubby. "The little wonder!" she said, as she hurried up to them. "What a little marvel! The clever little boy. He's a born player, isn't he, Miss Pepper?"

"Well — I wouldn't say *that*," said Miss Pepper. "He can't play a note, actually."

"Fancy that! It just shows how wonderful he is to make people think he *can* play!" prattled Miss Twitt. "I *quite* thought it was a real banjo. He really *ought* to join the pierrots, oughtn't he? Every one would come to hear him!"

Miss Pepper glanced at Snubby and was horrified to see a pleased and fatuous smile on his face. He was drinking it all in!

"Snubby's little tricks are quite all right to amuse his friends at school," she said firmly. "But that's really all they are. It's silly to think them anything else, Miss Twitt."

Fortunately they had now reached the inn. "I want a drink," announced Snubby. "All that twang-a-twanging has made me thirsty. Can I have a lemonade, Miss Pepper — two if you like. Oh, I say — wait a bit, though — I'd forgotten my five shillings. Drinks all round, please. What'll you have, Miss Pepper? Miss Twitt? Orangeade? Lemonade? Or go a splash and have ginger beer?"

Diana began to giggle. Snubby really could be very funny.

Miss Pepper ordered the different drinks and then sent all three children, and a very sleepy Loony, up to bed.

"It's late," she said. "Very late. Take your orangeade with you. No, Snubby, I don't care if you have five shillings or ten shillings, you can't have more than one orangeade. No, Loony can't have one either. Water is quite good enough for him."

Snubby went off sorrowfully. He had hoped to stay downstairs until Iris, Mr. Marvel and the Funny Man came back, and also Professor James, who had still not returned. Praise from

Miss Pepper sent all three children and a very sleepy Loony up to bed.

them would be worth a hundred times more than fulsome words from Miss Twitt.

Snubby was too excited to go to sleep that night. Roger snored gently and peacefully while Snubby tossed and turned, his mind full of wonderful plans. He would practise more and more imaginary instruments to play. He would appear on platforms in great halls. He would broadcast — perhaps he wouldn't, though, because people might think he was *really* playing

Snubby went up the staircase cautiously.

a banjo or zither or guitar — they wouldn't be able to *see* that he hadn't really got one.

Well, what about television, then? That would be the thing. And what about a drum? He was sure he could make that big BOOM-BOOM noise. He began to practise it very softly. Then he couldn't resist doing a very loud BOOM!

And then a most frightening thing happened. As soon as Snubby had delivered his BOOM, another BOOM came — a terrific one, muffled and very frightening. The inn shook. Snubby sat up in bed, scared.

"Bombs!" he thought. "No — can't be. Of course — it's an explosion in the Submarine Bay. Some experiment like the one we heard the other day."

He thought for a moment. "But wait a minute — this is the middle of the night — about half-past two, I should think. They wouldn't experiment then, and wake everyone up."

The noise hadn't, however, awakened Roger, who was in his deepest sleep. It hadn't awakened Diana either. Miss Pepper had heard it, and had sat up, listening. But as there was no more noise she had lain down again.

Snubby felt restless. He couldn't possibly lie down and go to sleep to-night. A thought flashed into his head. He would go up that little stairway that led to the skylight, open it, and peer out. He *might* be able to see something through that cleft in the cliff — something down in the Submarine Bay!

He slipped out of bed and went to the door. He opened it and went out on to the dark landing. Nobody seemed to be stirring. Probably they hadn't heard the noise then.

Snubby stole to the little door that shut off the steep staircase. He opened it quietly. Yes — there was the staircase — he could feel it with his foot though he couldn't see it. He went up cautiously. It was a clear night and Snubby could see stars shining through the little square of glass set in the middle of the trap-door that opened on to the roof.

He opened it, pushing it back carefully, so as not to make a sound. He looked out.

Gosh! Something *had* happened down in the Submarine Bay. Snubby could see quite clearly through the cleft in the cliff. Far away, on the other side of it, was the bay, and something was burning there, on the water. Searchlights were playing here and there. Snubby held his breath. Something had happened. Some awful accident, perhaps. He wished he could see more.

"Perhaps if I climb right out of the trap-door

I can find a bit higher place to see from," he thought. "It would be quite easy."

He climbed to the topmost stair and found it simple to get out on the roof, which, just there, was flat. Snubby looked round. There was a rise in the roof just to the right of him, where a set of chimneys rose up together. He could sit on the little rise, beside a chimney.

He made his way cautiously across to the rise in the roof, and crawled up it on hands and knees. Now he was by a chimney. But the wind swept him that side, so he crawled round in between two chimneys where he was well protected. One chimney was warm — good!

But to his disappointment he couldn't see much more of the bay than he had seen before, although he was now a little higher. Searchlights were still criss-crossing, and the flames of whatever was burning were still as high. Perhaps a submarine had exploded and was on fire?

Snubby cuddled up to the warm chimney, feeling very daring to be out on the roof in the middle of the night. He suddenly sniffed the air.

He could smell something. What was it? Cigarette smoke! Couldn't be! No one else was up on the roof in the middle of the night — smoking a cigarette too!

He craned his neck round the chimney, and saw, in the distance, a tiny glow, the red, burning end of somebody's cigarette. Someone else had heard the explosion then and had come to see what could be seen.

He saw the burning end of someone's cigarette.

He soon saw that the glowing end was just where the trap-door opened on to the roof. Somebody must be standing on the stairs there, looking out and smoking. Snubby was just about to give a low call to tell them that he, too, was there, and had heard everything, when he stopped himself.

No. He'd get into a frightful row for being out on the roof at night. If Miss Pepper heard of it she would be furious. There wouldn't be any second helpings for the rest of the holidays! Silence was best. But who *was* it there? Snubby screwed up his eyes, but he could only make out a blob of a head with the glowing end of the cigarette in front.

After a while the smoker finished his cigarette and threw it down the roof. Snubby heard the soft creak of the stairs. Somebody was going down them — but that somebody had closed the trap-door first! Snubby's heart missed a beat or two. He could imagine himself sitting out on the roof all night — falling asleep — rolling down the roof — oh, how simply horrible!

He crept across to the trap-door. As he got there, a light sprang up in the window of a room some distance away. Snubby stopped. Who was in there? Probably, whoever it was, was the smoker of a few minutes before — he must have returned to his room and switched on his light. Snubby decided to see who it was.

He crawled to another position, and found that he could look right across the roof into the lighted room. The curtains were drawn across, but there was a space left in the middle.

"Gosh! It's old Professor James!" said Snubby. "What a good thing I didn't let him know I was up here. He'd have told Mrs. Glump and Miss Pepper and got me into an awful row!"

He tried the trap-door with a trembling hand. Had the Professor slipped the catch into place, so that it could not be opened?

With an enormous sigh of relief Snubby found that he *could* open it. Thank goodness! He swung it back, and then clambered on to the narrow wooden stairway. He closed the trap-door quietly and then climbed down the stairs. He opened the door at the bottom, went on to the landing and back to again his room. Roger was still fast asleep.

Just as he was about to shut his door he saw a line of light under a door nearby. It was Mr. Marvel's door. So *he* had heard the explosion too. Snubby debated whether to go in and have a chat about it — surely Mr. Marvel would welcome him now that he had given such a fine performance in the show!

He decided against it, however. Mr. Marvel wasn't quite the person to enjoy a midnight chat. He might start to do a bit more unpleasant magic on Snubby!

In the morning the whole inn was agog with the news of the explosion in the night. So were the papers.

In the morning the whole inn was agog with news.

"GREAT EXPLOSION IN HUSH-HUSH BAY," said the headlines. "WAS IT SABOTAGE? ARE OUR SECRETS SAFE? INHABITANTS OF SURROUNDING TOWNS ALMOST HURLED FROM THEIR BEDS."

"What a lie!" said Snubby. "The bed just shook, that's all. And you didn't even wake, Roger. I did!"

"Did you?" said Roger. "Was it really a big explosion?"

"Terrific," said Snubby. "Tremendous. Louder than thunder. I got out of bed and went up that stairway to look out of the trapdoor — and I saw something burning like anything. And searchlights going like mad over the bay."

"Sh! Miss Pepper will hear you," said Diana. "She'd be furious if she thought you went wandering about at night — especially up to the roof."

"She didn't hear," said Snubby. He glanced round. Old Professor James was nearby reading a newspaper. He was deaf so he wouldn't have heard either. Mr. Marvel and the Funny Man were also near — they would have heard, but probably they didn't know about the staircase anyway.

"I did something else too," said Snubby, lowering his voice. "I got out on the roof and sat beside a jolly warm chimney. Somebody else came up the staircase and looked out too. The old Professor, I think. Fancy *him* hearing the explosion and not you, Roger!"

"I expect the vibration woke him, not the noise," said Diana. "I say — it's pretty serious, isn't it? One of our newest submarines blown up to the surface — and then burnt to nothing! I do wish you'd woken me up, Snubby!"

"You'd have hated seeing it," said Snubby. "Is it sabotage, do you think? I mean — would it be possible for any one to get into the bay and do a thing like that to damage us? I should have thought things were much too strict and closely guarded."

"It was probably an accident," said Roger. "You can't have successful experiments without accidents. Look at the things that happen in the lab, at school!"

"Oh well — we *plan* some of those," said Snubby. "A bit of well-planned trickery! All the same — I'd like to know if it *was* an accident. I don't want to think of people somewhere around planning to blow up more submarines — especially while we're staying here."

"Why? Are you afraid of being mixed up in another mystery?" asked Roger with a grin.

All that happened was that the handle came off.

"*Afraid!*" said Snubby with scorn. "I *like* mysteries. I dote on them. But this isn't a mystery, it seems to me. I bet it's an accident."

Whether it was or not they didn't learn from any of the papers that morning or evening. The Press seemed to shut down on the incident, which annoyed the children very much.

That afternoon was wet. The rain poured down and the children looked gloomy.

"It's a glumpish afternoon," said Snubby. "What shall we do? Shall I practise my banjo?"

"Not unless you go up on the roof or somewhere far away," said Roger. Snubby had produced his imaginary banjo, zither, guitar and harp at different times that day, and Roger and Diana were getting a little tired of the remarkable twanging, zizzing, buzzing sounds produced by Snubby.

"Let's go up that little stairway and see if the poor old submarine is still burning," said Snubby. "I promise I won't take any musical instruments with me!"

They ran upstairs to their landing and went to the little door that enclosed the staircase. Snubby turned the handle. But the door wouldn't open!

"What's the matter with it? Is it stuck?" he said, and pulled violently. All that happened was that the handle came completely off in his hand and he sat down heavily on a startled Loony.

"Ass! You *would* do that!" said Roger.

"Things always come off in my hand," complained Snubby. "Now what shall we do?"

"You'll have to go and own up to Mrs. Glump," said Diana. "Go on, Snubby. If you were brave enough to get out and sit on the roof last night, surely you're brave enough to confess to Mrs. Glump."

So Snubby had to go and find Mrs. Glump. She was in a peculiar little den, adding up rows and rows of figures, and didn't look at all pleased to see Snubby. He explained what had happened.

"But why did you pull at the handle so violently?" asked Mrs. Glump, resting her face on her four or five chins, and looking most majestic. Snubby wished he had a few chins he could look majestic with too. He felt very small beside Mrs. Glump, and she made him feel like a naughty little boy.

"Well, I pulled hard because the door stuck," said Snubby. "It's locked, I think."

"Locked! But the key would be in the lock anyway," said Mrs. Glump.

"There wasn't a key. I looked," said Snubby. "I'm sure it's locked, Mrs. Glump. I thought *you* must have locked it. I'm sorry about the handle. I've still got one and sixpence left out of the five shillings I won at the pierrot show yesterday. Would one and six pay for a new handle?"

"I expect so," said Mrs. Glump. "But I'm sure Dummy has an old one he could fix on quickly. Go and ask him. And I hear I must congratulate you on winning the prize yesterday. Let me see — you played the banjo, didn't you?"

"Not a real one. My imaginary one. Paid a hundred pounds for it!" said Snubby with a grin, and immediately began to play a jigging, strident tune, his voice twang-twanging exactly like a banjo.

Mrs. Glump began to laugh. She had a very curious laugh. It seemed to begin somewhere deep down and then rumbled all the way past her magnificent chins, and came out as a very hearty affair indeed.

Snubby stopped, bowed and grinned. "You're a caution," said Mrs. Glump. "Get on with you! Go and find Dummy about the handle. And don't shut my door too violently in case the whole *door* comes off in your hand."

Snubby went out, pleasantly surprised. She wasn't really glumpish at all! He made his way to the kitchen to find Dummy, who was polishing some horse-brasses one by one and making a very good job of it.

"Hallo, Dummy. Can I help you? I collect horse-brasses too," said the cheerful Snubby. "I say, did you hear about me winning the five bob at the show last night?"

Dummy listened and nodded. "You," he said. "You win. Good boy."

"My word, you *are* a chatterbox to-day," said Snubby, rubbing vigorously at a brass.

"What you do?" asked Dummy earnestly.

"This," said Snubby, and played his imaginary banjo again. To his enormous surprise, Dummy also picked up an imaginary banjo and began to twang it, making a most peculiar noise as he did so, almost as good as Snubby's!

"Here — what's all this?" said a voice, and the face of the young waiter poked round the door. "Some band performing here?"

Dummy fled at once, out into the back-yard. He sat down, blinking his eyes, confused. Years and years ago he had had a real banjo and he could play it. But when he had fallen from the rope, during a wire-walking act in the circus he was in he had hurt his head — and after that Dummy was different. Poor Dummy!

Dummy stared at Snubby and then leaned forward.

He sat till his mind cleared a little. He began to smile. Yes — he remembered his old banjo — and the tunes he played. He twanged imaginary strings again.

Snubby came into the yard to find him. "Oh, there you are, Dummy. I say, I forgot to tell you what I wanted you for. Have you got a spare door-handle? I've somehow pulled off the handle of the door that shuts in that little stairway leading to the roof."

"Roof," said Dummy. He stared at Snubby and then suddenly leaned forward. He whispered loudly in his ear. "Mind bad men up there! Bad men!"

Snubby drew back, startled. Dummy smiled and nodded at him. Then his face grew solemn again. "Bad, bad, bad," he whispered again. "Dummy see. Dummy watch. Dummy follow. Bad!"

Snubby looked at Dummy doubtfully. Poor old fellow — what peculiar imaginings had he got now? He couldn't imagine Dummy watching people and stalking them! Snubby decided to humour him.

"Snubby see. Snubby watch. Snubby follow,"

he said, equally solemnly. "Gosh, we sound like Red Indians or something! Dummy, where's an old door-handle? Let's find one and go in. I'm not too keen on sitting out here in the rain — twang-a-twang-twang-twang, zizz-a-zizz-ziz-ziz. Ker-plonk! There — I knew a string would bust if I played out in the rain. See that?"

He held out his imaginary banjo, and Dummy laughed delightedly. It was the first time Snubby had heard him laugh. It was a ripple, just like a very young child's. Snubby patted Dummy on the back.

"That's right. Laugh your troubles away! Have you such a thing as a door-handle, for the third time of asking?"

Mr. Marvel was standing outside his door.

Dummy had. He produced one from a shed and went upstairs. He was clever with his fingers and had soon fixed it. He gave it a pull.

"Locked," said Snubby. "And the key's gone. Who took it? And why? I tell you, Dummy, there were mysterious goings-on up here last night!"

"Indeed? And what were they?" said a voice.

Snubby jumped and turned round. Mr. Marvel the conjurer was standing outside his door. Snubby thought furiously. No — he wasn't going to give anything away and get himself into trouble.

"Oh, nothing," he said airily. "I was just putting the wind up old Dummy. I say, sir — that was a wizard act you put on last night. How did you do all that magic?"

"That's *my* secret," said Mr. Marvel. "Did you hear the explosion last night?"

"Yes. I jolly well did," said Snubby. "Did you?"

"No, I didn't," said Mr. Marvel, which surprised Snubby very much. Hadn't he seen a line of light under Mr. Marvell's door when he, Snubby, had come down from the roof to go to bed again?

"I saw a light under your door, though," blurted out Snubby, and could have kicked himself for saying so.

"Indeed? And what were *you* doing out on the landing at that time of night?" said Mr. Marvel at once.

"Just peeped out to see if any one was awake after the explosion," said Snubby. "I say, sir — you *were* clever at the show last night!"

But Mr. Marvel was gone. Snubby was left staring at a closing door. He made a face at it. All right — *be* snorty, Mr. Marvel! You *were* awake last night! Snubby shook a furious fist, marched into his own room, and slammed the door!

(Just in case you want to know — Snubby and Barney solve the strange mystery of Submarine Bay — but only after a great deal of excitement, and many mysterious goings-on!)

THE LITTLE MINER

One Sunday afternoon, when Uncle Nat and Peter and Mary were walking across the fields, Peter saw something that surprised him.

"Look at all those funny little hillocks," he said. "What made them?"

"Miner the Mole made them," said Uncle Nat. "Haven't you ever seen a mole? He's a fine miner. He has spades for hands."

"What do you mean, Uncle?" said Mary in astonishment.

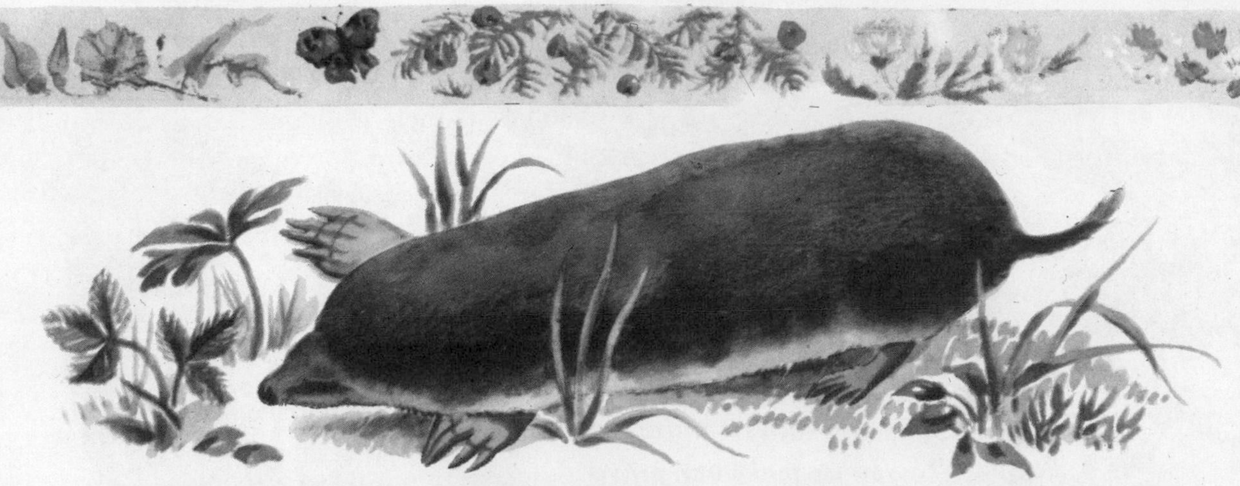

"Watch," said Uncle Nat suddenly, and he pointed down the field. "Is that a hillock I see coming up slowly in the grass?"

It was. Quietly the three hurried over to it and watched it rising. Miner the Mole must be there.

He was; for suddenly a little snout poked out of the ground. Quickly Uncle Nat picked up the little grey creature and showed him to the children.

"Here's the little miner of our fields. Feel his velvety coat, and notice that you can stroke the fur both ways, not just from head to tail as with most animals. You can't see his eyes because they are buried deep in his fur."

"Look at his hands," cried Mary. "Oh, you were right, Uncle; they are just like spades, and are turned outwards ready to dig. What big strong claws he has too! No wonder he throws up so much earth."

"Why doesn't he live above the ground?" asked Peter.

"He is always so hungry," said Uncle Nat. "He tunnels after grubs and beetles, worms and slugs. They live in the ground, so he has to dig a way after them. He gets rid of a lot of pests for us, so we must not harm him, except when he spoils our lawns or crops, and then he must be stopped."

"He's wriggling, Uncle. Put him down," said Mary. So Uncle Nat put down the mole — and then, to the children's great surprise, he seemed to sink right down in the earth and disappear!

"See how fast he digs down," said Uncle Nat. "Now — up comes the earth in a hillock. We shall be able to see the way he goes by the line of hills he makes. Funny little Miner the Mole!"

"I like him," said Peter. "Good hunting, little mole! Gobble up beetles and slugs by the hundred, and Uncle Nat will be pleased with you."

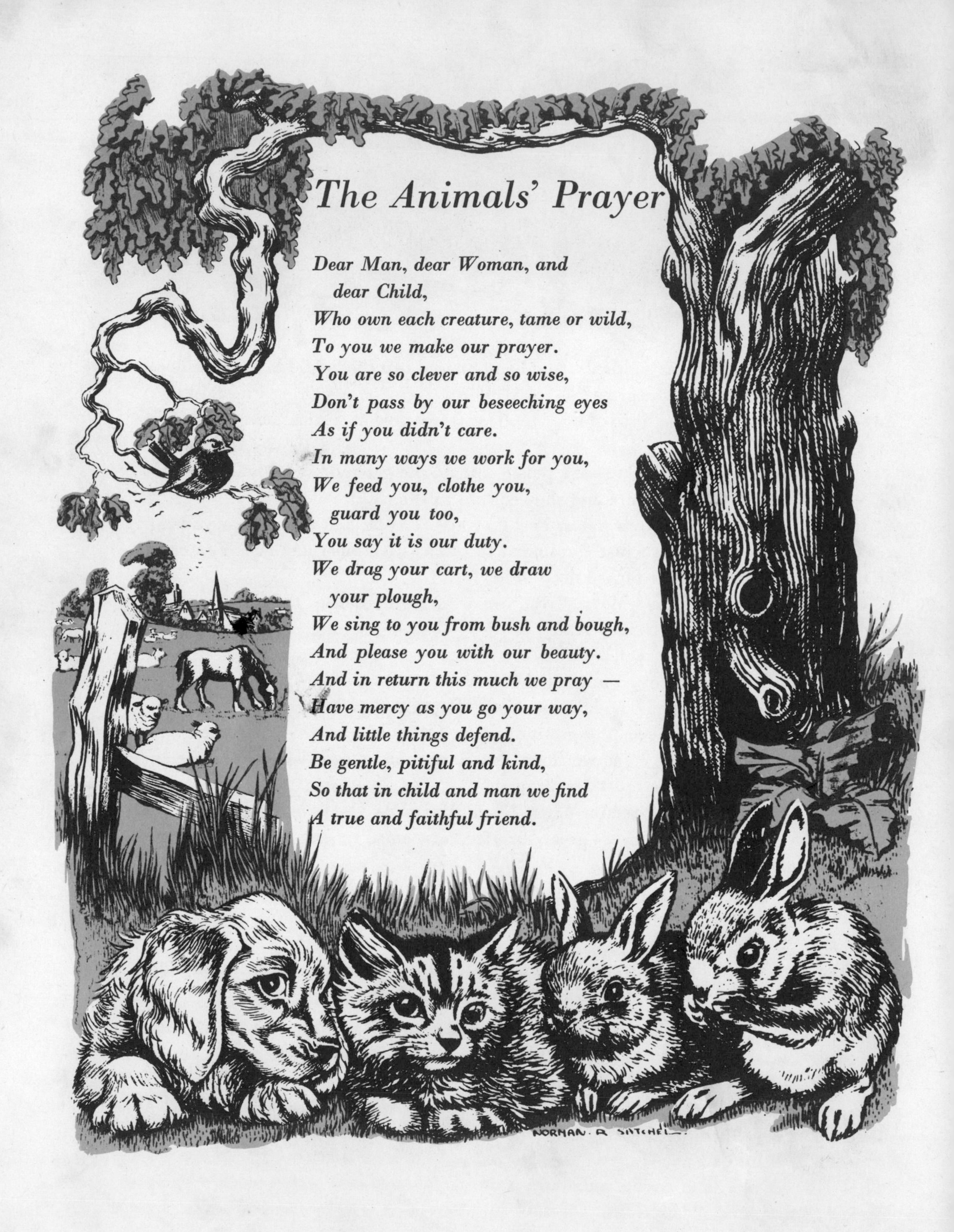

The Animals' Prayer

Dear Man, dear Woman, and
dear Child,
Who own each creature, tame or wild,
To you we make our prayer.
You are so clever and so wise,
Don't pass by our beseeching eyes
As if you didn't care.
In many ways we work for you,
We feed you, clothe you,
guard you too,
You say it is our duty.
We drag your cart, we draw
your plough,
We sing to you from bush and bough,
And please you with our beauty.
And in return this much we pray —
Have mercy as you go your way,
And little things defend.
Be gentle, pitiful and kind,
So that in child and man we find
A true and faithful friend.

Making a Bird-cake

TONY and Mollie were staying with their Uncle Jack and Aunt Jane at their little house in the country.

Aunt Jane had promised to show them how she made a splendid maize-cake for the birds each winter.

"Tony and I have cleaned the bird-table and spread it with food, and put fresh water into the dish," said Mollie. "The birds are having a fine time — but they say they *would* like a cake!"

"Dear me, you seem to understand their language very well," said Aunt Jane, laughing. "Come along, then, both of you — you shall make the maize-cake."

Aunt Jane put a big bowl on the kitchen table. She went to the store cupboard and took out some paper bags and tins. Mollie peeped into them.

"What's in these tins and bags?" she asked.

"This is maize meal," said Aunt Jane, shaking a large amount of it into the bowl. "It is very cheap. You can buy it at any seed-merchant's. The birds love it."

She took another bag and opened it. "You know what *this* is," she said, as she shook out the little brown seeds.

"Hemp-seed!" said Tony. "It is what we put on the bird-table each morning."

"Yes," said Aunt Jane. "And these little, round hard seeds in the tin are millet-seeds. Seed-eating birds really *love* those. Open the next tin for me, Tony, will you, and we'll put a little of the canary seed mixture into the bowl too."

"Can we help to mix all the seeds together?" asked Mollie, looking into the bowl. Aunt Jane nodded. Then the two children put in their hands and scrambled them about till the seeds were all well mixed. They liked feeling the little hard seeds running through their fingers.

"Now I want you to chop up some nuts for me," said Aunt Jane. "There are pea-nuts in that big bag — and there are brazil-nuts on the dish in the dining-room. Go and fetch seven or eight, Tony."

Soon the children were very busy chopping up the nuts with Aunt Jane's little kitchen knives. It was fun, though they had to be very careful not to cut their fingers.

"Now put the chopped-up nuts into the bowl," said Aunt Jane. "You have chopped them up nice and small."

Into the bowl went the nuts too. "What next?" asked Mollie. "It looks a good mixture, Aunt Jane."

"I've some fat melting in that pan on the stove," said Aunt Jane. "Last week's dripping. We pour that over the whole mixture next."

"Let *me!*" cried Tony. But Aunt Jane shook her head.

"No," she said, "children are not allowed to play about with boiling fat. *I* shall pour it in. If I hadn't any fat, I would use boiling water."

"Aunt Jane, let's put in a few currants too," said Tony suddenly, seeing a bag of currants on the dresser. "I should think the berry-eating birds would like those."

"They would," said Aunt Jane. "The thrushes and blackbirds never say 'No' to a currant. Very well, empty some in whilst I get the fat."

Tony shook in a good supply of currants, and then he and Mollie gave the mixture a last stir. Up came Aunt Jane with the pan of boiling fat. She poured it in carefully over the mixture, stirring with a long spoon.

"There!" she said. "Our cake is made."

"Do we cook it now?" asked Mollie.

"It doesn't need to be cooked," said Aunt Jane. "That's the nice part about this cake. I just put the whole mixture into a cloth and let it dry. Then, when it's dry, I shall take off

the cloth, and cut a slice from the cake whenever you want one for your birds."

"Will it keep, then?" asked Mollie.

"All the winter," said Aunt Jane. She took an old tea-cloth and emptied the mixture into it. Then she tied it all up tightly, and gave it to Tony to hang up in the garden-shed till it was dry.

"Then you and Mollie shall take off the cloth and see your bird-cake," she said.

"Oh, Aunt Jane, isn't it easy to do!" cried Mollie. "I'm surprised that more people don't make cakes for the birds. It's fun!"

"They would if they knew about it," said Tony. "I shall tell everybody now. Come and put it in the shed, Mollie. Thank you very much, Aunt Jane!"

When the cloth felt perfectly dry, in a day or two's time, the children unwrapped the cake.

"Oh, isn't it lovely!" cried Mollie. "It's hard and knobbly — and look, you can see the seeds and the currants all over it!"

"It's a funny shape," said Tony. "But that doesn't matter. Let's take it to Auntie and show her."

They carried it carefully to Aunt Jane. She gave them an old enamel plate to stand it on. "Now you shall cut the birds a slice for their table," she said. "Mollie, you can cut the first slice, and Tony can cut a slice tomorrow."

Mollie cut a good slice. It really looked delicious. "I wish I could have a bite," she said.

"No, you mustn't," said Aunt Jane at once. "It is not meant for children. It is always dangerous for girls and boys to eat food prepared for animals or birds. For one thing, there might be berries in a bird-cake — I often put them in if I have some by me — and yew berries, for instance, are very poisonous to children."

"Let's put the slice on the bird-table," said Tony. So they went outside and placed the slice of cake in the middle of the bird-table. Then they went to the dining-room window to watch.

All the birds loved the bird-cake! The sparrows and finches pecked the seeds out of it. The tits pecked at the chopped-up nuts. The blackbirds and thrushes took the currants, and the starlings liked the fat. Even the robins came to have a taste. It *was* fun to watch them all.

"I think our bird-table must be the most crowded one in the country," said Mollie. And I really think she was right.

Zerelda's Unfortunate Rehearsal

A chapter from one of Enid Blyton's stories about boarding-school life, taken from the "Malory Towers" series — THIRD YEAR AT MALORY TOWERS. Zerelda was an unusual newcomer to "Malory Towers". She was an American, and looked down on the ordinary English school-girl, considering herself much more grown-up — so she had rather a rough time, and many peculiar and amusing things happened to her. Here is one of them.

"Acting is marvellous!" said Zerelda.

THERE was great excitement when a notice was put up on the board. Miss Hibbert, the English mistress, was going to start rehearsals for "Romeo and Juliet". All third-formers were to go to the art-room to be tried out for parts.

"Blow!" said Gwendoline, who didn't like Miss Hibbert because she had so often ticked her off for being affected and silly in her acting. "I was hoping she had forgotten about the play. It's such a waste of time."

"Oh *no*, it isn't," said Zerelda, who had brightened up very much at the notice. "Acting is marvellous! That's a thing I really *can* do. I did Lady Macbeth over in . . ."

"Yes, we know you did," interrupted Daphne. "We ought to know by now, anyway! You tell us often enough."

"I suppose *you* fancy yourself in one of the chief parts, Daphne?" said Alicia. "What a disappointment you'll get! Anyway, if Zerelda's so good, she'll play Juliet — if she can get rid of that American drawl!"

Zerelda looked alarmed. "Do you think my way of speaking will stop me having a good part?" she asked.

"Well — I can't imagine Shakespeare's Juliet talking with a pronounced American accent," said Alicia. "Still — if you act the part well enough I don't see why you shouldn't get it!"

Zerelda had been rather subdued lately, but now she came to life again, with the hope of starring in "Romeo and Juliet"! She paid a tremendous amount of attention to her appearance and spent as much time as she dared in front of her looking-glass. She also tried to get rid of her American drawl!

This amused the class very much. Zerelda had never made the slightest attempt before to speak in the English way and had laughed at the English accent and called it silly. Now she badgered everyone to tell her how to pronounce the words the way they did.

"Well, try to say 'won*d*erful' with the D in the middle, instead of 'wunnerful', for a start," said Darrell. "And say 'twen*t*y-four' with the T in the middle, instead of 'twenny-four'. And couldn't you say 'stop' instead of 'starp' and 'shop' instead of 'sharp'? Or can't you hear the difference?"

Zerelda patiently tried to master the English way of speaking, much to Miss Peters' astonishment. She had felt quite pleased with Zerelda's efforts to keep up with the work of the form, but she was still annoyed with the girl's constant attention to her hair and appearance. Nor did she like Zerelda's still grown-up air, and her habit of appearing to look down on the others just because they were schoolgirls.

"Now I'll show them all!" thought Zerelda, studying the part of Juliet with great attention. "Now they'll see what I mean when I say I'm going to be one of the greatest of all film-stars!"

Miss Hibbert took a great deal of trouble in producing the school plays. She gave her time to each form in turn, and really achieved some excellent results. This term it was the third form's turn. They were to give the play towards the end of the term.

"Does Miss Hibbert choose the characters at the first rehearsal?" asked Zerelda.

"Oh no — she tries us all out in almost every part several times," said Darrell. "She does that for two reasons — she says that in that way she really does find the right actor for every part — and we all get to know every part of the play and work better as a team."

"Gee, that's wunnerful — I mean, won*der*ful," said Zerelda. "I've been studying Juliet's part. It's a lovely one. Would you like to hear me say some of the lines?"

"Well — I'm just going out to my lacrosse practice," said Darrell. "Sorry! Look — ask Alicia. She's got nothing to do this period."

But Alicia was not going to admire Zerelda's Juliet. She stood up hastily. "Sorry! I have to go to a meeting, Zerelda. But I'm sure you'd be just *wunnerful!*"

"I'll hear you, Zerelda," said Gwendoline, glad of an opportunity to please the American girl. "Let's go into one of the empty music-practice-rooms, where you won't be disturbed. It will be lovely to see you act. I'm sure you must be awfully good. As good as — what's the star you like so much — oh yes, Lossie Laxton!"

"Well, maybe I'm not up to her standard yet," said Zerelda, fluffing up her hair in the way Lossie did on the films. "Okay, Gwen — we'll go to a practice-room."

But they were all full, and music sounded from each of them, with the exception of one at the end. Irene was there, poring over a music score.

"I say, Irene," said Gwen, going in, "can you . . ."

"Go away," said Irene fiercely. "I'm busy."

"Well, you're not needing the piano, are you?" said Zerelda. "Can't you do your work, whatever it is, somewhere else?"

"No, I can't. I shall want to try it out on the piano in a minute," said Irene. "Go away. Interrupting me like that!"

Zerelda was surprised. She had never seen Irene so annoyed before. But Gwendoline had. She knew that Irene could not bear to be disturbed when she was concentrating on her music.

"Come on," she said to Zerelda. "Let's go."

"Yes. GO!" said Irene, with a desperate expression on her face. "You've stopped me just when it was all coming beautifully."

"Well, really, Irene, I do think you might let us use this room if you're only playing about with pencil and paper," began Zerelda. "I want to recite some lines of Juliet and . . ."

Then Irene went quite mad. She threw her music, her pencil and her music-case at the alarmed Zerelda. "You're daft!" she shouted. "Give up my music-hour for your silly acting! Oh yes, I know you're going to be a wonderful film-star, parading about in marvellous clothes, thinking of third-rate things if ever you *do* have a thought in your head — but what's all that compared to music! I tell you I'm . . ."

But Zerelda and Gwen did not wait to hear any more.

"*Well!*" said Zerelda. "If that doesn't beat all! Irene's mad!"

"Not really," said Gwen. "It's only when she feels sort of inspired, and music comes welling up into her mind and she has to write it down. She's got the real artistic temperament, I suppose."

"Well, so have I," said Zerelda at once. "But I don't go mad like that. I wouldn't have believed it of her."

"She can't help it," said Gwendoline. "It's only when she's interrupted. Look — there's Lucy going out of one of the practice-rooms."

They slipped into the room that Lucy had just left. Gwendoline sat down, ready to listen for hours if she could please Zerelda and make her feel really friendly towards her. Zerelda struck a lovesick attitude and began.

"Wilt thou be gone? It is not yet near day;
It was the nightingale and not the lark,
That pierced the fearful hollow of thine ear;
Nightly she sings on yon pomegranate-tree;
Believe me, love, it was the nightingale."

Gwendoline listened with a rapt and admiring expression on her face. She had no idea at all whether Zerelda was good or not, but that made no difference to her praise.

"It's marvellous!" she said, when Zerelda at last stopped for breath. "However have you learnt such a lot? My goodness, you do act well. And you really look the part, Zerelda, with your hair and all."

"Do I?" said Zerelda, pleased. She always enjoyed herself when she was acting. "I know what I'll do. I'll shake my hair loose. And I'll wrap this tablecloth round me. No — it's not big enough. The curtain will do!"

To Gwendoline's amusement Zerelda took down the blue curtain and swathed it round herself over her brown school tunic. She undid her brilliant hair and shook it all over her shoulders. She decided to put the tablecloth round her too. Ah — now she felt more like Juliet. Holding her hands out pathetically in front of her she began another speech. It sounded really a little queer because Zerelda tried very hard to speak in the English way but kept lapsing into her usual drawl, so that the whole effect was very funny.

Zerelda struck a lovesick attitude and began.

Gwendoline wanted to laugh but she knew how offended Zerelda would be. The American girl paraded up and down, declaiming her speeches most dramatically, the blue curtain dragging behind her like a train, her hair almost hiding one eye.

Someone looked in. It was Bessie, a second-former. She had come to practice, on the piano, but seeing two third-formers there, she fled. Then a fourth-former came. She was not scared of third-formers, but was very much astonished to see Zerelda and her strange raiment.

"I've come to practise," she said, at once. "Clear out."

Zerelda stopped indignantly. "Clear out yourself!" she said. "Gee, of all the nerve! Can't you see I'm rehearsing?"

"No, I can't," said the fourth-former. "And wait till a mistress sees you in that curtain — you'll be for it, Zerelda Brass. Clear out now, both of you. I'm late already."

Zerelda decided to go all temperamental like Irene. She caught up her book of Shakespeare's plays and threw it at the fourth-former. Most unfortunately at that moment Matron came by, and, as she always did, glanced into the practice-rooms to see that each girl there was practising. She was filled with astonishment to see someone wearing a curtain and a tablecloth, with hair all over her face, throwing a book at a girl about to sit down at the piano.

She opened the door sharply, making everyone jump. "What's all this? What are you doing? Oh, it's *you*, Zerelda. Why on earth have you wrapped the curtain round you? Are you quite mad? And what has happened to your hair? It looks a hundred times worse than usual. Janet, get on with your practising. Gwendoline, you shouldn't be here when a fourth-former is practising. As for you, Zerelda, if I see any more tempers like that, I shall report you to Miss Grayling! Throwing books at each another indeed!"

The girls couldn't get a word in, for Matron fired all this off at top speed. She pushed Janet firmly down on the stool, shooed Gwendoline out as if she was a hen, and took Zerelda firmly by the shoulder.

"You'll just come with me and let me find out if you've torn the cloth or the curtain," she said. "If you have you'll sit down in my room under my eye and mend it. And while I think of it — if you don't darn your stockings better than you have been doing, I shall have to ask you to come to me for darning lessons."

Angry and embarrassed, poor Zerelda had to walk down the corridor after Matron, trying to take the curtain and cloth away from her shoul-

She caught up her book and threw it.

ders and waist, and wishing she could tie her hair back.

But Matron would give her no time to re-arrange or tidy herself. This stuck-up, affected American girl had annoyed Matron so often — now Matron was getting a bit of her own back! Let everyone see Zerelda in this rumpled, ridiculous state!

And most unfortunately for Zerelda they met a whole batch of giggling second-formers, who stared at Zerelda in delighted amazement.

"What's she done? Where's Matron taking her? Doesn't she look *awful*!" poor Zerelda heard the twelve-year-olds say. She blushed miserably and looked round for Gwen. But Gwen had gone.

They met Mam'zelle at the bend of the stairs, and Mam'zelle exclaimed in surprise. "*Tiens*! What is this? Zerelda! Your hair!"

"Yes. I'm dealing with her, Mam'zelle," said Matron firmly. She and Mam'zelle were usually at war with one another, so Matron did not stop to talk, but swept Zerelda along to her room at top speed, leaving Mam'zelle to gape and wonder.

Fortunately for Zerelda, Matron could find no damage done to either the tablecloth or the curtain. She was quite disappointed! She did Zerelda's hair for her herself, and Zerelda was so overcome by Matron's briskness and ability to talk without stopping that she submitted without saying a word.

Matron plaited Zerelda's hair into two fat plaits! Zerelda had never had her hair plaited in her life. She sat there, horror-struck.

"There," said Matron, satisfied at last, tying the ends of the plaits with blue tape. She stepped back. "Now you look a proper schoolgirl, Zerelda — and very sensible and nice too. Why you want to go about pretending you are twenty, I don't know."

Zerelda got up weakly. She caught a glimpse of herself in the glass. How *awful*! Could that really be herself? Why, she looked a nobody — just like all the other English girls. She crept out of Matron's room and fled up to the dormy to try and put her hair right.

"Now you look a proper schoolgirl, Zerelda."

She met Miss Peters, who stared at her as if she didn't know her. Zerelda smiled a weak smile and tried to get by without a word.

"Well — *Zerelda*!" she heard Miss Peters say, as if she couldn't believe her eyes. Zerelda shot down the corridor, praying that she would not meet anyone else.

Gwendoline was in the dormy, and she too stared at Zerelda as if she was seeing a ghost.

"Did Matron do that to you?" she asked. "Oh, Zerelda — you look like a real schoolgirl now — not a bit like yourself. Oh, I *must* tell the others that Matron plaited your hair."

"If you dare to repeat such a thing I'll never speak to you again!" said Zerelda, in such a fierce voice that Gwen was quite scared. She shook her hair free of the plaits. "This horrible school! I'll never forgive Matron, never!"

MAWKINS THE HARE

A story from "Enid Blyton's Animal Lover's Book."

Richard and Susan love all animals, and have for their great friend Zacky the gypsy, who knows all the animals and birds in the countryside. Here he brings to them Mawkins the Hare.

RICHARD and Susan were out on a walk with their friend, Zacky the gipsy. They came to a thicket of gorse and briar. Here were big tufts of rank grass that made them stumble as they went. Zacky sat down on one and took out his hare-pipe.

"Zacky," began Susan, but he frowned quickly and she stopped, alarmed at the sound of her voice, suddenly loud in that deserted corner. She sat as still as a frightened mouse.

Zacky put his strange little pipe to his lips. The children expected a whistle to come from it, but instead there came a curious grunting noise, low and regular.

"Oont, oont, oont," said the pipe. Then Zacky stopped for a few seconds. He put the pipe to his lips again and once more the curious sound came. "Oont, oont."

There was the slightest rustling noise from a thick bramble not far off. The children held their breath and looked hard. Two great ears appeared, and then two enormous eyes. The hare!

Again the pipe sounded its call-note, and the hare leapt from the bush in one big bound. He fixed his eyes on Zacky, and with another leap was by his knee.

"Mawkins," said Zacky softly, in the special voice that he kept for animals and birds. "Mawkins, so you are still there. How's the leg, Mawkins? Can you run as fast as ever?"

The hare made exactly the same noise as the pipe had made, "Oont." The two children could hardly breathe. They had never in their lives kept so still. They looked and looked at the big hare.

He was lovely. His fur was russet-red on his back, and his ears were very long and were tipped with black. His great eyes took in everything around him. No wonder he could see danger a long way off with those enormous eyes!

Richard saw his strong back legs. He could leap high and far with those. The boy wished he could fondle the hare as Zacky was doing. He watched the gipsy scratch the fur under the hare's whiskered chin, while the animal stretched out his head in delight.

And then, almost in an instant, the hare disappeared! Something startled him and he was gone with one great leap. They could see him bounding down the hill.

"There he goes," said Zacky, putting away his pipe. "Do you notice how he leaps to one side now and again? That's to break the scent of his trail."

"Zacky, he's *lovely*," said Richard. "I never saw even a rabbit so close before. Tell us about your friend Mawkins. He doesn't live in a burrow like a rabbit, does he?"

"Oh, no — he's an open-air creature," said Zacky. "He lives in the thickets and fields. Let's see if we can find his resting-place somewhere here. It's called a form."

"Why?" asked Susan, thinking of the forms at school.

"Because it's just a big dent in the ground exactly the form or shape of the hare's body," said Zacky. "See — here is one, though whether it belongs to my friend Mawkins I don't know."

He showed them a dent in the long grass, the size and shape of the hare's long body. The hare had chosen the place, shuffled his body up and down in the grass until he had made a good depression there, and had then used it every day for a hiding-place. The blades of grass partly covered the "form".

"It's a good place," said Richard. "And I should think his colouring helps to hide him too, Zacky, doesn't it? Don't hares lie up in open fields, too? Can we find a 'form' in that field there, do you think?"

"Maybe," said Zacky, and they went to see. Zacky found one almost at once. It was just a dent in the ground, but now that the children knew what they were looking for they could quite well see that it was a hare's resting-place. The outline of his body was clear.

"When the doe — the mother-hare — has young ones, they are not born helpless," said Zacky. "They are covered with hair, and their eyes are wide open. Funny little creatures they are, half grown-up when they're born, seemingly! In no time at all they move away from their mother and make little forms of their own — and there they lie listening all day long, waiting for their mother to come to them."

"I wish I could see one," said Susan longingly.

"You'd love them," said Zacky. "Prettiest little things they are. I once took one and fed it from a bottle. It stayed with me for a long time and was as frisky as a skippity lamb."

"I wish things like that happened to me," said Richard. "Where's Mawkins the hare gone to now, Zacky?"

"He may be miles away," said Zacky. "He travels fast with those long legs of his leaping away — fifteen feet at a time he can jump when he wants to. No wonder the fox gives up the chase!"

"But can't the fox follow the scent of his trail?" asked Susan.

"I told you to notice how the hare jumps to one side now and again," said Zacky. "That big sideways jump breaks the scent, and puzzles the fox or the dog. And sometimes I've seen a hare run round and round in circles and then leap fifteen feet to one side and be off and away for good. When the dog comes up he follows the scent in the circle and he goes round and round till he's giddy. The trail is perfect in the circle, you see."

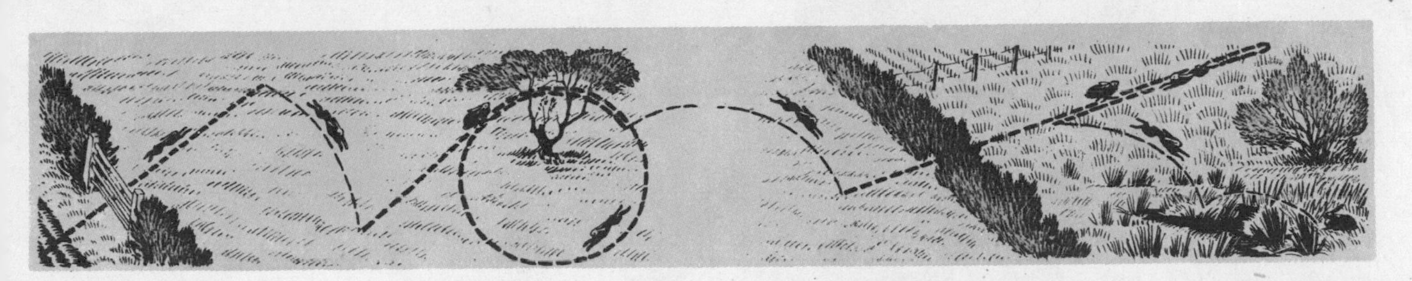

"That's clever," said Richard. "Very clever. I suppose the dog doesn't think that the hare might have leapt to one side. What else can the hare do?"

"Well, old Mawkins sometimes doubles back on his trail," said Zacky. "He'll be going along in a straight line, and he'll stop, turn round and run back on exactly the same trail. Then he'll do his trick of leaping to one side and breaking the trail — maybe into a marsh that won't hold any scent of him."

"I see! Up comes the dog on the trail and doesn't know the hare has doubled back — so there he is sniffing at a sudden end to the scent and he doesn't know why!" said Susan.

"Listen," said Zacky, suddenly, his eyes shining. "We're in luck! Listen."

They stood as still as statues, listening. On the evening air came strange sounds, something like

grunt and whistle combined. Then Richard recognised the noise.

"It's like your hare-pipe!" he said. "I can hear the 'Oont, oont' noise."

"Yes — it's two hares at play," said Zacky. "Sit down. Maybe they will come into view. You've heard folks say 'as mad as a March Hare,' haven't you? Well, maybe you'll see some mad hares in a minute!"

They sat down behind a briar bush and made spy-holes through it, looking down on a grassy hillside. And, quite suddenly, two hares came into view. Susan stared in amazement. They were certainly quite mad!

They leapt into the air continually, they bucked and they reared, they ran round and round in circles, and then they began to leap right over each other. "Oont, oont," they said, and danced about madly again.

"They played leap-frog," thought Susan, but she didn't dare to utter a word. Why, this was as good — no, better — than going to a circus!

And then a third hare came on the scene! He was a big fellow, and he joined in the mad antics. But one of the two hares didn't welcome him at all. He suddenly made a rush at the newcomer and struck him with a front paw.

In a trice both hares were up on their hind-legs, and were boxing each other with their fists! The children watched in amazement. Why, they were *boxing*! But one of them suddenly stopped boxing with his front paws, turned himself round, and, as he did so, kicked out with his strong back-legs at his opponent.

The other was knocked flat. He gave a squeal and got up. He took one look at the other hare and then ambled off. He had had enough!

Richard laughed — and the other two hares pricked up their long ears and were off like lightning! Down the hillside, and into the field and across it. As swift as the wind! How big they looked as they ran, their ears bobbing up and down, their bodies stretched to the utmost.

"Oh, *Richard*!" said Susan, crossly. "You've scared them away."

"Yes. I just couldn't help laughing," said Richard, vexed with himself. "I've never seen anything so comical in my life. But I didn't mean to frighten them like that."

"Never mind — they had about finished," said Zacky. "You're in luck's way this evening — watching a show like that!"

"Please could I just blow your hare-pipe and see if I can make Mawkins come?" asked Susan.

Zacky wiped it and gave it to her. She set it to her mouth. The rather mournful sound came out: "Oont, oont, oont."

"It sounds a bit like 'Don't, don't,' " said Richard. "I'm surprised that the hare who got such a kick didn't say 'Don't, don't', instead of squealing!"

"Hares always squeal or scream if they are hurt or frightened," said Zacky. "That's how I found Mawkins one night. He was caught in a trap and he screamed just like a child in pain, poor thing."

"What did you do?" said Susan, though she guessed, of course!

"I went out and found him, and brought him to my waggon," said Zacky. "His hurt leg mended well, as you saw. He's a good friend, is old Mawkins the hare — he's never forgotten me!"

Let's have a club of our own

2

(This is the second part of the "Let's have a Club" story, of which the first part showed you how to form a club and what to do about it. I told you how a group of children, very like yourselves, wanted to form a club, and how they held their first meeting, and decided such things as who should be Leader, what password to have, and what name to choose for their club — and the kind of badge. This time I am going to tell you of their second meeting, and how they decided what aims they meant to have, and what secret signal, and so on.)

IT was fun to be a club of six children — fun to meet and whisper the password, "cluck-cluck!" and exciting to think of the badges that the two girls were making for the Sturdy Six to wear! Friday evening seemed a long time in coming — but at last it was half-past five and the six were once again in the hen-house in Mark's garden.

It looked different! Katie had brought an old rug to sit on. Mark had found an old stool and a box or two. Dick brought a bottle of orangeade and two plastic mugs, which he proudly set down at the back, ready for the meeting's end. Eric produced a bag of peppermints.

"It's beginning to look quite homey," said Mollie, looking round the henhouse. "I'd better make a curtain for the tiny window."

Mark had arrived early, at twenty-past five, ready to admit and welcome each member, and to insist on the password being said. He knew that a certain amount of formality was necessary if the club was to be a serious one, and not a matter of giggles and nonsense. He meant the Sturdy Six to be a fine club, which would win respect from anyone outside it — not a stupid senseless one with no aims, no rules, no proper discussions. Yes — Mark was a good leader, and the others knew it when they chose him!

"Now, the meeting must begin," said Mark, when everyone had settled down. "First, the badges."

Mollie and Katie produced them proudly. They really were very good. They had begged fair-sized buttons from Mollie's mother, and had covered them with bits of navy blue material, on which they had embroidered the letters S.S. in red. At the back were small safety pins, sewn on strongly.

"Thanks awfully, Mollie and Katie," said Mark, as he handed them round. "They're smashing!"

"People will think we are the Secret Seven, not the Sturdy Six," said Katie. "S.S. stands for both."

"That doesn't matter," said Dick. "*We* know what our S.S. stands for! I must say I feel jolly proud of mine. Oh, Eric — you said the password 'cluck-cluck' so like a hen when you passed me in the school corridor yesterday that you made me jump!"

"Are we going to decide on a secret signal?" asked James. "I've thought of one, if so."

"What is it?" said Mollie.

"Just this," said James, and lightly touched his two shoulders, one with each hand, putting them down again at once.

"I don't see much point in that signal," said Katie.

"Well — the only point is — S for shoulders — two of them, so that's *S.S.* — and we're the S.S. or Sturdy Six," explained James. "So that makes the signal fit in with the badges — don't you see?"

"Oh — yes, I do see," said Katie, as James lightly and quickly touched his shoulders again, almost as if he were brushing away a little dust. "Yes — it's rather a clever signal —not very noticeable — but just right."

Everyone nodded, and James looked pleased. "Well, that shall be our signal," said Mark.

The six were once again in the hen-house in Mark's garden.

"Just a kind of recognition signal, like saying 'Hallo, secret comrade' which can be used from a distance. And I think we'll decide that if a signal is repeated *twice,* that means that something has happened, and the members must get in touch with one another at once."

"Oh, *good!*" said Katie, who really did love passwords and signals and all the rest of the Club customs. She touched her shoulders three or four times, as if signalling to someone urgently.

"Stop doing your gym exercises now, Katie," said Mark, and everyone laughed. "We'll get on to our next business. What shall this Club *do?* What shall be its aims? A Club is of no real use unless its members have some definite purpose."

"Let's do bird-watching down at the lake, for one thing," suggested Eric promptly.

Dick opened his mouth to say No, that was too dull — and then stayed silent. He remembered that Eric was lame, and couldn't go tree-climbing, or on long hikes — one of the Club's interests, at least, should be something *he* could do.

"A good idea, Eric," said Mark, at once. "We are all interested in birds and belong to the school's nature-club. We can do regular bird-watching, and write up what we see and hear for the School Nature Magazine — and we'll sign our article 'The Sturdy Six!' Any other suggestions?"

"Could we collect used postage stamps and tinfoil, and take them to the hospital?" asked Katie. "They sell them and buy toys for the children there. I know that Mollie and I already do this, but we'd get on much faster with our collections if we could *all* bring some to each meeting."

"Agreed!" cried everyone, and Mark looked at Katie. "You will be put in charge of that," he said to her. "Provide a bag for the silver paper or tinfoil, please, and a tin for the used stamps, and leave them here. We will bring what we have, each time there is a meeting —

and you and Katie will be responsible for taking the tin and the bag, when full, to the Secretary at the hospital."

"Yes, Mark," said both girls together. Ha — *now* they would soon get a good collection!

"And what about doing a play or something, and charging for the tickets?" said James. "You know the Head said the other day at Prayers that the school really must raise money to buy more books for the Class Libraries — and why shouldn't the Sturdy Six show what can be done?"

Everyone agreed in delight. "Yes! We'll do a show! We'll ask the Head if we can!" said Dick. "My word — we're going to be busy. But wouldn't it be better to do that at Christmas time?"

They discussed the matter thoroughly, and Mark looked at his Club members with approval. Who would have thought that at the second meeting the club would be going so strong — and that ideas would be pouring out, and everyone would be so eager and interested? He felt very pleased with the Sturdy Six!

He stopped the discussion at last, after having listened to everyone's suggestions.

"As far as I can gather, you are most of you in favour of a Christmas show," he said. "And it would certainly be something to do in the dark evenings next term. We'll put it to the vote. Hands up those who are in favour of doing the play now."

Not a hand went up! "Well, hands up for doing the play at Christmas," said Mark, grinning, and every hand shot up, of course! "That's decided, then," said Mark. "But couldn't we do something this summer, too — have a garden sale, or something?"

"Oh, *yes!*" said Katie and Mollie together. "A *jumble* sale would be wonderful," added Mollie. "Jumble sells like anything, and it's so easy to go round and ask people if they want to throw away anything, and if so, to give it to us instead, as we want to hold a sale in aid of — in aid of . . . well, what *shall* it be in aid

"Just this," said James and lightly touched his two shoulders, one with each hand.

of, because the *play* will be to get money for books for the Class Libraries. We shan't need any more money for that!"

"Ideas, please," said Mark, at once, and ideas came, of course!

"For the Sunshine Homes for Blind Children! For helping animals! For children in hospital! For buying a radio set for that poor blind old Mr. Sykes who sits at his window alone all day! For — for — for . . ."

"Enough," said Mark, putting up his hand. "You are full of good ideas! I don't see why we can't adopt *all* your ideas, and, when we've had the sale, and counted up the money we get, we could divide it between the things suggested."

"Yes! And if we raise any money on our own, that could go towards our ideas too," said Katie. "For instance, my father has promised me a shilling a week for keeping his bicycle clean. I'd willingly put that towards something."

"And I can take old Mrs. Lucy's two dogs out for a walk in the evenings, and earn *two* shillings a week," said Eric. "I can't walk very fast — but the dogs are old and fat and like ambling along."

"I can earn a shilling or two by doing the washing-up!" said Mollie.

"And I can earn *ten* shillings if I want to, by washing my uncle's car twice a week," said Dick proudly.

In fact, everyone knew how they could earn little or much, and they all became very excited in talking about it. Mark had to clap his hands loudly to get silence. "I shall really have to borrow my Dad's hammer," he said grinning, "and bang it on the floor for silence! This Club is about the liveliest in the country, I should think!"

"I never knew that discussing things like this all together, could be such fun," said Mollie, her face red with excitement. "Mark, I could walk to school and save my bus fare and . . ."

"Mollie, could you be silent for just one minute?" begged Mark. "ALL your ideas are good ones, and I can see that this is going to be a very alive Club indeed. But don't let us take on too much. One thing at a time! By all means let us earn money where we can, and save it for all kinds of things — but we'll have to have a Treasurer if we're going to deal with money! We want someone who will take the money, look after it, and keep an account of it. It's always best to have *one* person responsible for any money."

"I never knew that discussing things all together could be such fun," said Mollie.

"I vote Eric is Treasurer, then," cried Dick. "He's awfully good at figures — he's always top in maths."

"Yes. Yes, I think that's a *good* idea," said Mark. "Will you take on the post of Treasurer, Eric? We'll buy you a little account book — bring you any money at each meeting — and let you jot it down, and keep account of it, so that you can report to us at each meeting what is in our moneybox. We'll know then when we have enough to give money to some cause."

"Well — what with bird-watching — and collecting used postage stamps and tinfoil — and cleaning bikes – and doing the washing-up – and taking dogs for walks – and planning a Jumble Sale — and a show for Christmas — I really doubt if the Sturdy Six will have time to attend school," said Eric solemnly. "Certainly, I'll be Treasurer, Mark — I'll be proud to. I'll collect the money each time, jot it down, present the accounts, and keep the money safely at home locked in a drawer."

"I've an old money-box I don't use, with a key," said Katie. "I'll bring it to school and give it to you tomorrow, Eric."

"Right. Thanks," said Eric, who, of all the six, was the happiest — not because he could do all *they* could do — he couldn't, because of his crippled leg — but because they had chosen him to be one of them, and had given him a job of his own. He felt very proud and very happy.

The meeting came to a hilarious end, and Mollie ran up to the house for more mugs, and a jug of water for the orangeade. Her mother called to her.

"What a merry meeting you've had, Mollie!

I could hear your voices and your laughter from here! Do you want some biscuits to eat? I've a tin of home-made ones here for you."

"You're a pet, mother," said Mollie, pleased. "Oh, mother, our Club is *such* a good one! You've no idea what things we've been planning! And Mark is such a wonderful leader!"

"Well, so long as you follow out your ideas and really do something, I shall be proud of your club," said her mother. "But so many clubs begin well — and then just fade away."

"Not with a leader like Mark!" said Mollie, proudly. "You should see how he takes charge of our meetings, mother! And we've a Treasurer now, too — Eric!"

"My word — it's a *proper* club!" said her mother. "Well — if mere parents can ever be of any use to you, do tell me! I shall love to help if I can. Parents can be quite useful for such things as sales, and so on, you know!"

"Mother! How did you guess we meant to have a sale?" said Mollie, astonished.

"Oh, I couldn't help hearing one of you shouting out something about a Jumble Sale," said her mother, smiling. "Now, here are the biscuits. Run along with them."

Back went Mollie, and soon the Six were munching ginger biscuits, drinking orangeade, and sucking peppermints. Mark looked round at them all, and felt pleased.

"This is the kind of club to have," he thought. "Everyone friendly, full of ideas, and willing to work together. We can really DO things — not only bird-watching and things like that — but something even more worthwhile. I'm going to be proud of being leader of the Sturdy Six!"

You are, Mark! And your school is going to be proud of them too, and your friends are going to wish that *they* could wear those gay badges with S.S. embroidered in red!

Mollie ran up to the house for more mugs and a jug of water for the orangeade.

I wonder what the Sturdy Six will have done by the end of the year? How much money will they have earned? How many different birds will there be in their bird-watching books? How many used postage stamps, how much tinfoil will have been collected? Will old Mr. Sykes have his radio? Will their Jumble Sale go well — and their play bring the house down?

Well — what do *you* think? They are still going strong, and having meetings once a week — and Eric's account book shows a tremendous amount of figures!

It's such *fun* to have a Club! And now that *you* know how to start one from the very beginning, why don't *you* have fun, too? Well — if you do, don't forget to write and tell me all about it!

The little daughter of Jairus

A LITTLE girl was watching for her father to come home. She lived at Capernaum, the town to which Jesus often came.

"Where are you, Anna?" called her mother. The dark-eyed, dark-haired child called back:

"I am waiting for my father. He will play with me when he comes."

Anna was twelve years old, an only child, and her parents loved her with all their hearts. She went everywhere with them, and they were very proud of her.

Each day when Jairus, her father, came home they played a game together. Anna always looked forward to that. Now she was watching for him as usual.

"Here he is!" she cried, and ran to meet the big man whose eyes and hair were so like hers. They played their game and the mother heard them laughing and talking happily in the evening sunshine. She smiled happily, too.

But none of them smiled the next day. Anna felt ill. "My head is hot," she said. "It hurts. I don't want anything to eat. I don't want to play."

Her father was suddenly anxious. "Wife, the child looks really ill," he said. "Put her to bed. I will send for the doctor."

So Anna was put to bed. She tossed restlessly from side to side. The doctor came and left her some medicine.

"She is no better," said the mother that evening. "I am afraid she is worse. We will send for the doctor again."

The doctor was alarmed when he came. "I will fetch another doctor," he said. "The child is very ill. Perhaps a second doctor can help."

But in a day or two it was plain that Anna was desperately ill, and her father was in despair.

"She is my only child," he thought, "my dear beloved little Anna. What can I do for her? The doctor can do nothing. I cannot let her die!"

He sat by the child's bedside and watched her. He looked at his anxious wife, pale and sad.

"Have you heard of this new healer, the man called Jesus?" he said suddenly. "I've been thinking about Him. I think He is here, in the town."

"Go and fetch Him," said his wife at once. "He might come and lay His hand on our child and make her well. Go now, Jairus, before it is too late."

"Go and fetch Him," said the wife at once.

"I will go and ask where I can find Him," said Jairus. "He is a good man and He loves little children. Surely He would come to our little Anna."

Jairus stroked his little girl's hair and went quietly out of the room. He made his way into the town and asked people anxiously where he could find Jesus. He went to the house where Jesus stayed — but alas, He was not there!

"Go down to the lakeside," said the woman who opened the door to him. "He may be preaching there."

So Jairus went down to the blue water, and there he saw a great crowd of people. "Surely Jesus must be here," he thought gladly.

He pressed through the crowd. "Is Jesus here?" he asked. "Where is He?"

"No, He is not here," said someone. "He was with us only last night, telling us stories from Peter's boat. Then He sailed off over the lake. A storm blew up when it was dark and we hope Jesus is safe. We are waiting for the boat to come back."

"Will He be long?" said Jairus, in despair. Nobody knew.

"You can only wait," said a woman nearby, sorry for this man who looked so sad. So Jairus stood with the people and waited, straining his eyes to see across the lake. He thought of Anna, lying so ill. Was she still alive? Every minute mattered now. If only Jesus would come!

"There's a boat now," said somebody, and Jairus sighed with relief. But it was not Peter's boat. It was someone else's. Jairus's heart sank.

After a little while somebody shouted: "I can see the boat. Look, over there! Jesus is coming!"

Peter's boat sailed swiftly over the lake. Jairus could see a man standing in it. Yes, it was Jesus himself. The boat ran into shore, and willing hands helped to pull it in. Jesus sprang to the beach, and the disciples tried to keep back the people crowding round Him.

Jesus did not land near Jairus, and he had to push through the crowd. "Let me through," he begged everyone. "Do let me through."

"Go down to the lakeside," said the woman who opened the door to him.

The crowd opened to let him pass. They saw that he had something urgent to say to Jesus. Jairus knelt down in front of Jesus and begged Him to come and see his little girl.

"She is at the point of death," said Jairus, his voice trembling. "I pray you, Lord, come and put your hands on her that she may be healed. Then she will live."

Jesus saw that Jairus was desperate. "I will come at once," He said. "Let us go."

Everyone had been listening to what Jairus had said. "He's going to see the little girl," they said to one another. "Little Anna, you know. He'll do something wonderful! We must go and see."

The crowd jostled and pressed around Jesus and the disciples as they went with Jairus. They were excited and every moment more and more people came to join them.

Now, in the crowd, there was a poor, miserable

woman. She was ill with a disease that no doctor seemed to be able to cure. For twelve years she had spent all her money on doctors, and now she was worse.

She had heard of Jesus, of course. "I would never dare to speak to Him, or ask Him to heal me," she thought. "But suppose, in the crowd, I came near enough just to touch the hem of His robe or even the tassel on His cloak — why, that would be enough to make me well again. He is so good and so kind — yes, just to touch His cloak would heal me!"

So, as Jesus was walking along with Jairus, this woman made her way nearer and nearer to Him in the crowd. At last she was just behind Him. With a beating heart she put out her hand and touched the bottom of His cloak.

No sooner had she touched it than she felt herself healed! Her body was no longer ill and weak. It was suddenly strong and healthy. The woman was overcome with joy and wonder. Now she must slip away quickly and think of the marvellous thing that had happened to her.

But before she could go Jesus stopped and looked round. "Who touched me?" He said.

"I didn't, Master," said one nearby. "Nor did I," said another. Peter was astonished at his Master's question.

"Master, what do you mean, *who touched you?*" said he. "Look at the crowd round you, jostling against you all the time! Many people must have touched you."

But Jesus knew quite well that someone had

The crowd jostled and pressed around Jesus.

touched Him with a purpose, because He had felt goodness going out of Him as always happened when He healed someone. Some person had wanted His help, and had received it without even asking for it. Who was it?

Jairus did not want to stop. "Oh, hurry, hurry!" he thought. "There is so little time to be lost. My little Anna may be dying."

The woman in the crowd felt that Jesus was looking at her. She came forward and knelt down, trembling. She told Him of her disease.

"I knew that if I touched but the hem of your

Jairus suddenly saw the messengers pushing their way through the people.

cloak I should be healed," she said. "And it was so."

"Daughter," said Jesus gently, "because you trusted me so much, you were healed. Go in peace."

As the woman was slipping through the crowd Jairus suddenly saw messengers pushing their way through the people. "Where is Jairus?" they asked. "We want Jairus."

Jairus felt his heart go cold, for the faces of the messengers were grave and sad. "Sir," said one, "do not trouble the Master now. Your little girl is dead."

Jairus turned in despair to Jesus, tears in his eyes. It was too late after all!

Jesus spoke comfortingly to him. "Don't be afraid. Only believe in me."

He walked on with Jairus, and the crowd followed. When He came near the house Jesus turned and spoke to the people.

"Come no farther," He said. Then taking his disciples James and Peter and John with him, He went into the house with Jairus.

As soon as they were inside they heard a great noise of weeping and wailing and doleful singing and chanting. In those days when anyone died people were paid to come and wail for the dead, and already they were wailing for little Anna.

Jesus could not bear this noise. He knew that the people there had been paid to weep and wail, they were not weeping from their hearts for Anna. It was all make-believe, and Jesus did not like that.

"Why do you make this noise?" Jesus said to the weeping women. "The little girl is not dead. She is asleep."

Then they all laughed at Him, for they had seen that the child was dead. Jesus sent them all away, and then He followed Jairus into the room where Anna lay. His disciples went with Him, and they walked softly to the bed where the child lay so still.

The mother was there, weeping bitterly.

"You were too late, Jairus," she sobbed. "You did not even say goodbye to her, our poor little Anna."

Jairus looked at her in despair, and then turned to Jesus. No one but Jesus could do anything now.

Jesus stood by the bed, looking at the child who lay so still, her eyes closed, and her cheeks pale. He put out His hand and took Anna's in His. He held it firmly in His warm one.

"Get up, darling," He said.

Anna opened her eyes. She sat up, looking all round. She was surprised to see so many men round her bed. She smiled at her father. Then she rose up from her bed and walked a few steps in the room.

Her mother and father could hardly believe their eyes. "Anna!" said her mother. "My little Anna!"

And in a moment she was in the arms of her father and mother. They kissed her and fondled her, crying for joy. She was alive again! She was laughing and talking just as she always did!

Jesus watched them with gladness. It was always good to see love and happiness and He was glad that He could bring so much.

"Tell no one of this," He said to Jairus. Then he turned to Anna's mother. She was quite beside herself with joy. Jesus knew that He must give her something to do for her child.

"Give Anna food to eat," He said, and the mother went gladly to bring some .

Jesus went from the house with His disciples, leaving behind a family full of joy.

"I want to see that man again," said Anna, to her parents. "He is kind. I like Him."

And so, when Jesus visited Capernaum, and the children came round Him as they always did, little Anna was always there, waiting. She listened to His stories, gazing up into his clear, steadfast eyes. She would do anything in the world for Jesus!

He put out His hand and took Anna's in His.

BRER RABBIT'S CLEVER TRICK!

"BRRRRR! It's cold!" said Brer Rabbit, looking out of his window. "I'll have to wrap myself up warmly when I fetch some carrots out of my store."

So he wrapped his thickest scarf round his neck, put on two pairs of socks and some very old boots, and out he went.

But when he came to his store he stared in anger. "Someone's been here in the night! Someone's stolen half my carrots! Look at that now! It's Brer Bear, I know it is!"

Brer Rabbit looked in the snow to see if he could find Brer Bear's big footprints — but more snow had fallen that morning, and had covered whatever tracks there might have been.

"All the same, I'm sure it *was* Brer Bear," thought Brer Rabbit, and he marched off to Brer Bear's house at once.

Brer Bear was surprised to see Brer Rabbit marching so boldly into his garden. Brer Rabbit saw him at the window and yelled to him.

"You've been stealing my carrots! I know you have, Brer Bear. I can smell chicken a-stewing in your pot, and I know you like carrots with it!"

"You know wrong then!" shouted back Brer Bear. "I'm tired of carrots. I've put turnips in my pot instead. You have a look in my shed — you'll see it's full of turnips, not carrots."

Brer Rabbit went to the little shed and opened the door. Sure enough, there were turnips there! Brer Rabbit scrabbled among them, but couldn't find a single carrot. He went out into the front garden again — and was surprised to see a few turnips lying on the snow there. Why weren't they covered with the snow that had fallen earlier?

"Brer Bear — *I* know what you've done with my carrots!" shouted Brer Rabbit, dancing on the snow in a great rage. "You stole them last night — and you went to Brer Fox and swapped them for turnips — oh, yes, you did — those are Brer Fox's turnips, I know they are — because here are Brer Fox's tracks going to your shed,

and here are a few turnips he spilt on the snow!"

"Don't talk rubbish!" said Brer Bear, and slammed down the window.

Brer Rabbit was in such a temper that he went along the road kicking up the snow as hard as he could. He stubbed his toe against something hard and yelled.

A small head poked out of the snow. It was Brer Rabbit's friend, Brer Terrapin.

"Hey, stop kicking about like that," said Brer Terrapin. "You gave me a turn, so you did! What's the matter?"

Brer Rabbit told him. "That robber of a Brer Bear stole my carrots in the night — and exchanged them for the turnips that Brer Fox has been boasting about," he said.

"Well, you go and get your carrots," said Brer Terrapin. "Go tonight, Brer Rabbit."

"He'll see my tracks," said Brer Rabbit. "You can't go anywhere in this snow without leaving footprints behind you!"

"You carry me home to your nice warm fire and I'll tell you what to do," said Brer Terrapin. "I'm stuck in this snow, and it's cold."

So Brer Rabbit picked up Brer Terrapin and took him home. They sat in front of the nice warm fire, and talked.

"Now, you listen to me, Brer Rabbit," said cunning old Brer Terrapin. "You put on your largest boots, and then cut out some large pieces of cardboard in the shape of even larger soles, and tie them to the bottom of your boots."

"What's the use of that?" said Brer Rabbit.

"It's just so that you'll make tracks as large as Brer Bear makes when he wears those great boots of his," said Brer Terrapin. "Because, Brer Rabbit, you're going to pretend to *be* Brer Bear. You're going to get back your carrots from Brer Fox's shed, see, when it's nice and dark — and you're going to make old Brer Fox think it's *Brer Bear* that's been to get them."

"You've got brains, Brer Terrapin," said Brer Rabbit. "You're mighty clever! Right — I'll cut out those big cardboard soles — and when I go out with a sack tonight to collect my carrots from Brer Fox's shed, you can sit here and stoke up my fire for me."

"I'll do that — and I'll keep a pot of broth boiling so that we can have a feast of carrot soup!" said Brer Terrapin, pleased.

Well, that night Brer Rabbit put on his biggest boots, and tied the even bigger cardboard soles tightly underneath. You should have seen the enormous footprints he made in the snow, just like Brer Bear's!

He went to Brer Fox's house, and walked softly over the snow to his shed. He filled his sack — but there was still room in it for more. "Brer Fox has eaten some of my carrots already," he thought. "Well, I'll go up to Brer Bear's now and get a few of his turnips to make up for the carrots Brer Fox has eaten!"

So away he went up the hill to Brer Bear's, carrying the sack, his feet making big tracks as before. Into Brer Bear's shed he went, and filled up his sack with as many turnips as he could.

Down he went again, and then grinned. What a joke — in the morning Brer Fox would look out on the snow and see great footprints walking to his shed, and he would follow them right up the hill to Brer Bear's house — well, well, well — what a pity he and Brer Terrapin couldn't see what would happen when the two met next day!

When he came back again to Brer Fox's gate, he undid the large cardboard soles from his boots, and walked home properly, scuffling through the big footprints he had made when

he had walked from his own house to Brer Fox's gate. Now for a good meal of hot carrot soup!

Brer Terrapin chuckled when he heard all that Brer Rabbit had done. They sliced up the carrots and put them into the broth Brer Terrapin had made. "My, it smells good!" said Brer Rabbit.

Well, next morning Brer Rabbit took a walk to Brer Fox's, and found him in a great rage. He was by his shed — and it was empty, of course. "Do you know what's happened?" he shouted to Brer Rabbit. "That rogue of a Brer Bear came in the night and took my carrots. See his great footprints! Wait till I see him."

"He's coming down the hill this very minute," said Brer Rabbit, skipping behind a tree. "And my, isn't *he* in a rage! Listen to him grunting!"

Brer Bear was coming down the hill at a great pace, leaving just as big prints in the snow as Brer Rabbit had left the night before.

"Where's Brer Fox? Where's that thief of a Brer Fox?" he raged. "Didn't I give him all those carrots in exchange for his mouldy old turnips? And now he's been in the night and taken half my turnips as well! Wait till I get him!"

And Brer Fox was yelling too. "Brer Bear, how dare you come and steal my carrots! Didn't I give you turnips for them? You robber — I saw your big footprints, I knew it was you!"

And with that the two flew at one another, and Brer Rabbit danced with joy behind his tree to see such a fight. Biff! Slap! Bash! Grrrrr! Ooof! Whack! Biff!

"Serves them right," he said. "They won't take *my* carrots again in a hurry! Go it, Brer Bear! That's right, Brer Fox! Talk about a snow-storm! I can hardly see you for the snow that's flying up all around you! When you've finished, I might ask you in to dinner — I'VE SOME OF THE FINEST CARROT SOUP YOU EVER SAW!"

That made both the fighters stop the battle at once! "*Carrot* soup — where did you get carrots from? Your shed's empty!" cried Brer Bear.

"It's full again — but I've put a padlock on this time, Brer Bear," shouted Brer Rabbit. "Oooh — my carrot soup — it's DELICIOUS! Good-bye!"

And away he went, kicking up the snow, and laughing so loudly that the little Jack Sparrows flew off in fright. Poor Brer Fox and Brer Bear — still, it served them right!

FIVE - AND A HALF-TERM ADVENTURE!

Most children know the "Famous Five" — Julian, Dick, George (short for Georgina) and Anne — and, of course, Timmy the dog. Here is a story of an adventure they had during half-term holiday.

THE Five were at Kirrin Cottage for a short half-term holiday. For once in a way both the boys' school and the girls' school had chosen the same weekend!

"It hardly ever happens that we can spend half-term together," said Anne, fondling Timmy. "And what luck to have such lovely weather at the beginning of November!"

"Four days off!" said George. "What shall we do?"

"Bathe!" said Julian and Dick together.

"*What!*" said their aunt, horrified. "Bathe in *November*! You must be mad! I can't allow that, Julian, really I can't."

"All right," said Julian, grinning at his aunt. "Don't worry. We haven't any swim-suits here."

"Let's walk over to Windy Hill," said Dick. "It's a grand walk, by the sea most of the way. And there may be blackberries and nuts still to find. I'd like a good walk."

"Woof," said Timmy at once, and put his big paw up on Dick's knee. He was always hoping to hear that magic word "Walk!"

"Yes, let's do that," said Anne. "Aunt Fanny, shall we take a picnic lunch — or is it too much bother to prepare?"

"Not if you help me," said her aunt, getting up. "Come along — we'll see what we can find. But remember that it gets dark very quickly in the afternoon now, so don't leave it too late when you turn back."

The Five set off half an hour later, with sandwiches and slices of fruit cake in a knapsack carried by Julian. Dick had a basket for any nuts or blackberries. His aunt had promised a blackberry-and-apple pie if they *did* find any berries for picking.

Timmy was very happy. He trotted along with the others, sniffing here and there, and barking at a curled-up hedgehog in a hole in a bank.

"Now, leave it alone," said George. "You really should have learnt by now that hedgehogs are not meant to be carried in your mouth, Timmy! Don't wake it up — it's gone to sleep for the winter!"

"It's a heavenly day for the beginning of November," said Anne. "The trees still have their leaves — all colours, red, yellow, brown, pink — and the beeches are the colour of gold."

"Blackberries!" said Dick, catching sight of a bush whose sprays were still covered with the black fruit. "I say — taste them — they're as sweet as sugar!"

As soon as blackberries were to be seen on bushes here and there, the Five slowed up con-

"Now, leave it alone," said George.

siderably! The blackberries that were still left were big and full of sweetness.

"They melt in my mouth!" said George. "Try one, Timmy!" But Timmy spat the blackberry out in disgust.

"Manners, Timmy, manners!" said Dick at once, and Timmy wagged his big tail and pranced round joyfully.

It was a good walk but a slow one. They found a hazel-nut copse and filled the basket with nuts that had fallen to the ground. Two red squirrels sat up in a nearby tree and chattered at them crossly. This was *their* nut copse!

"You can spare us a few!" called Anne. "I expect you've hundreds hidden away for the winter."

They had their lunch on the top of Windy Hill. It was not a windy day, but, all the same, there was a good breeze on the top, and Julian decided to sit behind a big gorse bush for shelter. "We'll be in the sun and out of the wind then," he said. "Spread out the lunch, Anne!"

"I feel *terribly* hungry," said George. "I can't believe it's only just one o'clock, Julian."

"Well, that's what my watch says," said Julian, taking a sandwich. "Ha — ham and lettuce together — just what I like. Get away, Tim — I can't eat with you trying to nibble my sandwich, too."

It was a magnificent view from the top of the hill. The four children munched their sandwiches and gazed down into the valley below. A town lay there, comfortably sprawled in the shelter of the hills. Smoke rose lazily from the chimneys.

"Look — there's a train running along the railway-lines down there," said George. "It looks just like a toy one."

"It's going to Beckton," said Julian. "See — there's the station — it's stopping there. It really *does* look like a toy train!"

"Now it's off again, — on its way to Kirrin, I suppose," said Dick. "Any more sandwiches? What, none! Shame! I'll have a slice of cake then — hand over, Anne."

They talked lazily, enjoying being together again. Timmy wandered from one to the other, getting a titbit here and a scrap of ham there.

"I *think* I can see another nut copse over yonder — the other side of the hill," said George. "I vote we go and see what nuts we can find — and then we ought to be thinking of going back home. The sun is getting awfully low, Ju."

"Yes. It is, considering it's only about two o'clock," said Julian, looking at the red November sun hardly showing above the horizon. "Come on, then — let's get a few more nuts, and then go back home. I love that long path winding over the cliffs beside the sea."

They all went off to the little copse, and to their delight found a fine crop of hazel-nuts there. Timmy nosed about in the grass and brought mouthfuls of the nuts to George.

"Gosh — I must have forgotten to wind it up."

"Thanks, Timmy," said George. "Very clever of you — but I wish you could tell the bad ones from the good ones!"

"I say," said Dick, after a while, "the sun's gone, and it's getting dark. Julian, are you *sure* your watch is right?"

Julian looked at his watch. "It says just about two o'clock still," he said in surprise. "Gosh — I must have forgotten to wind it up or something. It's definitely stopped now — and it must have been very slow before!"

"Ass," said Dick. "No wonder George thought it was long past lunch-time when you said it was one o'clock. We'll never manage to get home before dark now — and we haven't any torches with us."

"That cliff-path isn't too good to walk along in the dark, either," said Anne. "It goes so near the edge at times."

"We'd better start back immediately," said Julian. "Awfully sorry about this — I never dreamed that my watch was wrong."

"I tell you what would be a better idea," said George. "Why don't we just take the path down into Beckton and catch the train to Kirrin? We'll be so late if we walk back, and Mother will be ringing up the police about us!"

"Good idea of yours, George," said Julian. "Come on — let's take the path while we can still see. It leads straight down to the town."

So away went the Five as fast as they could. It was dark when they reached the town, but that didn't matter, because the street lamps were alight. They made their way to the station, half-running down the main street.

"See — there's Robin Hood on at the cinema here," said Anne. "Look at the posters!"

"And what's that on at the hall over there?" said George. "Timmy, come here — oh, he's shot across the road. Come HERE, Timmy!"

But Timmy was running up the steps of the Town Hall. Julian gave a sudden laugh. "Look — there's a big Dog Show on there — and old Timmy must have thought he ought to go in for it!"

"He smelt the dogs there," said George, rather cross. "Come on — let's get him or we'll lose the next train."

The hall was plastered with posters of dogs of all kinds. Julian stopped to read them while George went in after Timmy.

"Some jolly valuable dogs here," he said. "Some beauties, too — look at the picture of this white poodle. Ah — here comes Tim again, looking very sorry for himself. I bet he knows he wouldn't win a single prize — except for brains!"

"It was the doggy smell that made him go to see what was on," said George. "He was really cross because they wouldn't let him in!"

"Buck up — I think I can hear a train coming!" said Dick, and they all raced down the road to the station, which was quite near. The train puffed in as they went to the booking-office for their tickets. The guard was blowing his whistle and waving his flag as they rushed on to the platform. Dick pulled open the door of the very last compartment and they all bundled in, panting.

"Gosh — that was a near squeak," said Dick, half-falling on to a seat. "Look out, Tim — you nearly had me over."

The four children got back their breath and looked round the carriage. It was not empty, as they had expected. Two other people were there, sitting at the opposite end, facing each

They all bundled in, panting.

other — a man and a woman. They looked at the Five, annoyed.

"Oh," said Anne, seeing the woman carrying a shawled bundle in her arms. "I hope we haven't woken your baby. We only *just* caught the train."

The woman rocked the little thing in her arms, and crooned to it, covering its head with a shawl — a rather dirty one, Anne noticed.

"Is she all right?" asked the man. "Cover her up more — it's cold in here."

"There, there now," crooned the woman, pulling the shawl tighter. The children lost interest and began to talk. Timmy sat still by George, very bored. Then he suddenly sniffed round, and went over to the woman. He leapt up on to the seat beside her and pawed at the shawl! The woman shrieked and the man shouted at Timmy.

"Stop that! Get down! Here, you kids, look after that great dog of yours. It'll frighten the baby into fits!"

"Come here, Timmy," said George at once, surprised that he should be interested in a baby. Timmy whined and went to George, looking back at the woman. A tiny whimpering noise came from the shawl, and the woman frowned. "You've waked her," she said, and began to talk to the man in a loud, harsh voice.

Timmy was *very* disobedient! Before George could stop him, he was up on the seat again, pawing at the woman and whining. The man leapt up furiously.

"Don't hit my dog, don't hit him, he'll snap at you!" shouted George — and mercifully just at that moment the train drew in at a station.

"Let's get out and go into another carriage," said Anne, and opened the door. The four of them, followed by a most unwilling Timmy, were soon climbing into a compartment near the engine. George looked crossly at Timmy.

"Whatever came over you, Tim?" she said. "You are *never* interested in babies! Now sit down and don't move!"

Timmy was surprised at George's cross voice, and he crept under the seat and stayed there. The train came to a little Halt, where there was a small platform, and stopped to let a few people get out.

"It's Seagreen Halt," said Dick, looking out. "And there go the man and woman and baby — I must say I wouldn't like them for a Mum and Dad!"

"It's *quite* dark now," said George, looking through the window. "It's a jolly good thing we just caught the train. Mother will be getting worried."

It was nice to be in the cosy sitting-room at Kirrin Cottage again, eating an enormous tea and telling George's mother about their walk. She was very pleased with the nuts and blackberries. They told her about the man and woman and baby, too, and how funny Timmy had been, pawing at the shawl.

"He was funny before that," said Anne, remembering. "Aunt Fanny, there was a dog-show on at Beckton, and Timmy must have read the

"It's Seagreen Halt," said Dick, looking out.

posters, and thought he could go in for it — because he suddenly dashed across the road and into the Town Hall where the show was being held!"

"Really?" said her aunt, laughing. "Well, perhaps he went to see if he could find the beautiful little white Pekinese that was stolen there today! Mrs. Harris rang up and told me about it — there was such a to-do. The little dog, which was worth five hundred pounds, was cuddled down in its basket one minute — and the next it was gone! Nobody was seen to take it, and though they hunted in every corner of the hall, there was no sign of the dog."

"Gracious!" said Anne. "What a mystery! How could anyone possibly take away a dog like that without being seen?"

"Easily," said Dick. "Wrap it in a coat, or pop it into a shopping basket and cover it up. Then walk through the crowd and out of the hall!"

"Or wrap it in a shawl and pretend it was a baby — like the little one in that dirty shawl in the train," said Anne. "I mean — we *thought* that was a baby, of course — but it could easily have been a dog — or a cat — or even a monkey. We couldn't see its face!"

There was a sudden silence. Everyone was staring at Anne and thinking hard. Julian banged his hand on the table and made them all jump.

"There's something in what Anne has just said," he said. "Something worth thinking about! Did anyone see even a glimpse of the baby's face — or hair? Did you, Anne — you were nearest?"

"No," said Anne, quite startled. "No, I didn't. I did try to see, because I like babies — but the shawl was pulled right over the face and head."

"And I say — don't you remember how interested *Timmy* was in it?" said George excited. "He's never interested in babies — but he kept *on* jumping up and pawing at the shawl."

"And do you remember how the baby whimpered?" said Dick. "It was much more like a little dog whining than a baby, now I come to think of it. No wonder Timmy was excited! He *knew* it was a dog by the smell!"

"Whew! I say — this is jolly exciting," said Julian, getting up. "I vote we go to Seagreen Halt and snoop round the tiny village there."

"*No*," said Aunt Fanny firmly. "I will not have that, Julian. It's as dark as pitch outside, and I don't want you snooping around for dog-thieves on your half-term holiday."

"Oh, I *say*!" said Julian, bitterly disappointed.

"Ring up the police," said his aunt. "Tell them what you have just told me — they'll be

"There go the man and woman and baby."

able to find out the truth very quickly. They will be sure to know who has a baby and who hasn't — *they* can go round snooping quite safely!"

"All right," said Julian, sad to have a promising adventure snatched away so quickly. He went to the phone, frowning. Aunt Fanny *might* have let him and Dick slip out to Seagreen in the dark — it would have been such fun.

The police were most interested and asked a lot of questions. Julian told them all he knew, and everyone listened intently. Then Julian put down the receiver and turned to the others, looking quite cheerful again.

"They were jolly interested," he said. "And they're off to Seagreen Village straightaway in the police car. They're going to let us know what they find. Aunt Fanny — we CANNOT go to bed tonight till we know what happens!"

"No, we can't!" cried all the others, and Timmy joined in with a bark, leaping around excitedly.

"Very well," said Aunt Fanny, smiling. "What a collection of children you are — you can't even go for a walk without something happening! Now — get out the cards and let's have a game."

They played cards, with their ears listening for the ringing of the telephone bell. But it didn't ring. Supper time came and still it hadn't rung.

"It's no go, I suppose," said Dick gloomily. "We probably made a mistake."

Timmy suddenly began to bark, and then ran to the door, pawing at it.

"Someone's coming," said George. "Listen — it's a car!"

They all listened and heard the car stop at the gate — then footsteps came up the path and the front-door bell rang. George was out in a trice and opened it.

"Oh, it's the police!" she called. "Come in, do come in."

A burly policeman came in, followed by another. The second one carried a bundle in a shawl! Timmy leapt up to it at once, whining!

"Oh! It *wasn't* a baby, then!" cried Anne, and the policeman smiled and shook his head. He pulled the shawl away — and there, fast asleep, was a tiny white Pekinese, its little snub nose tucked into the shawl!

"Oh — the darling!" said Anne. "Wake up, you funny little thing!"

"It's been doped," said the policeman. "I suppose they were afraid of it whining in the night and giving its hiding-place away!"

"Tell us what happened," begged Dick. "Get *down*, Timmy. George, he's getting too excited — he wants the Peke to play with him!"

"Acting on your information we went to Seagreen," said the policeman. "We asked the porter what people got out of the train this evening, and if anyone carried a baby — and he said four people got out — and two of them were a man and woman, and the woman carried a baby in a shawl. He told us who they were — so away we went to the cottage . . ."

He pulled the shawl away.

"Woof," said Timmy interrupting, trying to get at the tiny dog again, but nobody took any notice of him.

"We looked through the back window of the cottage," went on the policeman, "and spotted what we wanted at once! The woman was giving the dog a drink of milk in a saucer — and she must have put some drug into it, because the little thing dropped down and fell asleep at once while we were watching."

"So in we went, and that was that," said the second policeman, smiling round. "The couple were so scared that they blurted out everything — how someone had paid them to steal the dog, and how they had taken their own baby's shawl, wrapped round a cushion — and had stolen the dog quite easily when the judging of the Alsatians was going on. They wrapped the tiny dog in the shawl, just as you thought, and caught the next train home!"

"I *wish* I'd gone to Seagreen Village with you," said Julian. "Do you know who told the couple to steal the little dog?"

"Yes — we're off to interview him now! He'll be most surprised to see us," said the burly policeman. "We've informed the owner that we've found her prize dog all right — but she feels so upset about it she says she can't collect it till the morning — so we wondered if you'd like to keep it for the night? Your Timmy can guard it, can't he?"

"Oh *yes*," said George in delight. "Oh, Mother — I'll take it to my room when I go to bed, and Timmy can guard the tiny thing as much as he likes. He'll love it!"

"We looked through the back window."

"Well — if your mother doesn't mind you having *two* dogs in your room, that's fine!" said the policeman, and signalled to the second man to give George the dog in the shawl. She took it gently, and Timmy leapt up again.

"No, Tim — be careful," said George. "Look what a tiny thing it is. You're to guard it tonight."

Timmy looked at the little sleeping Pekinese, and then, very gently, he licked it with the tip of his pink tongue. This was the tiny dog he had smelt in the train, covered up in the shawl. Oh yes — Timmy had guessed at once!

"I don't know what your name is," said Dick, stroking the small silky head. "But I *think* I'll call you Half-term Adventure, though I don't know what that is in Pekinese!"

The two policemen laughed. "Well, good night, Madam, good night, children," said the burly one. "Mrs. Fulton, the dog's owner, will call tomorrow morning for her Peke. He won a hundred-pound prize today — so I dare say you'll get some of that for a reward! Good night!"

The Five didn't want a reward, of course — but Timmy had one for guarding the little Peke all night. It's round his neck now — the finest studded collar he has ever had in his life! Good old Timmy!

THE BRILLIANT LEAVES

"WELL," said Uncle Nat, as he met the children one fine October day, "what do you think of the country-side this morning?"

The two children gazed round. They saw the tree-covered hills and the hedges round the field, and, like Uncle Nat, they were filled with delight.

"Uncle, the trees aren't green – they're yellow and brown and red and pink and gold," said Mary. "Look at that wood over there — it looks as if someone had spilt a paint-box over it."

"We shall have a lovely walk today," said Uncle Nat. "We will go through the beechwoods, where the trees are the colour of golden sovereigns. Perhaps you have never seen a sovereign, but when you see the gold of the beech-leaves, you will know exactly what colour it is!"

There was colour everywhere that day. The creeper on the cottages was brilliant crimson. The birch-trees were a delicate yellow; the chestnut was golden, and so was the hazel.

"Uncle, soon the leaves will fall," said Mary sadly. "That's what all this brilliant beauty means—the fall of the leaf and winter-time."

"Don't look so gloomy," said Uncle Nat, amused. "Not every tree sheds its leaves. You will still have the yews and the firs, the pines and the holly. They keep their leaves all the winter through."

"Why do the leaves of some trees change colour?" said Peter. "It seems a queer idea."

"Does it," said Uncle Nat. "Well, when I tell you the reason, you will see that it is really a very *good* idea."

Mary picked up a brilliant pink leaf from a wild cherry tree. She held it up to the sun and it glowed like crimson fire. "Do tell me why this leaf is such a glorious colour," she said.

"Well," said Uncle Nat, "when the trees are about to cast away their leaves because they do not want them any longer this year, they collect all the rubbish they have and send it up to the leaves."

"What a queer idea! Why do they do that?" asked Mary in surprise.

"They want to get rid of their rubbish," said Uncle Nat, "and that is a very sure way to do it. The leaves will fall off when the frosty nights come — and the rubbish will go with them."

"I see," said Mary. "Is it the rubbish that makes the leaves turn those lovely colours?"

"Yes," said Uncle Nat. "You see, plant rubbish is never green. Green is the *good* colour for plants; reds, yellows, browns and so on are the 'waste' colours. So up into the leaves goes all the stuff that the trees want to get rid of — and hey presto, the leaves turn the most wonderful colours imaginable."

The children looked around at the brilliant trees and hedges. "It's a very good idea," said Peter. "The trees get rid of their rubbish, and they make themselves simply beautiful before they go to sleep for the winter. Uncle Nat, who really thinks of all these marvellous ideas?"

"Ah, there's a mystery for you!" said Uncle Nat. "Well, come along. We must go on with our walk. Let's collect all the different leaves and see how many colours we can find."

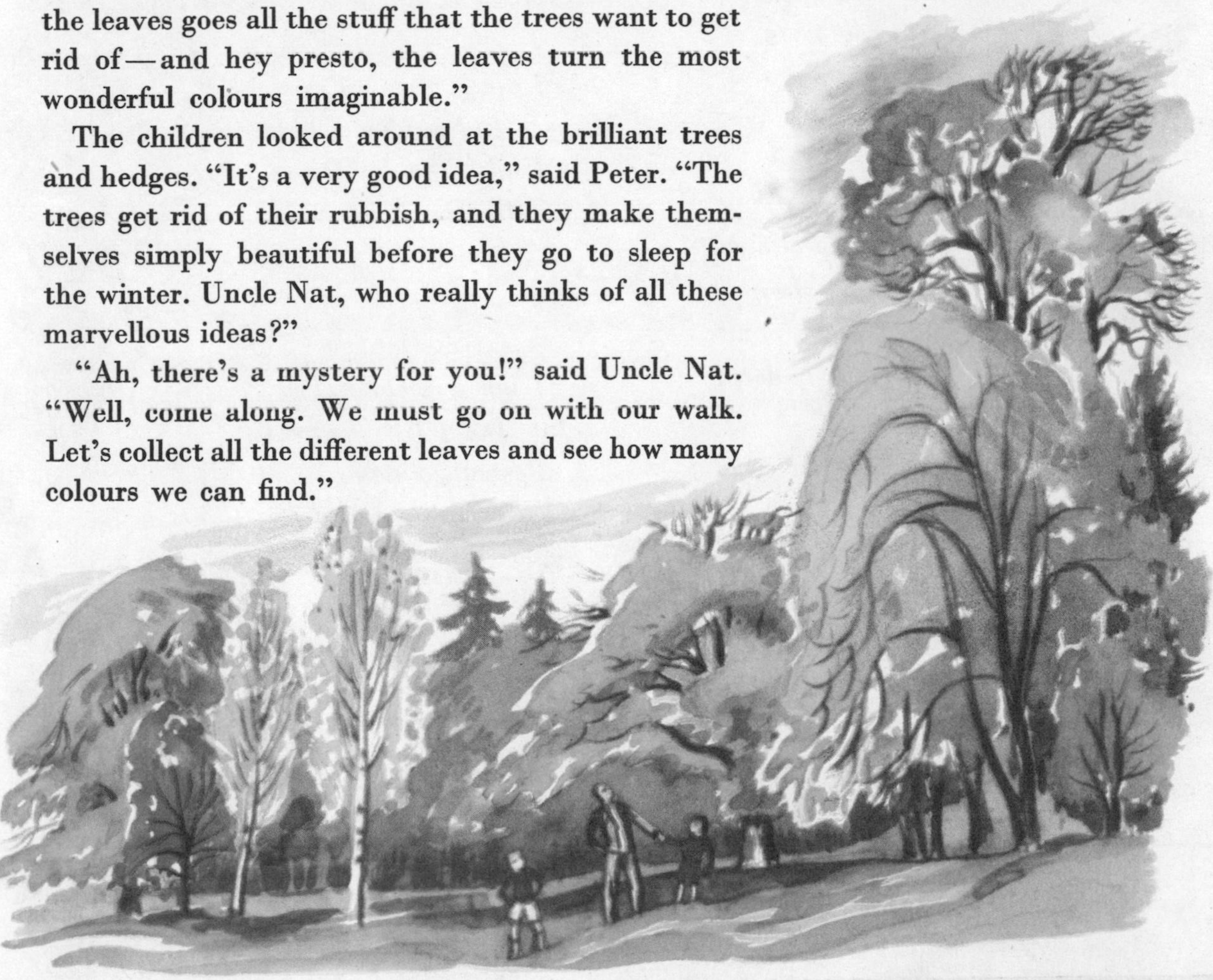

A PUZZLE POEM

(Find the right names of all the sleepers.)

I am a Slurriqe,
I sleep in a tree,
Curled up in my tail
As cosy can be.

I am a Tab,
When the winter wind blows
I sleep in a barn
Hung up by my toes!

I am a Doghegeh,
In ditches I creep,
Find a warm hole there
And roll up to sleep!

I am a Neque Paws,
And snugly I hide
Under the ivy-leaves
On the house-side.

I am a Gorf,
And soundly I sleep
Upside down in the pond
Where the water is deep.

I am a Dota,
And I like to crawl
Beneath a damp stone
Or under a wall.

And I am a Tribba,
Who all winter through
Is just as awake
And as lively as you!

PLEASE HELP ME

MR. PINK-WHISTLE!

Another tale of Mr. Pink-Whistle, the kind little man who likes to put things right when they have gone wrong. In this story he puts things right for Mark Brown.

"MR. PINK-WHISTLE, sir," said Sooty the cat, coming into the room where Mr. Pink-Whistle was having a little snooze. "Could you wake up for a minute?"

"Hallo? Dear me, was I asleep?" said Pink-Whistle, waking up with a jump. "What is it, Sooty? A visitor to see me?"

"Well, it's a little boy," said Sooty, "and he seems to want your help — but he's so shy that really I can't make head or tail of *what* he wants!"

"Send him in," said Pink-Whistle, and Sooty ran out of the room and went to the front gate. A boy of about nine was there, looking anxiously at the house.

"You can come in," said Sooty. "And do try to speak properly or you will waste my master's time!"

The boy followed Sooty into the little house, and blushed bright red with delight when he saw old Pink-Whistle — yes, the real, live Pink-Whistle, with pointed ears, green eyes and a very big smile.

"Hallo, my boy," said Pink-Whistle. "What's the matter? I hear you want my help."

The boy nodded his head but didn't say a word. "Sit down," said Pink-Whistle. "Now — tell me."

"P-p-p-p-please h-h-h-help m-m-m-m-m-m-me," said the boy, stammering dreadfully.

"I will," said Pink-Whistle. "What's wrong?"

"It's – it's – it's my st-st-stammer!" said the boy nervously. "I c-c-c-can't help it. And the others l-l-l-laugh at m-m-m-me and that m-m-m-m-akes it worse. And my m-m-m-mother gets c-c-cross, and that m-m-m-makes me w-w-w-worse t-t-too."

"Bad luck!" said Pink-Whistle. "You don't need to be nervous with *me*, you know. You will be glad to hear that I can cure you quite easily."

"C-c-can you!" said the boy, amazed.

"What's your name," said Pink-Whistle, "and your address? I'm going to send you something that will cure you."

"Hallo, my boy," said Pink-Whistle.

The boy beamed all over his face. "My name's M-m-m-mark B-b-brown," he said.

"Not a good name for a stammerer," said Pink-Whistle, and twinkled at the boy. "I told you that you don't need to be nervous with me. Take a deep breath and say it again, slowly."

"Mark Brown!" said the boy. "What are you g-going to send me, Mr. Pink-Whistle?"

"Aha! Something alive!" said Pink-Whistle, shutting up the notebook in which he had written Mark's name and address. "Something that will want to understand every word you say. Something that will never laugh at you. Something that will want you to talk and talk and

He rang up Mark's mother.

talk so clearly that he is never at a loss to obey your smallest word."

"Is it something magic?" asked Mark, not stammering at all in his wonder at what Mr. Pink-Whistle was saying.

"You wait and see," said Pink-Whistle. "Now, off you go — and I want you to visit me again in one month's time and bring my present back with you, so that I can see if you are getting along with it all right."

Mark ran off, puzzled and delighted. What did Mr. Pink-Whistle mean? What a KIND man he was — those twinkling eyes — that deep, happy voice! Yes — he felt sure that Mr. Pink-Whistle would cure him of his stammering — without any scolding or jeering, without any long, long exercises in speaking. Good old Mr. Pink-Whistle!

Mr. Pink-Whistle became busy as soon as Mark had gone. He went to his telephone and rang up Mark's mother. She was most astonished to hear who it was, and even more astonished when she knew that Mark had been to see him.

"It's his stammer he's worried about," said Mr. Pink-Whistle. "I can cure it — if you will allow me to give him a present."

He told her what the present would be, and she said, yes, she would let Mark have it as soon as it arrived — though for the life of her she couldn't see how it would help Mark's stammer!

Then Mr. Pink-Whistle went off to the nearby farm, and asked to see the little spaniel puppies there, that Floppy the lovely golden spaniel had in her basket. How pretty they were — and how they squirmed about, giving tiny little yaps all the time. Pink-Whistle longed to buy one for himself, but he knew that Sooty his cat wouldn't like that at all. He chose a fat little fellow, with a silky golden coat, ears that drooped beautifully, and eyes that would melt anyono's heart!

That night he took the puppy to Mark's home and gave it to Mark's mother. She had a little round basket all ready for it with a warm rug inside. She was very grateful to Mr. Pink-Whistle, and looked curiously at his pointed ears under his top-hat. What a strange little man — and what a kind face.

"This puppy won't cure Mark's stammer, you know," she said. "It's very *kind* of you to give it to him — but I'm afraid that not even

Mummy had some walnuts brown,
The shells she gave to me
Little half-shells, just like boats
To play with after tea.

I put a match-stick in each one,
And made a sail as well,
And now I've lots of fairy boats,
Each made of walnut shell.

I'll float them in a bowl, and puff
To make a little gale,
I wish that I could sit in one,
I'd have a lovely sail!

you can cure Mark. We've all tried and failed."

"Never mind. Just give it to Mark," said Pink-Whistle. "And tell him the puppy's name is Bonny."

"Oh dear — he'll *never* be able to say that!" said Mrs. Brown. "B for Bonny is one of his worst stammering letters."

"The puppy's name is *Bonny*," said Mr. Pink-Whistle firmly. "And it is on no account to be altered. Tell Mark he must train him properly, or else, at the end of a month, I shall take the puppy back. He must teach him what quite a lot of commands mean — 'Sit!' 'Come to heel!' 'Lie down!' 'Quiet!' and 'Down, sir, down!' I shall expect Bonny to obey all those commands in a month's time. Please give Mark this note for me.'

"Oh Mr. Pink-Whistle — he *really* won't be able to say a single command without stammering," said Mrs. Brown. "It's no use, you know."

Mr. Pink-Whistle raised his hat, said good-bye and went. How he wondered what Mark would say when he saw the puppy!

Mark's mother crept upstairs with Bonny in the basket. The little thing was tired and was now fast asleep. She set the basket down gently in Mark's room and went out. The boy was fast asleep, too, and didn't stir at all.

Bonny slept peacefully — but he awoke in the middle of the night and wanted his mother. Where was she? He couldn't feel her or smell her. He was very, very lonely indeed. He sat up in the basket, frightened, and began to whine.

Mark woke up at once, and he, too, sat up — what *could* that noise be? He listened in astonishment. It sounded like the whining of a dog!

He switched on his light, and at once saw the tiny golden spaniel sitting forlornly in his basket, crying for his mother.

"Oh!" said Mark, "It's a dream! Surely I'm dreaming!" He leapt out of bed and went over to the puppy. The little thing cuddled up to him, still whining. Then Mark saw a big white envelope in the basket, and picked it up. "From Mr. Pink-Whistle to Mark" was written on the outside. Mark tore it open.

"Here is the cure for your stammer, Mark," said the note. "Be sure Bonny understands every word you say. He doesn't even know what stammering *is!* Teach him all the things he ought to know. Your mother will tell you what I said. Love from Pink-Whistle."

Mark put the note down and stared at the tiny puppy. He cuddled it in his arms, and put his chin down on its soft head. "Bonny!" he said softly. "Yes, you're Bonny — it's a good name for you. So this is Mr. Pink-Whistle's gift."

The puppy whined and cuddled closer. He liked this boy. He was warm and friendly and kind — the kind of boy that all dogs liked.

"I can't let you sleep alone in your basket the

"*You wait and see.*"

"Let me hold him, Mark!"

very first night!" said Mark. "I'll take you to bed with me, Bonny, and hope that Mother won't be cross — it'll only be just this once."

He cuddled the puppy again, loving its soft silky fur and beautiful ears. "I haven't stammered once to you, have I?" he said. "You wouldn't mind if I did — but it would puzzle you if I called you B-b-b-b-bonny, wouldn't it? It might even frighten you. You'll never laugh at me or be angry with me; you'll be my friend. And I shall be yours. If only I could tell Mr. Pink-Whistle how happy I am!"

Mark was so happy next day that he hardly knew how to stop singing and whistling. Bonny followed him about like a shadow. Everyone in the house loved the tiny creature, especially Janie, Mark's tomboy sister.

"Let me hold him, Mark, do let me!" she said.

"No-n-n-no," said Mark, with his usual stammer.

"There! You're stammering!" said Janie. "And yet you don't stammer when you talk to Bonny. You *can* help it, you see."

"I c-c-can't when I t-t-talk to p-p-people like you, who l-l-laugh at me so often," said Mark. "I'm not afraid that B-bonny will laugh."

"Listen, Mark — let me hold Bonny sometimes, and I promise, word of honour, I won't *ever* laugh at you again," said Janie. "Or mimic you. Not ever."

"All right. That'll b-be a help," said Mark. "Bonny — here's my sister. She'll love you, too!"

It certainly was a most extraordinary thing, but whenever Mark spoke to Bonny he never once stammered. He soon began to teach the little thing how to behave. At first Mark was sure he would not be able to say "Down, sir, down" without stammering over the D, but it never bothered him at all. Mr. Pink-Whistle was right as usual!

Mark remembered that Pink-Whistle had told

He told Bonny all that happened at school.

him to be sure to talk and talk and talk to Bonny, so that he would soon understand every word that his little master said to him. So, as soon as he came home from school, Mark went to fetch Bonny, took him to the playroom, and played with him, and talked all the time.

He told Bonny all that had happened at school. He showed him how to play ball, and talked to him about it. He told him over and over again of his visit to Mr. Pink-Whistle. His mother heard all the talking going on one day, and popped her head in to listen. How amazed she was! Why, Mark wasn't stammering once — not ONCE.

But when he saw her looking in, he stammered immediately he spoke to her! "Oh, M-m-mother, you made me j-jump!"

"Sorry!" said his mother. "Oh, Mark — I've

been listening to you talking to Bonny — you didn't stammer at all then."

"I know," said Mark. "He wouldn't *mind* my stammering, but it might muddle him a bit — and, besides, I don't even *think* about stammering when I'm with him. He's my friend. I know he won't laugh or jeer, so I don't have to think before I speak, and then get afraid and stammer. He's curing me, Mother!"

"Yes. He is," said Mrs. Brown. "Mr. Pink-Whistle was right. Go on chattering to Bonny, Mark — you'll soon be so used to talking without a stammer that you won't be afraid of stammering even when you talk to *people*!"

At the end of the month Mark was sure he was cured. He had talked so much to Bonny, had taught him so many commands, and had quite forgotten to be afraid or nervous. Now he talked just as Janie did — fast and confidently without a single stammer!

"It's a miracle!" said Mrs. Brown.

"No. Just common sense," said Mark's father. "I'd like to meet this Mr. Pink-Whistle!"

But Mark went alone to see the kind little man, taking Bonny with him. The puppy already knew how to walk to heel, and was as good as gold.

"Hallo! Nice to see you again!" said Pink-Whistle. "Well, did the cure work all right?"

"Oh *yes*! I never stammer now!" said Mark. "Do you want to see how well I've trained Bonny?"

"Dear me, yes — if he's not been properly taught, I must have him back," said Pink-Whistle.

Then Mark gave all kinds of commands to

"Oh M-m-mother, you made me j-jump!"

little Bonny. "Sit! Lie down! Bark! Quiet now! To heel, sir, to heel! On guard, boy, on guard!"

Mr. Pink-Whistle watched and listened. He felt very very pleased. Mark turned to him with a flushed face and shining eyes. "There, sir!" he said. "I can keep him, can't I? I love Bonny, he's my friend and I'm his. He's cured me, just as you said he would."

"Well done, Mark!" said Mr. Pink-Whistle. "Of course you can keep him. You deserve to

Mr. Pink-Whistle watched.

have him — and he deserves to have you. Share him with Janie sometimes."

"I will," said Mark. "She helped me, too, because she never once laughed at me after I let her hold Bonny whenever she wanted to. I'm cured, aren't I?"

"You certainly are. You're quite a chatterbox now!" said Pink-Whistle. "Let yourself out, will you — Sooty, my cat, doesn't like puppies, I'm afraid."

"Good-bye, Mr. Pink-Whistle — and thank you very much!" said Mark. "I'm going to tell EVERYONE how to cure a stammer — just get a puppy-dog to talk to!"

Well — it certainly *does* seem a very good idea, doesn't it?

Miss Hannah's Red Indian Hats

THE children next door had a great many Red Indian things, which Jack, Lucy and Jane envied very much. They had Red Indian suits and head-dresses, and a lovely wig-wam.

"It's the feathered head-dresses I like the best," said Jack. "Miss Hannah, aren't they lovely? I suppose you don't know how to make them?"

"Oh yes I do," said Miss Hannah. "If you badly want Red Indian hats, we'll make them! They're really very easy."

"Oh, good!" said the three children.

"I shall want a *brave's* hat," said Jack. "You know, one that not only has feathers all round it, but that fall right down my back too. But the girls mustn't have one like that. They're only squaws. They can only wear bands with feathers in."

"Oh, that's not fair," said Jane, at once.

"Well, it is really," said Miss Hannah. "It is only the Red Indian braves that are allowed to wear feathers down their back. The squaws mustn't. But I expect Jack will lend you his sometimes."

"What do we want for the head-dresses?" said Jack. "Do let's begin! I'm longing to be able to wear mine."

"We want feathers, of course," said Miss Hannah. "The gayer the better. I wonder if Cook has any old pheasant feathers. If not we'll get ordinary hen feathers and dye them!"

"Oh, I've got lots and lots of all kinds of feathers!" said Jane, joyfully. "I've saved them up for years, and I never thought they'd come in so useful. I've hen feathers, and duck feathers, and pheasant feathers, and even parrot feathers! Old Miss Lawson, who used to keep a parrot, gave me all the ones that Polly dropped. I've enough for all of us!"

"Good!" said Miss Hannah. "Get them then." So Jane fetched them from the cupboard. Certainly she had a wonderful collection of all colours and sizes!

"Now we must first make the band for the feathers to go in," said Miss Hannah. She took some pieces of material and cut them into long

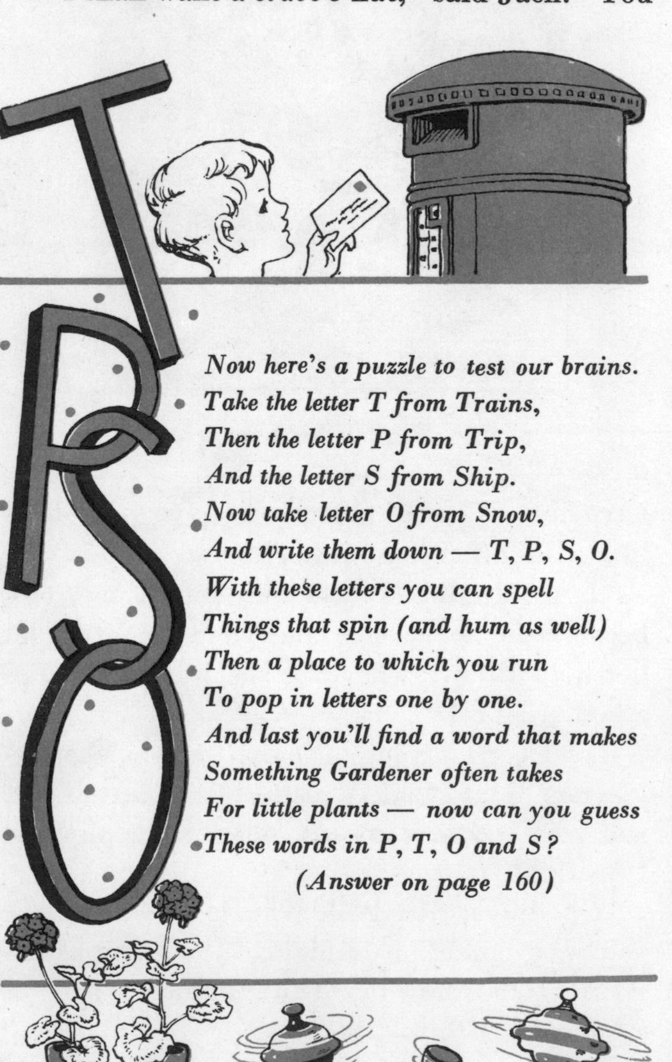

Now here's a puzzle to test our brains.
Take the letter T from Trains,
Then the letter P from Trip,
And the letter S from Ship.
Now take letter O from Snow,
And write them down — T, P, S, O.
With these letters you can spell
Things that spin (and hum as well)
Then a place to which you run
To pop in letters one by one.
And last you'll find a word that makes
Something Gardener often takes
For little plants — now can you guess
These words in P, T, O and S?

(Answer on page 160)

The squaw's head-dress. *The brave's head-dress.*

strips. Then she measured each child's head.

"Now each strip must be folded in half." she said. "The feathers have to be set inside the fold and sewn into place."

"But I *can't* sew," said Jack, in alarm.

"Well, you can sort out the feathers and arrange them in the folds," said Miss Hannah. "Big ones at the front, of course. Choose gay colours. Then I and the girls will sew them into place."

It wasn't long before Jack had sorted out the best and longest feathers and arranged them in each fold of material. Then Miss Hannah and the girls set to work to sew them in tightly. After that the ends were sewn together.

"We ought to decorate the bands with bright stitches and sew beads on," said Miss Hannah. "I saw some beads in your bead-box that would do nicely, Jane. Get them. Jack, sort out more feathers, to hang down your back. You'll want plenty!"

Miss Hannah cut another, much longer strip of material into which to set the tail of feathers to hang down Jack's back. It began to look very exciting, as she deftly sewed in feather after feather.

The girls were busy decorating the bands of their own head-dresses. Soon they looked very gay indeed. Lucy glanced out of the window.

"I say, look — it's stopped raining! Do let's go out and play Red Indians! We can wear our feathers, and make the children next door go green with envy. We've made much better ones than theirs!"

So out they went, with their Red Indian feathers on, looking very grand indeed. They yelled and gave such fierce war-whoops that Mother came to the window in surprise.

"Good gracious — so *that's* what they've been so quiet over all afternoon!" she said. "Well, they're making up for their quiet now!"

TWO LITTLE PUZZLES FOR YOU

I am a creature in a little round house.
Take off my head and I will grow on
your fingers. Change my head and you
will see me from the station platform.
Now add yet another head and I am
something left by my first!
(Answers on page 160)

Sit down in me and take your ease
Behead me — (brush me nicely, please)
Behead me once again and lo
You breathe me everywhere I go!
(Find the three words!)
(Answers on page 160)

But little Madame Fifi dared!

Beware the Bears!

This is an incident from Enid Blyton's exciting book THE CIRCUS OF ADVENTURE, which tells of four children — Jack, Philip, Dinah and Lucy-Ann — and their adventures with a travelling circus. There is trouble because the bears had escaped from their cages.

THERE came a sudden shouting from the other end of the camp — then screams. People began to stream away towards the two boys, shouting in fear.

"The bears! The bears! They're out!"

Toni came bounding up to Jack. "Where's Philip, that friend of yours you said could manage animals? Oh, there he is. The bears are loose — they've broken three of the bars of their cage. See if your friend can help. Fank, their keeper, can't even get out of bed."

Philip knew nothing about the bears, of course, and Jack hurriedly told him the details as they ran to the other end of the field. "I hope you *can* do something with them, Philip. It will be a terrible loss to the circus if the bears get loose and have to be shot."

One bear was still in the broken cage, afraid to go out because of the crowds. He was making a terrible noise. No one dared to go near. In a nearby cage Feefo and Fum, the two chimpanzees, were wailing in fright. Madame Fifi made sure they were locked in and ran over to Jack.

"Don't go near that bear, you two boys. He's dangerous. And look out for the others."

"Can't someone block up those broken bars?" said Philip. "The bear will be out soon."

"Nobody dares," said Toni. But little Madame Fifi dared! She ran to a brilliant flaring torch, stuck in a holder nearby, plucked it out and ran back to the cage. She thrust the pointed bottom end of the torch into the ground, just in front of the cage. The bear shrank back at the bright light and crouched down in a corner. He was afraid of the brilliance.

"That settles *him*," said Philip, pleased.

The bear licked Philip's hand.

"Now — where are the others?"

"Over there — sniffing round the Boss's caravan," said Jack, pointing to two dark shapes. "I bet the Boss is shivering in his shoes inside the van!"

"Where can I get some meat?" panted Philip as they ran across the field towards the bears. "Or better still, can I get honey anywhere — or treacle?"

"Treacle! Yes, Ma's got a whole jar of it," said Jack, remembering. "I'll get it."

He raced off to Ma's caravan, burst in and demanded the treacle. Ma didn't seem to be at all surprised. "On the shelf," she said.

Jack found the big stone jar and fled back to Philip with it. Philip had now gone close to the bears, who turned to look at him suspiciously.

"They've already injured one man," said Jack, in a low voice. "Look out, won't you, Philip?"

"I'll be all right," said Philip. "Keep out of sight, Jack." He took the jar of treacle, dipped his hands in it and smeared them up to the wrists with the thick, sweet syrup.

Then he walked towards the bears, pouring a little of the syrup out on the grass as he went. The bears growled warningly. Philip turned and went back again. He sat down with the jar of treacle and waited.

By now many people were watching. Who was this boy? What was he doing, meddling with two dangerous bears?

Jack stood out of sight — but near enough to run to Philip's help if necessary! He didn't think it *would* be necessary; he had absolute faith in Philip's ability to manage any animal.

The bears soon smelt the syrup that Philip had spilt here and there on the grass. They loved the sweetness of treacle. Fank, the keeper, sometimes gave it to them for a treat.

They sniffed, and went towards the first spots of treacle on the ground. One bear found them and licked eagerly. The second bear growled at him and tried to push him aside — but suddenly smelt another few spots of treacle further on!

He lumbered on clumsily and licked in delight.

As soon as the bears realised that there was treacle about, they began to grunt excitedly. They had refused food for two days now, and they were hungry. They sniffed eagerly for more treacle.

The watching people held their breath as they saw the two great clumsy creatures getting nearer and nearer to the boy sitting on the ground. Surely he was in danger?

"Who is he? He ought to be warned!" they said. But Toni and Bingo hushed them.

"Be quiet! He is Jack's friend, a wonder with animals! Give him a chance! He can run if the bears threaten him!"

The first bear was now quite near Philip, his head close to the ground as he sniffed about for more treacle. Philip put his hand into the jar he held, and took it out, waving it slowly in the air so that the bear could get the full scent of it.

The bear raised his head and saw Philip. He backed away a little and gave an angry grunt. Who was that sitting on the ground? His eyes gleamed an angry red in the light from a nearby lamp. A little sigh of fear went through the anxious crowd.

And then Philip spoke. He spoke in what Jack called his 'special' voice — the voice he always kept for animals. It was a low, monotonous voice, a gentle, kindly voice, but somehow it was a voice that had to be listened to.

The bear listened. He grunted again, and backed away, bumping into the second bear. But still Philip's voice went on. What was he saying? Jack couldn't hear. How did he know how to talk to animals like this? And why did they always listen? The watching circus-folk knew that most animal-trainers used a special tone of voice when they petted their animals — but here was a strange boy talking to frightened and suspicious bears — and yet they listened!

The second bear came a little nearer, his ears pricked. He sniffed. He sniffed not only the treacle, but Philip's own particular smell. He liked it. It was a friendly smell. The bears always

The bears followed licking their lips.

sorted out people into two kinds — those whose smell they liked and those they didn't.

He lumbered right up to Philip and sniffed at him, ready to strike if the boy moved. A little scream came from someone in the crowd, but the bear took no notice.

Philip went on talking, and now his voice was so honeyed and persuasive that even the crowd began to feel his spell. The bear licked Philip's hand, which was covered in treacle. Philip did not move. The bear went on licking, quite unafraid.

The other bear came up, and, seeing how unafraid his brother was, he took a quick lick at Philip's other hand. In two or three seconds both bears were grunting in delight at so much treacle. This boy was a friend!

Philip talked all the time, monotonously and kindly. He thought he could now dare to move, so he lifted one hand slowly, put it into the jar beside him, and then took it out covered with treacle again.

One bear lay down beside him to lick in comfort. Another sigh at once went through the tense crowd. Philip gave the jar to the other bear, and then with his free hand began to fondle the bear lying beside him. It grunted in pleasure.

Now the bears were happy and at peace. They had found someone they liked and trusted. Philip knew that he had them under control — if only the crowd didn't do something silly — make a sudden noise, or come surging towards him. But the circus folk knew better than that.

Philip stood up, doing nothing quickly — all his movements were smooth and slow. He picked up the jar, and with his other hand on one bear's neck, began to walk to the cage. The bears followed, shambling along quietly, licking their lips.

Philip took them right to the cage, undid the door and let them shuffle in. He put the treacle jar inside, shut the door, and went quietly outside.

And then HOW the people cheered!

Lullaby

Sleep, bonnie prince, you come with the Spring,
Sweet is your lullaby,
For you the robin and thrush will sing
And the wind go rollicking by.

So sleep, little babe, for when you awake,
Daffies will dance in joy,
Fluffy wee ducklings out on the lake
Will wait for the new little boy.

Close your eyes, little babe, and sleep,
While bells ring out from the steeple,
You need no cot, for you're cradled deep
In the hearts of a loving people.

This lullaby was written for the baby Prince Andrew, born to the Queen in 1960. If you have a baby in your home, sing it to him, to the tune of "The Skye Boat Song".

THE LAND OF FAR-BEYOND

This is an incident from Enid Blyton's book, THE LAND OF FAR-BEYOND, in which three children, with great burdens on their backs — burdens of selfishness, cruelty, dishonesty and the like — go with others to find the Land of Far-Beyond, where they hope to lose their burdens. On their way they meet many people, both good and bad. In this chapter they are not far from the Land they seek, and have met with a kindly youth called Charitable. The book is a new kind of Pilgrim's Progress — for children.

"I DO like Charitable, don't you?" said Peter to the others as they set off down the path again, quite dry and cheerful. The flood-water had begun to go down, but they could not see Intolerance who was far away on the other side.

"Yes, Charitable is as good to be with as Intolerance was hateful," said Anna. "It is a mercy that we find both good and bad along this road. If we found all bad I am sure I would have turned back."

"Well, we've no need to turn back now!" said Peter, cheerfully. "We're nearly there! We've only the Steps of Impatience to climb, and to deal with some dragons or other."

"I don't much like the sound of the dragons," said Patience.

"Bless us all, you don't need to worry about old-fashioned things like dragons!" said Mr. Scornful, contemptuously. "Dragons! I didn't even know there were any nowadays. I must say I was very surprised to find that a giant was alive, too. I didn't really believe in him till I saw him."

"Yes — Giant Cruelty was a terrible creature," said Anna. "I hope I never meet *him* again! I'm glad that Mercy and Pity steal into his castle so often without his knowing it."

Talking cheerfully, they went along the way until the sun sank down. Mr. Scornful looked around. "I wonder where we could shelter for the night," he said. "I don't see anywhere. Perhaps we had better go on. We might see a cottage with a light in the window."

They went on and on. Suddenly the sun disappeared and night began to fall. A few stars twinkled in the sky, but the night was so pitch-black that the children could hardly see their hands in front of their faces.

And then, in the dark, they came to the Steps of Impatience. It was just after Anna had lost her temper with Mr. Scornful.

Anna was feeling tired. She stumbled over a stone in the dark, and caught at Mr. Scornful's hand. He jerked her up rather roughly.

"Oh! You nearly pulled my arm off!" cried Anna, crossly. "Oh, dear! Why didn't we find a nice place to rest in when it was light? Now we can't see a thing."

"Don't get cross about it. That won't help matters," said Mr. Scornful in a sneering voice.

"Don't talk to me like that!" cried Anna. "I'm tired. I want to rest. You shouldn't take us children on and on into the night."

"Oh, be quiet," said Mr. Scornful, impatiently. "I never did like children — always having to bother about them, and run round them!"

"Well, children don't much like *you*," said Peter, taking Anna's arm. "You're never kind or patient — you always sneer and jeer at others not so big or so clever as yourself."

They were all tired and cross. Each one felt irritable, and they wanted to quarrel — and just at that very moment they found themselves going up some curious steps!

They couldn't see what the steps were like in the dark — but they were very steep to climb up, and seemed to be made of clay, so that their feet stuck to them.

"Oh, bother, bother, bother!" cried Anna, as she tried to go up quickly. "Why must these steps come just when it's dark and we are all tired?"

Patience remembered her name and tried to go up the never-ending steps patiently. But it was very difficult.

Peter lost his temper and stamped on one particularly steep step. "Horrid step! Of course you would be steep and sticky just as my legs are tired, and my burden is extra heavy! How I hate you!"

"I must say they are the most tiresome steps I've ever climbed," said Mr. Scornful, in a vexed tone. "It's so sickening not to be able to see them — or to see where we are going. We can't possibly stay and sleep on them. They are so steep that if once we fell asleep and rolled off one, we'd go bouncing to the bottom in no time."

Anna cried. Patience tried not to. Peter grumbled. Mr. Scornful sneered at them all for grumbling, and for being babies. Everyone felt unhappy and cross.

Suddenly, not far off, they heard a loud bellow. They all stood still in fright. Then there came the sound of another bellow and another. It was not like the noise made by any animal they knew.

"It's the Dragons!" cried Anna, in a panic. "It must be! Don't you remember that Charitable said we had to pass the Dragons of Fatigue? Oh, dear — to think we had to meet them now, when we don't at all feel like it."

The bellows came again. It sounded as if the dragons must be lying in wait a few steps above. What was to be done?

"They sound pretty fierce," said Mr. Scornful. "I don't know that I want to face them."

"We haven't anything to keep them off if they come at us, except our sticks," said Peter.

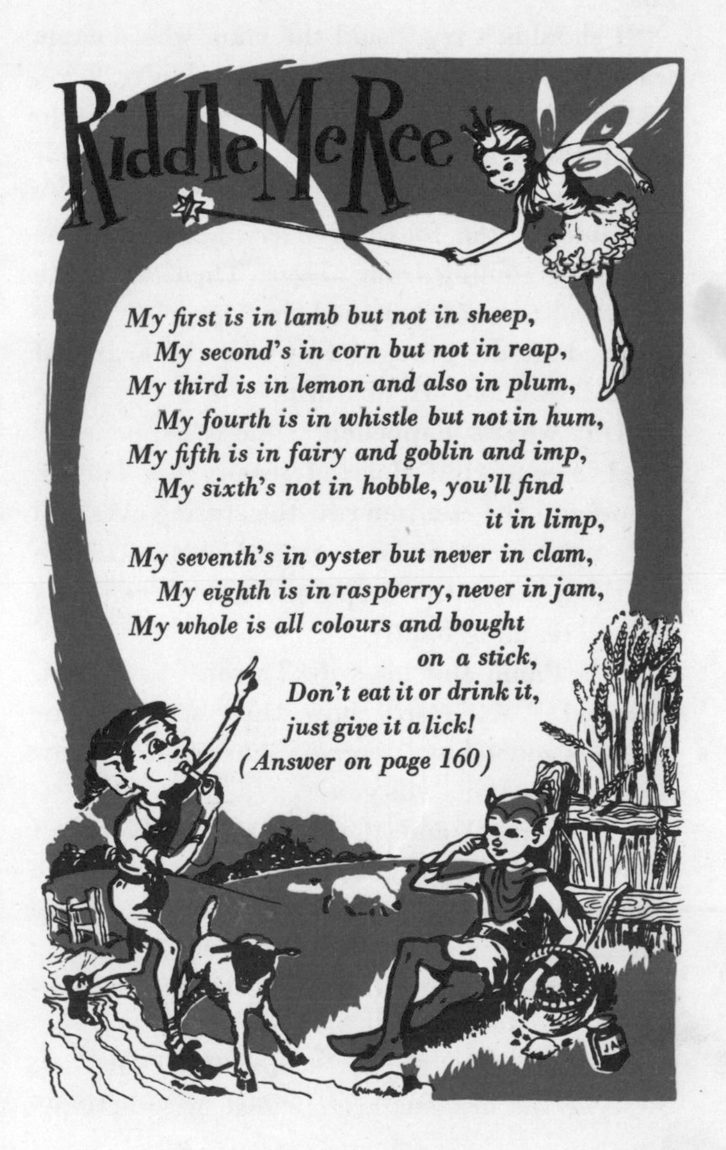

"I'm frightened and miserable," sobbed Anna. "Let's go back down the steps till to-morrow."

"What — and walk up them all over again!" cried Mr. Scornful in horror. "I should just think not. No — either we stay here on these steps till daylight comes — or we go up and face the dragons."

"Here comes somebody with a lantern," said Patience, suddenly. "He's coming down the steps."

A voice hailed them. "Who are you? Why do you climb here in the night?"

"We are four travellers," said Mr. Scornful. "We have climbed up these tiresome steep steps — and now we hear the bellows of those dragons. We don't know if we can pass them safely or not."

"I shouldn't try," said the man, whose name was Half-Hearted. "I really shouldn't. Why, just now I warned two other travellers not to go by the dragons, and they did — and goodness knows what has happened to them!"

Suddenly the four travellers heard screams and yells coming from above. Then down the steps rolled and bounced two people, whose terrified shouts brought fear into the hearts of the children and Mr. Scornful.

"Oh, what's happened, what's happened?" cried Anna. Half-Hearted swung his lantern round and the children saw the staring eyes and wide-open mouths of a man and woman rolling by them down the Steps of Impatience. They were screaming loudly.

"It's Panic and his wife Terror," said Half-Hearted. "My word, how they scream! The dragons must have scared them terribly. Now don't you go on, will you?"

Mr. Scornful and the children really didn't know *what* to do. They couldn't stay on the steps. They didn't want to go down to the bottom again, and yet they felt afraid of going up towards the dragons they could still hear bellowing.

"We'd better go up," said Peter at last. "Maybe the dragons are chained or something.

If they weren't, surely they would be down the steps after Panic and Terror!"

So up the four of them went, very cautiously indeed, leaving Half-Hearted and his lantern behind. The roaring and bellowing of the dragons sounded very fierce as they drew near to them. At last they could see three pairs of eyes glowing like red embers in the pitch darkness.

"The eyes of the dragons!" whispered Anna. "Oh, I can't bear it! I don't want to go on."

Peter spied some one coming along in the darkness wearing a shining white robe that showed like the wings of a moth in the night. He called out, "Who's there?"

"It is I, Sleep," answered a calm voice. "I have come to seek you. My sister, Rest, is looking for you too. Charitable sent us word that you were coming."

At the sound of that calm, soothing voice, the two girls stopped crying. Sleep went up to them and put her soft arms around them. "Come with me," she said. "Rest is waiting for you, with warm, soft beds."

The four travellers followed Sleep upwards. She led them right by the bellowing dragons, whose red eyes gleamed wickedly in the night. "Don't take any notice of them," said Sleep. "They are afraid of me and Rest!"

The dragons stopped bellowing as Sleep passed by. The children sidled by as quickly as they could, dragging their tired feet along. They came to a little house in whose window was set a shining light that pierced through the darkness most invitingly.

Sleep's sister, Rest, pulled the children and Mr. Scornful inside. Not one of the travellers waited to undress or to have anything to eat and drink. They all fell straightway on to the soft white beds, and in a moment were sound asleep.

They slept all through the night, never once hearing the bellowing of the dragons outside, and quite forgetting Half-Hearted, Panic and Terror. In the morning they awoke and stretched themselves lazily.

Peter jumped up and went to the window. He wanted to see the Dragons of Fatigue! But there were no great beasts to be seen, and no enormous bellows to be heard. How strange!

"Where are the dragons?" he asked Sleep, who came in to wake the others.

"Over there," said Sleep, pointing to a nearby glen on the hillside, where three small, strangely shaped beasts with snake-like tails lay asleep in the sunshine.

"What!" cried Peter in amazement. "Those *can't* be the dragons! They simply can't! Didn't you hear their enormous roars last night? Didn't you see their gleaming eyes?"

"Oh, you were tired last night, and couldn't see things properly," said Sleep. "The Dragons of Fatigue always look small and harmless in the morning, and there isn't a bellow in them. At night they frighten travellers with their roars, and make troubles seem bigger and harder. The best thing to do is to let Rest and me look after you for a night — and then things seem quite different in the morning!"

Peter looked down the hillside. He saw the Steps of Impatience stretching down and down. How steep they were! He turned to look out of the other window, to the top of the hill. How far was it?

But they *were* at the top! At the very very top! And there, spread before them, looking not very far away, was the wonderful City of Happiness itself, shining brilliantly in the early morning sun! They were almost there! Yes, really, they were almost there!

ANOTHER NODDY ADVENTURE

NOW once when Noddy was driving along a country road his car suddenly made a peculiar noise, and then stopped.

"Good gracious! What's wrong with you?" said Noddy, in alarm, and he jumped out to see. "Your wheels haven't a puncture, you've plenty of petrol. Then WHY don't you go?"

"Parp-parp," said the car dolefully, and gave a little rattle.

"I'll have to take you to the garage and get you mended," said Noddy. "Something has gone wrong. But dear me, I'll have to push you all the way because this is a very lonely place and there's nobody to help me."

So he began to push and push, and how he panted and puffed. "I sound like an engine going up a hill!" said Noddy. "Oh dear, I shall never get you to the garage!"

He pushed the car round a corner of the lane, and then he suddenly heard a noise. "Hrrrumph! Help! Hrrrrumph!"

"Now what can *that* be?" said Noddy, and he stood and listened.

"Nay - hay - hay - hay - hay! Hrrrrumph! Help!"

"Why — it's a horse in trouble!" said Noddy, and he squeezed through the hedge to find it. Sure enough, in the field beyond was a small horse, neighing and snorting loudly.

"What's the matter?" called Noddy.

"I walked into this muddy bit," said the horse, "and look — my front legs have sunk down into the mud and I can't get them out!"

Noddy ran to him. "I'll pull you out!" he said. "What part of you shall I pull?"

"My tail," said the horse. "It's a very strong tail. Hold hard — pull. PULL! Pull HARDER. I'm coming. I'm coming!"

Noddy pulled hard at the wooden horse's tail, and, quite suddenly, the horse's front legs came out of the mud, and the horse sat down hard on Noddy.

"Oooh, don't!" said Noddy. "I'm squashed to nothing. Get up, wooden horse. Don't sit on me like this."

"Sorry," said the horse, and got up. "You are really very kind. It was lucky for me that you came by just then in your car."

"Yes, it was," said Noddy. "But I wasn't in my car. Something's gone wrong with it, and now I have to push it all the way into Toyland Village. Goodness, I shall be tired."

"You needn't be," said the wooden horse. "I am quite used to pulling cars. I could pull your car for you, if you like, all the way to the garage! I'd be glad to do you a good turn, little Noddy."

"Oh, *thank* you!" said Noddy. "How lucky I am! Come along — I'll get my ropes and tie you to the car. What fun!"

And now, there goes Noddy sitting in his car, steering it carefully, and the little wooden horse is walking in front, pulling it well. How everyone stares!

"Aren't I lucky?" calls little Noddy, "My car broke down — and I found a little wooden horse to pull it!"

You *are* lucky, Noddy — but, you see, you're kind too, and kind people are *always* lucky!

The GANG

Here is an incident from Enid Blyton's book, THE SIX BAD BOYS. It is about a gang of little ruffians, and what happens to them when they are found out. Bob unfortunately gets involved with them, and becomes one of the gang.

DOWN in the town there was a little gang of boys. The youngest was eight, the oldest was fifteen. There were four of them, Len, Jack, Patrick, a wild Irish boy, and Fred. They met each evening, and every Saturday and Sunday; their favourite playground was a terrace of half-ruined old houses that were to be pulled down.

Under one of these houses was a cellar. The four boys had found it by accident one day, and were delighted.

"Coo! Look here," said Len, peering down some stone steps. "What's this? Underground tunnel or something? Let's play spies! This would be a fine hiding-place!"

It certainly was! Down the stone steps was a small dark stone cellar. The walls were damp, and the place smelt musty and bad. But the boys didn't mind. It was a hidey-hole, a place where nobody could find them.

Jack thought of the idea of making it a proper meeting-place, and proposed that they should try and furnish it in some way.

"We could get a few boxes, see?" he said. "And what about pinching a bit of old carpet from somewhere? And we could get a candle from home. My mum would give me one."

This hidey-hole was one of the greatest pleasures of the little gang. To it they brought their treasures; an old pack of cards, dirty and sticky, Len's little clock-work engine, some comics, a broken candlestick for the candle — and, oddest thing of all, a toy telephone!

This was brought by Fred the eldest boy. He was very proud of it indeed. He had seen it in a toy-shop and had stolen it when the shop was fairly full and nobody had been looking.

He had seen cinema films of rich men at the cinema with telephones crowding their desks, and although he himself had never used a telephone it seemed to him that it was a sign of power and of riches. He must have one too, even though it was only a toy one.

So there stood this little telephone on a box, and the other three boys used to listen with bated breath while Fred talked down it, giving orders to mythical spies or gangsters in an American voice!

Sometimes they brought food down there and

shared it. They planned raids on this garden and that when fruit was in season. They thought out silly tricks, such as knocking at doors and then running away.

Len was the youngest, and his brother was Fred, the fifteen-year-old. Jack was eleven, Patrick was twelve, loud-voiced, fiery-tempered, amusing and cunning.

Len and Fred had no father. They ran completely wild. Their mother didn't bother about them in the least. They cheeked her, took money from her purse when she left it about, and were quite out of control.

Patrick had no mother, only a father who had no time for him, but beat him regularly "just to keep him in order", so he said. Patrick hated his father and kept away from him as much as he could.

Jack had both mother *and* father, and two brothers and three sisters. But as they all lived together in two rooms the boy escaped from home as much as he could.

The two rooms were dirty and smelly and untidy. No one could eat, sleep or read in comfort. Jack hated his home, and though he really loved his mother he couldn't bear her whining voice and miserable face. Poor woman, she had long ago given up all hope of getting a place big enough for her large family, and had lost heart. It was no wonder the boy went to find happiness somewhere else — and to him the little hidey-hole down in the cellar was heaven.

None of the boys was very clever. Patrick had a streak of cunning that the gang found useful, but they had a very healthy respect for the two policeman of that district, and kept out of their way as much as possible.

"We're the Four Terrors Gang," Fred had announced one night. "We aren't afraid of the coppers or anybody, and don't you forget it."

"We aren't afraid of nobody!" said Patrick. It wasn't true, of course. They were afraid of their teachers, the "coppers", one or two shopkeepers who shouted at them — and Patrick was terribly afraid of his father. But they liked

Bob worked hard and well.

pretending that they were quite fearless. For a little while they felt grand and on top of the world!

Fred picked up the receiver of the toy telephone, and at once his three "men" were respectfully silent. They listened eagerly. Fred was grand on the telephone.

"Is that Number 61045?" said Len, in the short sharp voice he used at times. "This is the Chief here — the chief of the Four Terrors. Here's my orders. You'll take five men with you and the big car, and you'll go to Scarface and get his orders — then you'll . . ."

The one-sided conversation would go on for about two minutes. Then Fred would put down the little receiver and say, "Well, that's settled, boys. The men are on the job!"

The gang always wanted money — money to buy food, money to go to the pictures, which they loved above everything else. To sit in a comfortable seat in a warm place and see

Four boys sat in the candle-lit cellar.

people being chased and shot, to see horses galloping at top speed, cars tearing along at eighty miles an hour, aeroplanes being revved up . . . this was all glorious to them. They didn't have to think, or use their brains at all — they only needed to sit back and look.

It was into this gang that Bob stumbled one night. It was about a week after his mother had begun to take the keys of the house with her, so that he couldn't get in till she came back at half-past six. She left him some cake on a shelf in their little garden shed, but he never touched it.

"Leaving out food for me as if I was the cat next door!" he grumbled to himself. "I'll wait till she comes home, and have supper — proper supper, even if she has to cook it when she's tired."

But it was difficult to fill in the time between afternoon school and half-past six. The evenings were quite dark now, and cold.

"You can always go to the Mackenzies," his mother said to Bob. "They'll be pleased to have you, goodness knows why!"

But Bob didn't go. He was ashamed to have to tell anyone that he couldn't get into his own house. He only went once, when the Mackenzies asked him to come to tea and help with something they were making. He worked so hard and well that Mr. Mackenzie was amazed.

"Come again," he said. "You're good with your hands. You've done twice as much as old Donald here! Come in any time you can. I want to get this ship finished for Christmas."

Most nights Bob wandered down into the town by himself. He kicked his away along moodily, his school satchel on his back. He stared into any shops that were open, and into any lighted living-rooms. Other people's families had a kind of obsesssion for him.

One night it was pouring with rain. Bob was down in the town. He wondered if he should go home and sit in the shed — or should he go to the Mackenzies? No, he wouldn't. He'd find shelter somewhere.

He came to where some houses were half-tumbled-down. "I'll shelter here," he thought, and scrambled over fallen bricks to find a corner of a ruined room.

And then he suddenly heard a voice coming from below him — a short, staccato voice, issuing orders. Bob stood in astonishment.

"Hallo! That Number 678345? This is the Chief speaking. What do you mean by not coming along when I told you? Here we've been waiting an hour or more! You afraid of being ticked off for failing in that job you had to do? Well, you know what happens to men who're yellow! Unless you come along straight away, look out for trouble! The Four Terrors will be after you!"

Bob was simply amazed. What was this? Who was speaking like that, just below him?

Then he saw a dim light somewhere down below. He bent down and saw that he was near some stone steps that led underground. He felt excited. What was all this? Had he discovered some secret hiding-place?

He cautiously put one foot on the top step. Then down another step, and another. The rain pelted down all the time, making a great noise, so that it hid the sound of his feet on the rubbly stone steps.

He came in view of the cellar, and stared in astonishment. He saw a little square place with damp walls. Boxes were here and there, and an old piece of damp carpet was on the floor. A big box stood in the middle for a table, and on it was a pile of comics and a candle set in a ginger-beer bottle. On another box stood a telephone — the little toy telephone that Fred was so proud of.

Four boys sat in the candle-lighted cellar. All were reading comics. They hardly ever read anything else. Bob stood and stared: it looked so cosy and exciting and most surprising to him.

Patrick suddenly looked up and saw him. He shouted. "Hey! Look there! Who's that?"

Then Bob had a real brain-wave. He grinned widely and said:

"I'm Number 678345! You telephoned me just now. I've come along to report to the Chief."

There was dead silence in the cellar. All four boys stared at Bob, extremely startled by what he had said. Who was he? How did he know anything about them? Had he really "come to report"?

Fred rose to the occasion. He had sized Bob up at once — a boy a bit above them in station, a daredevil, someone with a sense of humour. He might be useful!

"Come in, Number 678345," he said. "Good thing you came along! I was just going to send someone for you!"

Bob went right into the cellar. Fred took his precious telephone off its box, and pushed the box over to Bob for a seat. "I suppose you heard me telephoning," he said.

"Yes," said Bob. "I couldn't make it out! Were you *really* telephoning with that telephone?"

Fred didn't answer. He sometimes almost persuaded himself that he really *was* telephoning to distant members of the gang, and he didn't want to admit that he wasn't. He lived in a curious world of make-believe.

"It's pouring," said Bob. "Do you mind if I shelter here for a bit! I like this place. Cosy, isn't it — a home from home!"

"Stay as long as you like," said Fred. "We're all pals together here!"

He couldn't do it!

I REALLY must tell you how James Jonathan Brown got the better of a clever wizard called Mr. Talk-a-Lot. It happened on a Saturday, when James had his weekly spending-money in his pocket.

His father always gave him a shilling a week if his weekly school report was good. His mother gave him a shilling if he ran all her errands without grumbling, and his Granny gave him sixpence a week simply because she loved him.

So that morning he had two shillings and a sixpence jingling in his pockets. He thought he would go to the farm over the hill, and buy some corn for his three hens, Hinny, Henny and Honey.

"I'll go through the wood," he thought. "And I'll see if that funny little house is still there that I saw last time, almost hidden by trees. Nobody seems to know anything about it."

So he went through the wood, and tried to

find the little house. It had six chimneys, which James thought rather a lot for such a small cottage. "Six chimneys mean six fire-places — and six fire-places mean six rooms," he thought. "And that cottage doesn't look as if it had more than two tiny rooms, at the most!"

He couldn't see the cottage anywhere — but he suddenly saw someone rushing through the trees at top speed, a bright red and black cloak sweeping behind him. "Now who's that?" thought James. "And why go about in fancy dress? I'll see where that fellow goes."

He ran after the red and black cloak, which billowed as its owner sped along — and then James saw the little cottage with six chimneys

"Well, you can come in! Wipe your feet please!"

that he had been looking for! The red and black cloak disappeared in at the front door, and there came a loud slam.

"Oh — so there's the cottage again — and that fancy dress person must be the owner," thought James. "Very interesting! If I believed in wizards and witches, which I don't, I might have thought that cloak belonged to one of them. Well — there's no harm in making a call!"

So he went to the little cottage and knocked sharply on the door. "Who is it, bothering me this morning? Go away, I'm busy, I don't like visitors, they're a nuisance, for goodness' sake don't stand there, but . . ."

"What a talker!" thought James, and knocked loudly again. He called out at the top of his voice. "May I have a drink of water, please?"

"Oh — it's a child, is it?" shouted the voice from inside. "Well, you can come in! Wipe your feet please!"

And the door swung open, a long arm reached out, and there was James, feeling rather surprised, inside the little cottage. He had a great shock when he looked round!

"Good gracious — I thought this was a cottage — but it's AWFULLY big!" said James, staring round a very big room indeed — so big that it had six fire-places, one on each of its six sides. "But — but, I say — how is it that it looks so small outside, and yet inside, it's . . ."

"Oh, don't talk so much," said the person who had pulled him inside. He really was most extraordinary. He was very tall, wore a gleaming red cap, and had on the dazzling black and red cloak in which James had first seen him. His hands were never still, and his eyes shone as green as a cat's.

"I say, sir — what big green eyes you have!" said James, in astonishment.

"Oh, don't speak to me as if you were Red Riding Hood speaking to the wolf!" said the green-eyed man. "Haven't you seen a wizard before? Dear, dear, what in the world do they teach you at school these days? Now why do you want a drink of water? You're not thirsty.

James snatched the wand out of his hand.

You're just inquisitive, you're . . ."

"Just stop talking for a minute, please," said James, rather alarmed at all this. "Let me explain. I only want a . . ."

"Well, you don't. You never did," said the wizard. "By the way, my name's Talk-a-Lot. Don't tell me yours. I can see it written down in the notebook you carry in your pocket — James Jonathan Brown — what a name!"

"You surely can't see into my notebook when it's in my pocket!" said James, startled. "Are you *really* a wizard? Do you do magic?"

"All day long! It's my hobby!" said Talk-a-Lot. "I make magic and spells and wishing-wands, and now I'm trying to make dry water. Water's so *wet*, you know — all right when you want to have a bathe, but . . ."

"I think that's rather silly," said James. "Water's *always* wet. If it wasn't, it wouldn't be water. Anyway, what would be the use of *dry* water?"

"Well, suppose you did your washing with dry water!" cried Talk-a-Lot. "You wouldn't need to hang it out on the line to dry, would you? And just think of not having to wipe dishes and plates dry, or bothering to have towels to wipe your hands and face, or . . ."

"Please let me get a word in," said James. "I like magic as much as anyone, but not *silly* magic."

The wizard was so angry when James said this, that he caught up a little sparkling wand and jabbed him with it. "I'll turn you into a hippopotamus, and send you to live in the wettest river that ever was," he began. But James snatched the wand out of his hand.

"*I'll* have this!" he said. "How many wishes will it make come true?"

"Only one," said Talk-a-Lot. "Put it down. You're a dangerous boy. All the same, I rather like you. Like to see me do a few tricks?"

"Well, yes, I would," said James, still holding on to the little wand. "Go ahead!"

"Tell me what you want me to do," said Talk-a-Lot, "but don't expect me to bring thunder and lightning down, and that sort of thing. I'm a bit scared of storms."

"All right. See that teapot on the table?" said James. "Make it hop into the air and pour out tea."

Talk-a-Lot immediately began to sing out a string of magic words at the top of his voice, and as he went on and on, the teapot rose slowly into the air, swung across to James, and tipped itself over so that the spout poured warm tea all over him.

"Hey! I didn't say pour tea over *me*!" cried James, darting away. "Don't be spiteful!"

"I'm not spiteful. I might have made the tea boiling hot, but I didn't," said Talk-a-Lot.

"Teapot, sit down again. Well, what next, James Jonathan?"

"Er — let me see — make all your six fires die down a bit," said James. "This room's too hot."

Talk-a-Lot at once began a kind of sing-song again, magic words running off his tongue at top speed. And then, almost immediately, streams of water appeared in front of all six fire-places and the fires sizzled loudly as the water poured over them. Black smoke billowed out into the room, and James began to cough and choke.

"Stop the water!" coughed James. "Quick!"

Talk-a-Lot waved his hands about and croaked out a few words. He was almost choking too! The water disappeared, the smoke gradually went — and, of course, all the fires had gone out!

The teapot rose slowly into the air.

"Look at that — no fires!" cried the wizard. "What a silly fellow you are! See what's happened now! I've a good mind to keep you here and make you light the fires and stoke them for me all day long! That's all an idiot like you is any use for! Why did I say I liked you? I don't! You're a nuisance, and a . . ."

"Oh, stop TALKING!" said James. "Don't you know enough magic to get those fires lighted again without wood?"

"No, I don't," said Talk-a-Lot sadly. "I haven't come to the lesson on 'How to Light Wet Wood' in my book of magic. It comes under the letter W right at the end of the book. Anyway, who are *you* to talk? I can do hundreds of things *you* can't do — and there isn't a single trick you can do that I couldn't do twice as quickly! Ha!"

"Ha to you!" said James. "I bet I could do a trick that you couldn't do at all!"

"Go on then — do one! If you can do a trick I can't do at once, I'll — I'll — I'll . . ."

"You'll give me this little wishing-wand, with its one wish, for my own," said James. "Ha! You're afraid of saying you will, because you think I might know a trick that you *don't* know!"

"Rubbish! Nonsense! Stupid boy! Tell me the trick — and see me do it straightaway!" cried the wizard, his eyes shining like a cat's at night.

"All right. I want a glass, please — that tumbler over there will do," said James. Talk-a-Lot fetched it and put it on a table, that was covered with a green cloth. "What next?" he said.

"We need a sixpence, and two shillings," said James, and took his money out of his pocket. "One or two pennies will do, but I haven't any."

"You're not to use your own money — it might be magic," said Talk-a-Lot fiercely.

"Don't be silly," said James. "I don't carry magic money about with me. I'm not a wizard! I'm a schoolboy. It's a trick I've often played on my friends at school. Now I'm going to play it on you!"

He placed his sixpence on the table, and put

James took the money out of his pocket.

the glass over it, so that the coin was right in the middle. Then he took two separate shillings and put them under the rim of the upturned glass, so that the edge of the glass rested on them.

"There!" he said. "See that? The little sixpence is in the middle, under the glass. The edges of the glass rest on the shillings, which are half under the glass and half outside. Now listen — *can you get that sixpence out from under the glass without touching either the shillings OR the glass?*"

Talk-a-Lot stared at the glass and the three coins. He rubbed his chin. He frowned. "I don't know the spell for that," he said. "But I expect I'll think of it."

"You won't," said James. "Go on — try a few magic words. See what happens!"

Talk-a-Lot waved his hands about and muttered some strange-sounding words. The glass slowly changed to a bright green — but the sixpence still lay under it, unmoving.

"Hm!" said the wizard. "*That* spell's no good. I'll try another." So he tried again, and the strange words he said made James feel quite shivery. He stared at the sixpence, wondering if such magic *might* move it out from under the glass. But no — it didn't move. All that happened was that the shillings turned black!

"You aren't using very clever magic," said James, scornfully.

"Well, what words do *you* say, then, to get that sixpence out from under the glass, without touching either the coins or the glass?" asked Talk-a-Lot crossly. "Tell me them, and I'll use them."

"Right," said James. "Anything to help you! All I say is 'Come along, little sixpence, come along! Come along to me!' "

"I don't believe it," said Talk-a-Lot. "But I'll try it." He waved his hand over the glass, and chanted loudly, "Come along, little sixpence, come along! Come along to me!"

But the sixpence didn't move. It lay there, shining under the green glass, between the two black shillings.

James laughed. "You might change the glass back to its right colour, and the shillings too," he said. "Then I'll show you how to do the trick. It's very, very simple."

"If it was simple, I'd be able to do it," said Talk-a-Lot, sulkily. He muttered a few words, waved his hands, and the glass lost its green colour, and the shillings shone silver again.

"Thanks," said James. "Now watch. I'm going to say my own magic words, and just scrape the cloth with my finger like this. Very very magic, you know!"

And James bent over the table, put his hand down on the cloth near the edge of the glass, and began to scrape it sharply with his forefinger. As he scraped he chanted his own words.

"Come along, little sixpence, come along! Come along to me!"

And sure enough, the little sixpence moved under the glass, and over the cloth, and slipped out under the rim, between the two shillings! There it was, lying outside the glass — and James hadn't touched either the glass or the shillings — nor had he touched the sixpence!

"Wonderful!" said the wizard, in amazement. "Terrific! Marvellous! Where did you learn your magic?"

"From my Grandad," said James. "He taught me this trick — and plenty of others too. Well — I'll be off now. Thanks for the wishing-wand!"

He picked up the wand, and Talk-a-Lot cried out at once. "No, wait! I didn't think you'd do a trick I couldn't do! Wait! I *can't* give you that wand. There's still a wish left in it. How do I know what dreadful wish you'd wish? You might wish me away to the moon!"

"I might. But I shan't," said James. "I rather like you, you see, Talk-a-Lot. But I'll tell you what I *am* going to wish, if you like."

"Yes. You tell me. I'd feel safer if you do," said the wizard, looking quite worried.

"Well, I'm going home with it — and I'm going to wave it over my mother, and wish her a new washing-machine," said James. "You're smiling! Well, I thought that would make you laugh! It'll make my mother laugh too — with joy! You've no idea how hard she has to work when she washes all my dirty things, and my brother's and sister's and Dad's too. So *that's* what I'm going to use the wish for — I shouldn't DREAM of wasting it on you!"

"No. No, of course not," said Talk-a-Lot. "I see that now. But wishing-wands aren't usually used for washing-machines, you know."

"Well, there has to be a first time for everything," said James, taking his sixpence and shillings off the table, and holding fast to the little wishing-wand. "Goodbye, Talk-a-Lot. It's been a very pleasant morning."

"Yes. It has," said the wizard. "I really do like you, Jonathan James. You might come and see me some time again. I *could* teach you a few magic tricks, you know."

"Ha! You mean *I* could teach *you* some!" said James, with a chuckle. "All right — I'll be along some day. Meantime, you practise the magic trick *I* taught *you* — and don't forget the magic words!"

And away he went with the magic wand. What a wonderful surprise his mother is going to have!

As for the wizard, he is still practising the Sixpenny Trick! You can hear him any day saying, "Come along, little sixpence, come along! Come along to me!"

You can do it, too, you know. Try it, and astonish all your friends!

"Come along, little sixpence, come along!"

The Whistler

This is a story from Enid Blyton's "Hedgerow Tales".

In the lovely month of May the hedgerow was beautiful to see. The hawthorn-leaves were a brilliant green, the brambles threw graceful branches into the air, full of tender young leaves, and the ivy shone dark and glossy. When the may blossom came it lay along the hedgerow like drifts of summer snow, and its fragrance brought a myriad bees, moths, butterflies and other insects to it. The hedgerow animals smelt it too, and rejoiced because it was a summer smell — a smell belonging to warm days and happy times.

The oak-tree was now full of leaf. It was the last of all the trees to put out its tender, feather-shaped leaves, and the birds whose nests were among its branches were glad of their shelter. They liked the soft green light that the leaves made, and they liked to see them waving in the wind. It was good to have a nest in the oak-tree in May.

On the bank below there were many flowers, glad of the hot sun. The cow-parsley foamed there, and in the wet ditch great clumps of golden kingcups raised their heads to the sun. Lilac milkmaids, the pretty cuckoo-flower, grew in the field and danced gaily all day long. Buttercups made a carpet of gold, and red clover raised its sweet head to the humming bees. All day long the cuckoo called, over and over again. It was a summer sound and the hedgerow folk liked it.

At sunset, when the buttercups glowed even more golden, and the shadow of the oak-tree was long, so long that it stretched half-way along the field, a strange sound was heard. It was a clear low whistle, rather bird-like. It came from the big pond that lay not far from the oak-tree. The hedgerow folk heard it, and knew what it was.

It was the otter whistling to his mate. She lived in the pond, for it was very deep in places, and big fish could be found there. It had once been part of a stream that had run into the river not far away, but the stream had been altered in its course so that it emptied itself into the river at a different place — and the big pond was all that was left of the old part of the stream.

In long ago days many otters had swum in the pond when it had been part of the stream, and even now, when it was only a pond, they came to it, travelling over the fields. It had the alder-trees they loved, and beneath the roots of the alders were fine hiding-places, holes where an otter could rest in peace, well hidden from all eyes. It was a good pond.

In the autumn before, two otters had come to the pond. The hedgerow knew them well, both in the water and out. The birds knew the least about them, for the otters were night-time creatures, and most birds sleep through the night. The owl knew them best, and sometimes hooted to them when he heard the otters whistling to each other.

The otters were dusky-brown creatures covered with dense fur — so thick that not a drop of water could wet their warm bodies. They were large creatures, about four feet long. The inquisitive hedgehog often sniffed at the "spur" or footprint left by the otters in the mud at the side of the pond. These prints showed the otters to have rounded toes, webbed for swimming, for they were marvellous swimmers.

Sometimes at sunset the late robin could see two flat black heads moving about on the pond surface. Then he knew that the otters were astir. He watched them swimming and playing, rolling their oily bodies round in a circle, as clever as fish in the water. They swam with their front paws only, and used their long flattened tails as rudders. It was wonderful to watch them.

The alder-trees knew the otters very well indeed, for had they not made their nursery under their roots? The alders sighed in the wind and remembered. The mother otter had found the big hole one day and had whistled to her mate to come and look. To get to the hole under the roots they had to dive right into the water, and then scramble into the underground chamber as best they could. The hole led upwards, criss-crossed by alder-roots. At its top end it was dry and roomy.

"This will do for our nursery," said the otter to her mate. "No one will find us here. There will be plenty of room for all of us when the babies come. I shall bring rushes and grass here, and the purple flowers of the great reed, and make a soft nest."

And that winter, during a warm spell, the mother otter laid her three little ones there in the big, dark hole under the alders. They were quite blind, but they were already covered with a warm, downy fur. The mother was very proud of them and licked them all over. So did the father. They smelt sweet, those tiny otters, and were so warm and playful.

"You must go hunting for us," said the mother to her mate. "It is cold tonight, and I must not leave these little ones to get chilled. Go and bring us some fish. I am hungry."

The big otter slid into the water. He closed his short, rounded ears all the time he was under the surface so that no water should get into them. He went to the deepest part of the pond where he knew there were big fish, and very soon chased and caught one. Back he went to the hole.

The mother otter bit a large piece out of the fish's shoulder, and then ate the fish all the way down to the tail. This she left, for in the otter family it is not good manners to eat the tail. The tiny otters sniffed and snickered round the little bits of fish the mother had left. The smell excited them.

The alder-trees often felt the little otters scrambling about over their roots, and they liked it. And then one evening, when the sun had just gone down, leaving a golden glow in the western sky, the mother otter took her young ones into the pond for the first time. What an adventure for them!

They had often been to the edge of the water that lapped into their dark hole. One of them had even slipped into it, and had been pulled out by its mother, who scolded it and bit it sharply for a punishment. But this was the first time they had ever been out into the great world beyond their small, dark home under the alder-roots.

"Come!" said the otter to her three young

ones. She slid into the water and one by one the three small otters followed her. They did not feel the chill of the water, for by now they had thick, dense fur coats — two coats each, one of short fur and one of longer hairs.

At first they floundered about, not at all sure what to do in the water — but their mother was patient with them. She took them quickly up to the surface, for she knew they could not at first go very long without breathing. Then she showed them how to swim properly.

"Use your tail to guide you," she said. "Use your front paws for swimming. Let your back paws drag loose."

The young otters were clumsy at first, but

they enjoyed the adventure. What a fine place the world was! They watched their mother and father swim gracefully here and there, turning and tumbling easily through the water. They gazed in amazement as they saw a large fish chased and caught, and they snickered together in terror when they spied their mother chasing a startled moor-hen, which, taking to its wings, escaped just in time!

All through the spring-time the young otters learnt many things from their parents. They learnt how to turn over the big stones to hunt for crayfish. They found out how to twist and turn swiftly in the water to catch a darting fish. They were taken on land and found that they could run easily on their four webbed feet. They caught frogs for themselves, and grew fat and strong.

One night the father otter whistled good-bye to his mate. "The youngsters are big now," he said. "I am going away to the sea."

"Why is that?" asked his mate.

"This pond is drying up a little," answered the otter. "I am afraid that it may disappear altogether if the summer is hot. Even the river near by may dry up, and as I count on the current to take me down to the sea, I shall go whilst there is plenty of time. I shall spend the summer in an old sea-cave I know, where many bats live. In the autumn I will come back to you."

The big otter swam to the edge of the pond, shook the water from his thick coat like a dog and disappeared in the long grass. He had gone to the river. The robin, who loved the long twilit evenings of summer followed him, flitting along the hedgerow beside him. She saw him enter the swiftly flowing river, and, with front paws pressed under his chin, float gently down with the current.

His mate missed him sadly. The hedgerow folk often heard her whistling for him on these warm May evenings when the sunset glow lasted for a long time in the western skies. She wanted him to see what lusty fellows their cubs were now; she wanted him to swim and play with her on these sweet warm nights. But he had gone.

The weather grew hotter. The pond, never very full since a hot summer two years since, grew lower. The mother otter found that her underground chamber was now hardly under water. It would soon be no longer a safe hiding-place. She hunted round the pond for another. But there was none big enough for four otters.

"We must part," said the mother to her young ones. "You are old enough to go your own way now. You can fish and swim and dive, and you can walk for miles on the land if need be. You know how to avoid traps. I have taken you to the river and shown you how to let the current carry you along. You have often found holes big enough to hide in. Now the time has come for you to work for yourselves."

"But where will *you* go?" asked the smallest of the three.

"I may go down to the sea, too, as your father did," said the otter. "There are many things there to eat that we do not find inland."

"Is there fish there?" asked the biggest otter, hungrily.

"Shoals and shoals!" said his mother. "I shall come back in the late autumn, maybe to this very pond, and perhaps your father will come, too, to find me and play with me as he used to do. Ah, it is good to go up the rivers in the autumn! For then there are many eels coming down to the sea, and they are very good to eat!"

"Good-bye!" whistled the young otters, and they swam away from their mother. One went overland to the stream and swam along it. One went to the hole under the alder-roots and lay there, sorrowing to think that the happy family life was broken. And the third went to a marshy place he knew in a withy-bed two miles off. The mother otter swam once round the pond she knew so well, and then, whistling clearly, she left it and made her way to the river.

"I shall return in the autumn!" she called to the inquisitive robin. "Look for me then!"

"THE snow is still thick on the ground," said Uncle Nat. "What about going out and doing a little detective work?"

"Oooh — I should like that," said Peter. "But what exactly do you mean?"

"I mean we'll go out and see if we can tell by the tracks in the snow who has been about last night and this morning," said Uncle Nat. "No — I don't mean burglars, so don't hope for that. I mean animals and birds."

They went out. The snow lay thick and white—but the surface had plenty of marks.

"Now, look," said Uncle Nat. "Those are bird-tracks — what kind of a bird went just there, Peter?"

"I should think a sparrow — or a chaffinch," said Peter. "The prints are in little pairs, which makes me think they have been made by a bird that hops, two feet together, like a sparrow."

"Good boy," said Uncle Nat. "Now what about *these* marks?"

"Well, I should think those were made by a bird that can *run*, like a blackbird," said Mary, "and these must have been made by a duck from the frozen-up pond. I can see the marks made by the web between his toes."

"Very good," said Uncle Nat, really pleased. "Now, here again are two sets of prints — animal prints this time.

One is a dog's, and the other a cat's. Can you say which is which?"

"Mary couldn't, but Peter did. "I know," he said. "This must be the cat's because there are no claw-marks showing — and this must be the dog's because there are. I know our cat draws in her claws when she walks — so they wouldn't show in her prints, would they?"

"Quite right," said Uncle Nat. "Top marks. Now this print here, in the road. What made that?"

"Horse!" said both children at once.

"And this one?" said Uncle Nat, showing them another track, inside the field-gate.

"That's the mark of a hoof too — but a hoof split in half," said Peter, puzzled. "Of course — a cow. It has a cloven hoof, hasn't it, Uncle?"

"Right," said Uncle Nat. "Now look at all these marks, heaps of them together — more hoof-marks. What animals made them?"

"Rather like the cow — cloven — but much smaller," said Mary. "Sheep! The sheep went along here, Uncle Nat, a whole flock of them."

They found a rabbit's prints, and they even found a fox's, which was very like that of the dog, except that here and there the mark of his brush showed where it had sometimes touched the snow.

"Have we been good Snow Detectives?" asked Mary.

"Excellent!" said Uncle Nat. "I'm glad I'm not a burglar. I'm sure you would both track me down at once!"

(Can you do some snow-tracking?)

THE STORY OF THE CHRISTMAS TREE

A Tale from "The Christmas Book".

THE children were helping Mother to dress the Christmas tree.

"Mother," asked Susan, "who thought of the first Christmas tree? It's such a good idea."

"It is, isn't it," said Mother, cutting some coloured string into small pieces, so that she might tie small presents on the tree. "Well, I don't exactly know who thought of the first Christmas tree, as *we* know it — but there is a rather nice old story about it."

"Tell us, please!" said Ann, who loved a story of any kind.

"Well," said Mother, "one stormy Christmas Eve, long long ago, a forester and his family were sitting together round a big fire. Outside, the wind blew, and the snow made the forest white.

"Suddenly there came a knock at the door. The family looked up, startled. 'Who can be in the forest at this time of the night,' said the forester, in surprise, and went to open the door.

"Outside stood a little child, shivering with cold, tired out and hungry. The forester picked him up in amazement, and brought him into the warm room.

" 'See,' he said, 'it is a little child. Who can he be?'

" 'He must stay here for the night,' said his wife, feeling the child's ice-cold hands. 'We will give him hot milk to drink, and a bed to sleep in.'

" 'He can have my bed,' said Hans, the forester's son. 'I can sleep on the floor tonight. Let us put the child into my warm bed.'

"So the hungry, cold child was fed and warmed, and put into Hans' bed for the night. Then the family went to sleep, Hans on the floor beside the fire.

"In the morning the forester awoke, and heard an astonishing sound. It seemed to him as if a whole choir of voices was singing. He awoke his wife, and she too heard the sweet singing.

" 'It is like the singing of angels,' whispered the forester. Then they looked at the child they had sheltered for the night, and saw that his face was dazzling bright. He was the Christ-Child Himself!

"In awe and wonder the forester and his family watched the Holy Child. He went out-of-doors to a fir-tree, and broke off a branch. He planted the branch firmly in the ground.

" 'See,' He said, 'you were kind to me, and you gave me gifts of warmth and food and shelter. Now here is my gift to you — a tree that at Christmas-time shall bear its fruit, so that you may always have abundance.'

"And so, at Christmas-time, the Christmas tree shines out in beauty, and bears gifts of many kinds."

Mother stopped, and looked round. The children were all listening, and for the moment had forgotten, their task of decorating the tree.

"That was a nice story," said Ann. "I wish the Christ-Child had come to *me*, I would have given up my bed to Him, and He could have had my toys as well."

"Does the Christmas tree have real fruits?" asked Peter, trying to remember. "This one hasn't any — only just its many branches of prickly leaves."

"Oh, you must have seen the *cones* on the spruce firs," said Susan. "Surely you have! You know what fir-cones are, silly!"

"Of course!" said Peter, remembering. "Yes — they hang down from the branches, don't they?"

"The cones of the spruce fir do, but not the cones of the silver fir," said Benny, who loved trees. "They sit upright. You can always tell the spruce from the silver fir by its top, too — the spruce has a sharp spear-like point but the silver fir has a bushy top."

"Oh, that's easy to remember," said Ann. "Why hasn't our Christmas tree any cones on

it, Benny? I wish it had. I would paint them silver and make them look lovely!"

"Well, it's only a baby tree," said Benny. "It hasn't borne cones yet. If we plant it in the garden and let it grow year by year, it will grow cones, of course. Let's do that. It has good roots, and should grow well if we plant it out."

"Then we can have the same tree year after year for our Christmas tree!" said Ann. "I should like that."

"I like its prickly needle-like leaves," said Peter. "See, Ann — they look as if someone had combed them neatly down the middle of the branch, and made a parting — just like you do to your hair!"

The others laughed. Peter was right — the little boughs did look as if someone had made a parting down the middle of the close-set needle-leaves.

"The fir-tree isn't only useful as a Christmas tree," said Mother, "its straight trunk is used for lots of things that need to be quite straight. Perhaps you can think of some."

"Masts of ships!" said Benny at once.

"Telegraph posts!" said Susan.

"Scaffolding poles!" said Peter.

"You've said all that I was going to say," said Ann. "Are they right, Mother?"

"Quite right. The fir-tree gives its trunk for all those things," said Mother. "People say that its name 'fir' should really be 'fire'. It should be called the fire-tree, not the fir-tree, because once upon a time its gummy, resinous branches used to be broken off, lighted, and used as flaring torches."

"Have you noticed that the fir-tree's roots are very shallow?" said Benny, fixing a shining yellow ornament to a bough. "They stand out above the ground in the wood. I should think the firs would easily fall in a strong storm."

"Oh, they do," said Mother. "And sometimes, if one fir falls, it knocks down the next, and that one falls and knocks down a third tree, and so they go on, all through the forest, making quite a path of fallen trees."

"Like a row of dominoes each knocking down the next," said Ann, remembering how she often stood up her dominoes in a row, and then touched the first one, which caused the whole row to fall, one after the other.

"I'm going to put the star on the top of the tree now," said Benny, fetching a chair. "Mother, I suppose we put a star at the top to represent the Star of Bethlehem, don't we?"

"Yes," said Mother. "The Christmas tree should always have the Star of Bethlehem shining at the top."

"Have we had the custom of decorating the Christmas tree for hundreds and hundreds of years, just as we have had for the holly and mistletoe?" said Ann.

"Oh dear me no!" said Mother, "It's not much more than a hundred or so years ago that the first Christmas tree was set up in England. It was first known in Germany, then spread to other countries, and at length came to England. It is the kind of simple and beautiful idea that spreads into all lands. Who first thought of it we don't really know, nor quite how long ago. The idea itself may be old, but our English custom is certainly not older than the last century. Prince Albert, the husband of Queen Victoria, set up a Christmas tree at Windsor in 1841 — and after that the tree was used more and more, all over England."

"It must be nice to begin a custom like that," said Ann. "I wish I could begin one of my own. Mother, may I put the candles into Susan's clips?"

"Isn't the tree beginning to look lovely?" said Susan, stepping back a little to see it. "How the ornaments shine — and the tinfoil strips gleam — and the Star glitters. I'm longing for the time when the candles will all be lighted."

It took the children all the morning to decorate the tree properly, but they loved every minute of it. By the time it was finished there was not a bough without a candle, present or ornament, and the frosted cotton-wool and strips of tinfoil gave the tree a glitter and shine that made it very beautiful.

The Star shone at the top, and under it stood the fairy doll, a silver crown on her head, silver wings on her back and a silver wand in her hand. Little presents for every member of the household hung here and there, wrapped in coloured paper.

"They are *proper* presents," said Mother, "not just useful gifts, which should never be put on a Christmas tree, according to old beliefs — but beautiful little gifts which will bring joy and pleasure to everyone."

"How lovely!" said Ann, dancing round. "Now the tree is beautiful. Mother, I wouldn't be surprised if all the other trees in the garden came close to the window and looked in when we light our Christmas tree!"

"You do say funny things," said Benny, laughing, but they all thought secretly that it was rather a lovely idea of Ann's, and could quite well imagine the hollies and the yews, the birches and the oaks pressing themselves against the window to see the beauty of the lighted Christmas tree!

Answers to Puzzles

ANSWER TO T.P.S.O.

Tops, Post, Pots, and if you are very clever, you will find a fourth word — Spot.

TWO LITTLE PUZZLES

Answers to first little puzzle.
Snail, Nail, Rail, Trail.
Answers to second little puzzle.
Chair, Hair, Air.

Answer to Riddle Me Ree: LOLLIPOP.

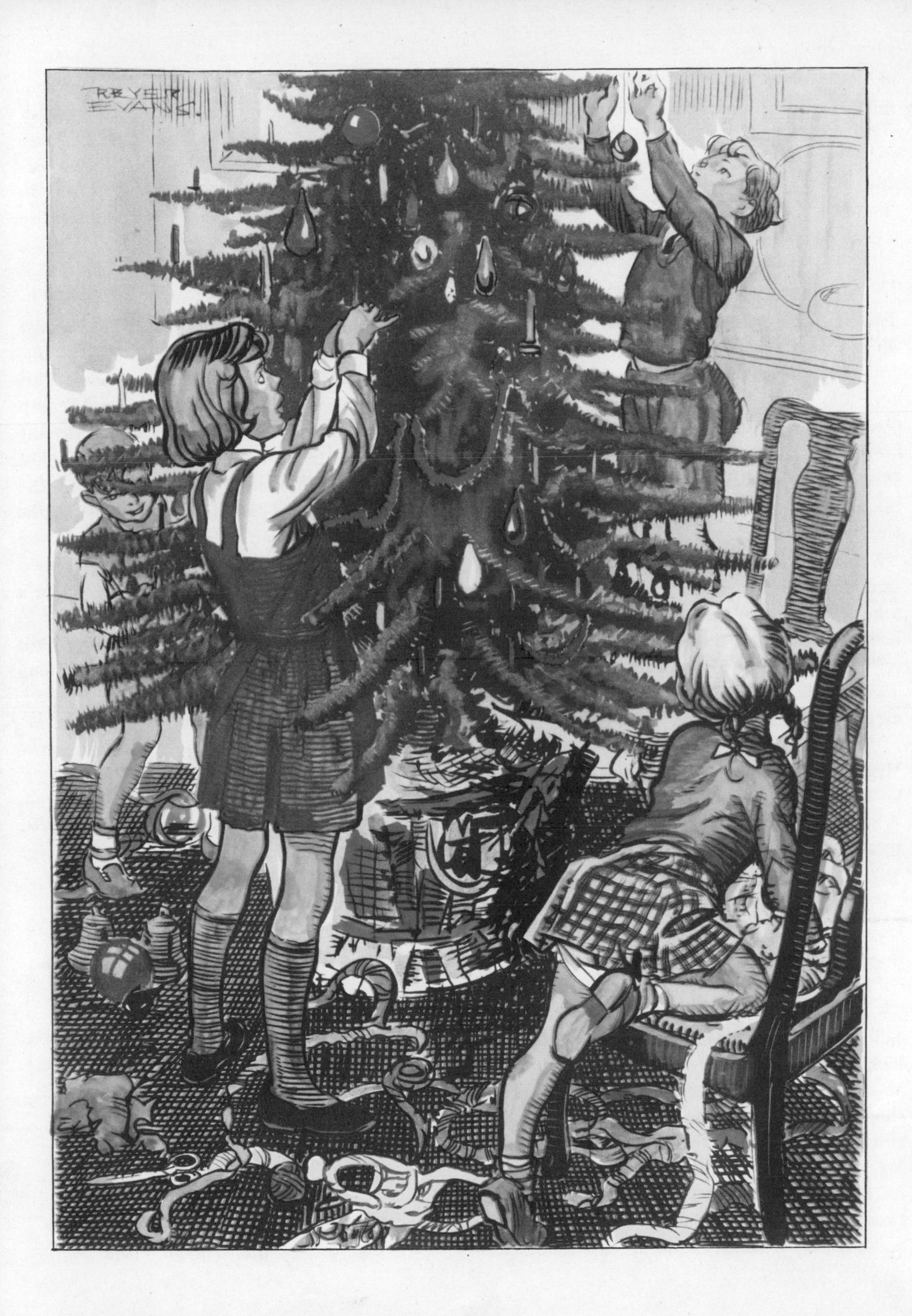
TREYER
EVANS

Mr. Twiddle and the dog

This is a story about dear old Mr. Twiddle, who always tries to be helpful, but somehow makes a dreadful muddle, no matter what he does!

ONCE Mrs. Twiddle looked after a friend's dog for a week. It was a nice little dog, called Scamp. It was most obedient, always wiped its paws on the mat when it came indoors, and said, "Wuff-wuff" for its food.

"Really, I'm quite sorry to part with the dog," said Mrs. Twiddle, patting it. "Twiddle, will you take it back for me, please? My friend, Mrs. Gubbins, would like to have it this morning."

"Certainly, my dear, certainly!" said Mr. Twiddle. "Shall I go now? There's a bus I can catch in about ten minutes' time."

"Yes — get your hat and go along," said Mrs. Twiddle. She gave the dog a biscuit, brushed his coat well, and fastened the lead to his collar.

"Dear, dear!" she said, feeling the collar. "You must gave grown fatter this week, Scamp. Your collar is too tight for your neck. I'll loosen it!"

She undid the collar and slipped the buckle along to another hole. The dog liked its collar loose. It knew it could slip it off then!

"Dear little thing," said Mrs. Twiddle. "Now, Twiddle, hurry along or you'll miss that bus."

Twiddle looked for his hat, put it on, and then, looking at his watch, he found that he only had about five minutes. He took hold of the lead and shot off down the garden-path, with the dog trotting after him. When he came to the gate Mr. Twiddle found that he had forgotten to put on his glasses. He had cleaned them and left them on the table. Bother!

"Well, never mind, I shan't really need them," said Mr. Twiddle, hurrying along. "I shall miss the bus if I don't walk fast."

Now very soon the dog met a friend. This friend was a beautiful little Pekinese, and Scamp thought she was marvellous. The Pekinese wagged her plumy tail and Scamp wagged his.

"Stop a minute and talk to me," said the Pekinese. So Scamp did a kind of double-wriggle, and slipped his head neatly out of his loose collar. He wagged his tail, ran to the Pekinese, and joyfully licked her nose. He was ready for a jolly good game!

The Pekinese looked after the hurrying Mr. Twiddle in astonishment. "Does he *mind* going without you?" she asked.

"I haven't asked him," said Scamp. "I say, doesn't my collar look funny running along the road without me, on the end of the lead!"

With a bound Scamp ran round the corner and began to have a fine game with his little

Very soon Scamp met a friend.

Pekinese friend. Mr. Twiddle didn't even see him go. He trotted along down the street, pulling the lead and empty collar behind him, whistling a little tune, and keeping a sharp look-out for the bus at the corner.

He met his friend, Mr. Jinks, who stared in astonishment at the sight of Twiddle hurrying along pulling a dog collar behind him.

"Where are you going?" he called.

"Just taking this dear little dog back to its owner," said Twiddle, beaming. "Isn't it a good little soul, trotting along behind me so happily?"

Mr. Jinks thought that Mr. Twiddle must be a little mad that morning, but there wasn't any time to say so, because Twiddle hurried on so quickly. Mr. Jinks stared at the collar running along behind Mr. Twiddle, and began to laugh.

Mr. Twiddle came to the corner just at the same moment as the bus. He jumped in pulling the lead and collar behind him.

"Now just go under the seat little dog, and lie down quietly," said Mr. Twiddle, peering round for Scamp. He couldn't see him, so he thought he must already have gone under the seat.

"Good dog," he said to the empty collar there. "Very good dog! Conductor, I want a twopenny ticket for myself, and a ticket for my dog."

"What dog?" asked the conductor in amazement.

"Really, some people do ask silly questions. said Mr. Twiddle. "Don't you know a dog when you see one? Perhaps you thought I had a cat or a canary on my lead."

The conductor looked offended. He thought that if Mr. Twiddle really wanted to buy a ticket for a dog that wasn't there, he might as well let him. So he gave him a twopenny ticket and a dog's ticket as well.

A very big woman got in with a small dog under her arm. She tried to sit down beside Mr. Twiddle.

"Madam, I have a dog under my seat," said Mr. Twiddle. "Perhaps it would be better if you took the seat over there. Our two dogs might fight."

The big woman looked under the seat and saw no dog at all. Only an empty collar! She thought it was a trick to make her take another seat and leave Mr. Twiddle comfortably alone in his.

So she sat down opposite to him and glared at him with large black eyes. Mr. Twiddle felt most uncomfortable.

"I suppose you think you are very clever," said the big woman in a freezing sort of voice.

Mr. Twiddle was astonished. He had never thought himself clever, to begin with — and he couldn't imagine why the big woman should think he did. He felt more and more uncomfortable as he sat under the glare of the woman's big black eyes, and he bent down and spoke to Scamp, who he still thought was lying under the seat.

Mr. Jinks stared in astonishment at the sight of Mr. Twiddle hurrying along pulling a collar behind him.

It was dark under the seat, and Mr. Twiddle hadn't his glasses on, so he couldn't see a thing. He spoke in a quiet voice.

"Good dog, Scamp. Lie down quietly now."

Not a sound came from under the seat, which wasn't at all surprising.

"You *do* think you're funny, don't you?" said the big woman in a scornful sort of voice.

"Well, Madam, no, I can't say that I have ever thought myself funny," said Twiddle. He stood up to go, because he couldn't bear to think what this strange big woman would say next. "Come on, Scamp!" he said. "Come on."

"Mind he doesn't bite you!" called the big woman after him. He jumped off the bus, and, with his nose well up in the air, he hurried along.

Mr. Twiddle blinked at the empty collar.

"Hie! Your dog's gone to chase a cat!" a boy shouted after him.

"Dear me, I wonder why children are so stupid this morning," thought poor Twiddle. "Ah — here is Mrs. Gubbins's house!"

He went up the path and knocked at the door. Mrs. Gubbins opened it. "Oh, do come in," she said. "I wondered if you'd bring back my darling Scamp today!"

"Then you wondered right," said Twiddle happily, pulling the collar behind him into the hall. "I've brought him — and he's been as good as gold all the time!"

He looked round to see Scamp, but the hall was dark, and he could see nothing. "He must have gone under the chest there!" he said.

"But he didn't come in with you," said Mrs. Gubbins, puzzled. "At least, *I* never saw him!"

"He was just at my heels," said Mr. Twiddle, "I had him on the lead."

He pulled at the lead — and the empty collar slid over the floor to Mr. Twiddle's foot.

"Good gracious!" he said. "He's slipped his collar, the rascal. Well, I'm sure he's under the chest. Mrs. Gubbins. You call him and see. I must go now or I'll miss the bus back. Good-bye, Scamp, dear little chap! Good-bye!"

He trotted off down the path again to the bus, whilst Mrs. Gubbins looked all about for a dog she couldn't find. Twiddle caught the bus and was soon walking home down the street.

"Well!" said Mrs. Twiddle, opening the door to him, "and where have *you* been all this time? Didn't I tell you to take Scamp back to Mrs. Gubbins for me?"

"Well, my dear, I did," said Twiddle, in surprise. "He was as good as gold all the way, and I left him safely under the chest in the hall at Mrs. Gubbins's."

"Oh — and I suppose he caught the bus back, and arrived home before you did," said Mrs. Twiddle, in a rage. "Scamp! Come here!"

And to poor Twiddle's enormous astonishment Scamp came rushing out of the kitchen, put his front paws on Twiddle's middle, and tried to lick his chin!

"But I've just taken you to your mistress!" cried Twiddle, sitting down in alarm. "Wife, there must be two Scamps. There really must."

"Well, it's a good thing there are not two Twiddles!" said Mrs. Twiddle with a snort. "Now *I* shall have to take Scamp home myself — and without a collar and lead too. Really, Twiddle, I've a good mind to BOX YOUR EARS."

She looked so fierce that poor Twiddle ran out to the garden-shed and sat there for the rest of the day. And he *still* cannot think how it was that he took Scamp back to Mrs. Gubbins — and yet found him waiting for him when he arrived back home!

To poor Mr. Twiddle's enormous astonishment Scamp came rushing out of the kitchen

FIRE-EATING AND OTHER THINGS!

An extract from FIVE HAVE A WONDERFUL TIME, a story about the Famous Five — Julian, Dick, George, Anne and Timmy the Dog, and their caravan holiday among the Fair Folk.

A BIG figure loomed up in the twilight. It was Alfredo, the fire-eater. "Jo! Are you there?" he said. "Your aunt invites you to supper — and all your friends too. Come along."

"Thanks," said Julian. "We'd be pleased to come. Do you mean now?"

"That would be nice," said Alfredo, with a little bow. "I fire-eat for you? Anything you say!"

This was too tempting to resist. Everyone got up at once and followed the big Alfredo over the hillside to his caravan. Outside there was a really good fire, and on it was a big black pot that gave out a wonderful smell.

"Supper is not quite ready," said Alfredo. The five children were relieved. After their big tea they didn't feel ready even for a meal that smelt as good as the one in the pot! They sat down near it.

"Will you really eat fire for us?" asked Anne. "How do you do it?"

"Ah, very difficult!" said Alfredo. "I do it only if you promise me not to try it by yourselves. You would not like blisters all over your mouth inside, would you?"

Everyone felt certain that they wouldn't. "I don't want you to have blisters in *your* mouth, either," added Anne.

Alfredo looked shocked. "I am a very good fire-eater," he assured her. "No good ones ever make blisters in their mouths. Now — you sit still and I will fetch my torch and eat fire for you."

Someone else sat down beside them. It was Bufflo. He grinned at them. Skippy came and sat down too. Then the snake-man arrived, and he sat down on the opposite side of the fire.

Alfredo came back carrying a few things in his hands. "Quite a family circle!" he said. "Now watch — I will eat fire for you!"

Alfredo sat down on the grass, some way back from the fire. He set a little metal bowl in front of him, that smelt of petrol. He held up two things to show the children.

"His torches," said Mrs. Alfredo, proudly.

Alfredo called out something to the snake-man, dipping his two torches into the bowl. They were not alight yet, and to the children they looked like very large buttonhooks, with a wad of wool caught in the hook-part.

The snake-man leaned forward and took a burning twig out of the fire. With a deft throw he pitched it right into the metal bowl. Immediately it set light to the petrol there, and flames shot up in the darkness.

Alfredo had held his torches out of the way, but now he thrust first one and then another into the burning petrol in the bowl.

They flared alight at once, and red flames shot up as he held one in each hand. His eyes gleamed in the brilliant light, and the five children sat still, spellbound.

Then Alfredo leaned back his head — back and back — and opened wide his great mouth. He put one of the lighted torches into it, and

The Lucky Ducks

The ducks go out on rainy days,
And never wear goloshes,
And no one calls to them and says
"Put on your macintoshes!"

They never wrap their necks about
With scarves when it is chilly,
And never take umbrellas out,
They wouldn't be so silly.

But when it rains I have to do
Exactly what I'm told,
And put a hat and gloves on too,
In case I catch a cold.

And with umbrella out I tramp,
In macintosh and coat,
Goloshes to keep out the damp,
And scarf around my throat.

But though the ducks wear none of these,
And never, never will,
I haven't heard them cough or sneeze,
Because they've caught a chill!

And when it's raining very hard,
I wish I had the luck,
To go splish-splashing round the yard
And be a dripping duck!

closed his mouth over it, so that his cheeks glowed a strange and unbelievable red from the flames inside his mouth. Anne gave a little scream and George gasped. The two boys held their breath. Only Jo watched unconcerned.

Alfredo opened his mouth, and flames rushed out of it, gushing like a fiery waterfall. What with the other torch flaring in his left hand, the burning petrol in the bowl, the torch in his right hand and the flames from his mouth, it really was an extraordinary scene!

He did the same with the other torch, and once more his cheeks glowed like lamps. Then fire came from his mouth again, and was blown this way and that by the night breeze.

Alfredo closed his mouth. He swallowed. Then he looked round, opened his mouth to show that he no longer had any flames there, and smiled.

"Ah — did you like to see me eat fire?" he said, and put out his torches.

"It's marvellous," said Julian, with great admiration. "But don't you burn your mouth?"

"What, me? No, never!" laughed Alfredo. "At first maybe, yes — when I began years and years ago. But now, no. It would be a shameful thing to burn my mouth."

"But — how is it you *don't* burn your mouth?" asked Dick, puzzled.

Alfredo refused to give any explanation. That was part of the mystery of his act and he wasn't going to give it away.

"*I* can fire-eat too," announced Jo, casually and most unexpectedly. "Here, Uncle, let me have one of your torches."

"You! You will do nothing of the sort!" roared Alfredo. "Do you want to burn to bits?"

"No. And I shan't either," said Jo. "I've watched you and I know just how it's done. I've tried it."

"Fibber!" said George at once.

"Now you listen to me," began Alfredo again. "If you fire-eat I will whip you till you beg me for mercy. I will . . ."

"Now, Fredo," said his wife, "you'll do nothing of the sort. *I'll* deal with Jo if she starts any

Then Alfredo opened his great mouth wide.

nonsense here. As for fire-eating — well, if there's to be anyone else fire-eating here, *I* will do it, I, your wife."

"You will *not* fire-eat," said Alfredo obstinately, evidently afraid that his hot-tempered little wife might try to do it.

Anne suddenly gave a scream of fright. A long, thick body glided between her and Julian — one of the snake-man's pythons! He had brought one with him, and the children hadn't known. Jo caught hold of it and held on for dear life.

"Let him be," said the snake-man. "He will come back to me. He wants a run."

"Let me hold him for a bit," begged Jo. "He feels so smooth and cold. I like snakes."

Julian put out his hand gingerly and touched the great snake. It did feel unexpectedly smooth, and quite cool. How extraordinary! It *looked* so scaly and rough.

The snake slithered all the way up Jo and then began to pour itself down her back. "Now don't you let him get his tail round you," warned the snake-man. "I've told you that before. He'll squeeze you till you yell."

"I'll wear him round my neck," said Jo, and proceeded to pull at the snake's long body until in the end he hung round her neck like a fur. George watched in unwilling admiration. Anne had removed herself as far from Jo as possible. The boys gazed in astonishment, and felt a new respect for the little gypsy girl.

Someone struck up a soft melody on a guitar. It was Skippy, Bufflo's wife. She hummed a sad little song that had a gay chorus in which most of the fair folk joined.

It was exciting sitting there round the glowing fire, listening to the thrum of the guitar, and the sound of Skippy's low, clear voice — sitting near a fire-eater too, and within arm's length of a snake who also seemed to be enjoying the music! He swayed about in time to the chorus, and then suddenly poured himself all down Jo's front and glided like magic to his master, the snake-man.

"Ah, my beauty," said the funny little man, and let the python slide between his hands, its coils pulsing powerfully as it went. "You like the music, my beauty?"

"He really *loves* his snake," whispered Anne to George. "How can he?"

Alfredo's wife got up. "It is time to go," she

The snake hung round Jo's neck like a fur.

told the audience. "Alfredo needs his supper. Is it not so, my big bad man?"

Alfredo agreed that it was so. He placed the heavy iron pot over the glowing fire again, and in a few seconds such a glorious smell came from it that all the five children began to sniff expectantly.

"Where's Timmy?" said George, suddenly.

"He crept away with his tail down when he saw the snake," said Jo. "I saw him go. Timmy, come back! It's all right! Timmy, Timmy!"

"*I'll* call him, thank you," said George. "He's *my* dog. Timmy!"

Timmy came, his tail still down. George fondled him and so did Jo. He licked them both in turn. George tried to drag him away from Jo. She didn't like Timmy to show affection for the little gypsy girl — but he always did!

The supper was lovely. "*What* is in your pot?" asked Dick, accepting a second helping. "I've never tasted such a delicious stew in my life."

"Chicken, duck, beef, bacon, rabbit, hare, hedgehog, onions, turnips . . ." began Alfredo's wife. "I put there everything that comes. It cooks and I stir, it cooks and I stir. Perhaps a partridge goes in one day, and a pheasant the next, and . . ."

"Hold your tongue, wife," growled Alfredo, who knew quite well that the farmers round about might well ask questions about some of the things in that stew.

"You tell me to hold my tongue!" cried little Mrs. Alfredo angrily, flourishing a spoon.

"Woof," said Timmy, receiving some nice tasty drops on his nose, and licking them off.

"Oh, Aunt Nita, do give Timmy a spoonful out of the stew," begged Jo, and to Timmy's joy he was given a big plateful all to himself.

"Thank you very much for a very nice supper," said Julian, feeling that it really was time to go. He stood up and the others followed his example.

"And thank you for fire-eating for us, Alfredo," said George. "It doesn't spoil your appetite!"

"Poof!" said Alfredo, as if such a thing would never enter his head!

(A story from *Enid Blyton's Twelfth Bedside Book*)

THERE were once four wise men who travelled in a strange country with their servant. They rode upon horses, and when night came and the world was dark, they leapt from their horses and told their servant to make a shelter for the night.

But as he was doing this, the horses gave a frightened whinny and galloped away into the darkness! The wise men scolded the dismayed servant and bade him catch the horses.

"But, sirs, how can I do that?" asked the servant. "It is a black night and I do not know where the horses have gone. You should have tied them to a tree. I was building you a shelter, and did not know that you had left the horses loose."

"That is the worst of having a foolish man for a servant!" said one of the wise men. "If he had been as wise as we are, such a thing would never have happened!"

Just then he bumped into something enormous, and he stood still in surprise. It was an elephant who had come wandering by, and had frightened the horses, who did not like the smell of the strange beast. The wise man ran his hands over the great side of the elephant. He pushed it. It did not move.

"Here is a great rock!" cried the wise man. "We will shelter beneath it for the night!"

The others came up. One felt the elephant's trunk-like leg, and laughed. "This is no rock!" he said. "This is a tree — a great forest tree! Its branches will shelter us well!"

The third wise man put out his hand to feel, and he took hold of the trunk, which wriggled and tried to get away from his hand.

"It is a snake," he cried in fear. "How can you say it is a rock or a tree? You are mad! Come away from here. I tell you it is a snake."

The fourth wise man also put out his hands to feel, and touched the tusks.

"It is a cow!" he said. "I feel its horns. Now we shall be able to have milk to drink."

"Does a snake have horns?" snorted the third wise man in scorn.

"It's a tree, I tell you!" said the second wise man, feeling the elephant's leg again.

"No, a great rock!" said the first one, pounding the elephant's hard side.

They then fell to quarrelling and fighting, and the poor servant stood in fear, wondering what would happen if they all killed each other.

"Masters, masters!" he cried. "You cannot all be right — and you cannot all be wrong, for you are so wise! Let me light my lantern and we will see what you have found."

"Foolish servant!" said the wise men.

And they all said again what they thought — one said a rock, another a tree, the third a snake, and the fourth a cow. The servant trembled and lighted his lantern. He held it up in the air and all five men looked to see what they had found.

"An elephant!" cried the servant in joy. "We will ride him to the nearest town. Masters, you are all wrong!"

"I tell you it was a rock!" said one. "No, a tree!" "No, a snake that wriggled!" "No, a cow with horns!"

"Well, I will leave you to your wisdom!" said the servant, climbing on to the elephant's neck. "I am but a foolish man, and it seems to *me* that this is an elephant. Better to be foolish and safe than wise and in danger! Good night, masters!"

He rode off — and what happened to the four wise men nobody ever knew!

THE SECRET ISLAND

(The first of the Secret Island Series)

The four children have run away from unkind homes, and under the guidance of Jack the farm-boy have come to a little secret island on a lake. Here they plan to live together — but first they must have somewhere to live. The following extracts tell how they built their tree-house from young, growing willow trees.

What fun it was to wake up that first morning!

WHAT fun it was to wake up that first morning on the island! Jack awoke first. He heard a thrush singing so loudly on a tree near by that he woke up with a jump.

"Mind how you do it," said the thrush, "mind how you do it!"

Jack grinned. "I'll mind how I do it all right!" he said to the singing thrush. "Hi, Mike! Wake up! The sun is quite high!"

Mike awoke and sat up. At first he didn't remember where he was. Then a broad smile came over his face. Of course — they were all on the secret island! How perfectly glorious!

"Peggy, Nora! Get up!" he cried. The girls awoke and sat up in a hurry. Wherever were they? What was this green bedroom — oh, of course, it was their heathery bedroom on the secret island!

Soon all four children were up and about. Jack made them take off their things and have a dip in the lake. It was simply lovely, but the water felt cold at first. When they had dried themselves

Jack made them undress and have a dip.

on an old sack — for they had no towels — the children felt terribly hungry. But Jack had been busy! He had set his fishing-line, and, even as they bathed, he had seen the float jerk up and down. It was not long before Jack proudly laid four fine trout on the sand of the cove, and set about to make a fire to cook them.

Mike went to fill the kettle to make some tea. Peggy took some big potatoes out of the sack and put them almost in the fire to cook in their skins. Jack found the frying pan in their storeroom and put a piece of margarine in it to fry the fish, which he knew exactly how to clean.

"I don't know what we should do without you," said Mike, as he watched Jack. "Goodness! How I shall enjoy my breakfast!"

They all did. The tea did not taste very nice without milk. "It's a pity we can't get milk," said Jack. "We shall miss that, I'm afraid. Now, Peggy, wash up, and Nora, too. Put everything away — and we'll start on our house!"

In great excitement everything was washed up and put away. Then Jack led the way through the thick willow-trees, and they came to the little clear place in the centre of them.

"Now, this is how I mean to build the house," he said. "Do you see these little willow-trees here — one there — one there — two there — and two there. Well, I think you will find that if we climb up and bend down the top branches, they will meet each other nicely in the centre, and we can weave them into one another. That will make the beginning of a roof. With my axe I shall chop down some other young willow-trees, and use the trunks and thicker branches for walls. We can drive the trunks and branches into the ground between the six willow-trees we are using, and fill up any cracks with smaller branches woven across. Then, if we stuff every corner and crevice with bracken and heather, we shall have a fine big house, with a splendid roof, wind-proof and rain-proof. What do you think of that?"

The other children listened in the greatest excitement. It sounded too good to be true. Could it be as easy as all that?

"Jack, can we really do it?" said Mike. "It sounds all right — and those willow-trees are just the right distance from one another to make a good big house — and their top branches will certainly overlap well."

"Oh, let's begin, let's begin!" cried Nora, impatient as usual, dancing up and down.

"I'll climb up this first willow-tree and swing the branches over with my weight," said Jack. "All you others must catch hold of them and hold them till I slip down. Then I'll climb another tree and bend those branches over too. We'll tie them together, and then I'll climb up the other trees. Once we've got all the top branches bending down, touching one another, and overlapping nicely, we can cut long willow-sticks and lace our roof together. I'll show you how to."

Jack swung himself up into one of the little willow-trees. It was only a young one, with a small trunk — but it had a head of long, fine branches, easy to bend. Jack swung them down, and the girls and Mike caught them easily. They held on to them whilst Jack slid down the tree and climbed another. He did the same thing there, bending down the supple branches until they reached and rested on top of those bent down from the other tree.

"This is how I mean to build a house," said Jack.

"Tie them together, Mike!" shouted Jack. "Peggy, go and find the rope I brought."

Peggy darted off. She soon came back with the rope. Mike twisted it round the branches of the two trees, and tied them firmly together.

"It's beginning to look like a roof already!" shouted Nora, in excitement. "Oh, I want to sit underneath it!"

She sat down under the roof of willow-boughs, but Jack called to her at once.

"Get up, Nora! You've got to help! I'm up the third tree now — look, here come the top branches bending over with my weight — catch them and hold them!"

Nora and Peggy caught them and held on tightly. The branches reached the others and overlapped them. Mike was soon busy tying those down, too.

The whole morning was spent in this way. By dinner-time all the six trees had been carefully bent over. Jack showed Mike and the girls how to weave the branches together, so that they held on one another and made a firm close roof.

"You see, if we use the trees like this, their leaves will still grow and will make a fine thick roof," said Jack. "Now, although our house has

They bent down the branches of the willow trees.

no walls as yet, we at least have a fine roof to shelter under if it rains!"

"I want something to eat," said Nora. "I'm so hungry that I feel I could eat snails!"

"Well, get out four eggs, and we'll have some with potatoes," said Jack. "We'll boil the eggs in our saucepan. There's plenty of potatoes, too. After the eggs are done we'll boil some potatoes, and mash them up. That will be nice for a change. We'll nibble a few carrots, too, and have some of those cherries."

"We do have funny meals," said Peggy, going to fetch the saucepan and the eggs, "But I like them! Come on, Nora, help me get the potatoes and peel them whilst the eggs are boiling. And, Mike, get some water, will you?"

Soon the fire was burning merrily and the eggs were boiling in the saucepan. The girls peeled the potatoes, and Jack washed the carrots. He went to get some water to drink, too, for everyone was very thirsty.

"You'd better catch some more fish for to-night, Jack," said Peggy. "I hope our stores are going to last out a bit! We do seem to eat a lot!"

"I've been thinking about that," said Jack, watching the potatoes boiling. "I think I'll have to row to land occasionally and get more food. I can get it from Grandad's farm. There are plenty of potatoes there, and I can always get the eggs from the hen-house. Some of the hens are mine — and there's a cow that's *really* mine too, for Grandad gave her to me when she was a calf!"

"I wish we had hens and a cow here!" said Peggy. "We should have lots of milk then and plenty of eggs!"

"How would we get hens and a cow to our island?" said Mike, laughing. "I think Jack's idea of rowing across to land sometimes is a good one. He can go at night. He knows the way, and could get back before day breaks."

"It's dangerous, though," said Peggy. "Suppose he were caught? We couldn't do without Jack!"

The children ate their dinner hungrily. They thought that eggs and potatoes had never tasted so nice before. The sun shone down hotly. It was simply perfect weather. Nora lay down when she had finished her meal and closed her eyes. She felt lazy and sleepy.

Jack poked her with his foot. "You're not to go to sleep, Nora," he said. "We must get on with our house, now we've started. You two girls clear up as usual, and Mike and I will get back to the house. We'll start on the walls this afternoon."

"But I'm sleepy," said Nora. She was rather a lazy little girl, and she thought it would be lovely to have a nap whilst the others got on with the work. But Jack was not going to let anyone slack. He jerked Nora to her feet and gave her a push.

"Go on, lazy-bones," he said. "I'm captain here. Do as you're told."

"I didn't know you were captain," said Nora, rather sulkily.

"Well, you know now," said Jack. "What do the others say about it?"

"Yes, you're captain, Jack," said Mike and Peggy together. "Ay, ay, sir!"

Nobody said any more. Nora and Peggy washed up in the lake and cleared the things away neatly. They put some more wood on the fire to keep it burning, because Jack said it was silly to keep on lighting it. Then they ran off to join the boys in the willow thicket.

Jack had been busy. He had chopped down some willow saplings — young willow-trees — with his axe, and had cut off the longer branches.

"We'll use these to drive into the ground for walls," said Jack. "Where's the old spade, Mike? Did you bring it as I said?"

"Yes, here it is," said Mike. "Shall I dig holes to drive the sapling trunks into?"

"Yes," said Jack. "Dig them fairly deep."

So Mike dug hard in the hot sun, making holes into which Jack rammed the willow wood. The girls stripped the leaves off the chopped-down trees, and with Jack's knife cut off the smaller twigs. They trimmed up the bigger branches nicely.

Everyone worked hard until the sun began to go down. The house was not yet built — it would take some days to do that — but at any rate there was a fine roof, and part of the wall was up. The children could quite well see how the house would look when it was done — and certainly it would be big, and very strong. They felt proud of themselves.

"We'll do no more to-day," said Jack. "We are all tired. I'll go and see if there are any fish on my line."

But, alas! there were no fish that night!

"There's some bread left and a packet of currants," said Peggy. "And some lettuces and margarine. Shall we have those?"

"This food question is going to be a difficult one," said Jack thoughtfully. "We've plenty of water — we shall soon have a house — but we must have food or we shall starve. I shall catch rabbits, I think."

"Oh no, Jack, don't do that," said Nora. "I do like rabbits so much."

"So do I, Nora," said Jack. "But if rabbits were not caught, the land would soon be overrun with them, you know. You have often had rabbit pie, haven't you? And I guess you liked it, too!"

"Yes, I did," said Nora. "Well, if you are sure you can catch them so that they are not hurt

Soon the fire was burning merrily and the eggs were in the saucepan.

or in pain, Jack, I suppose you'll have to."

"You leave it to me," said Jack. "I don't like hurting things any more than you do. But I know quite well how to skin rabbits. It's a man's job, that, so you two girls can leave it to Mike and me. So long as you can cook the rabbits for dinner, that's all you need worry about. And ever since Peggy said she wished we had a cow and some hens, I've been thinking about it. I believe we could manage to get them over here on to the island — then we *would* be all right!"

Mike, Peggy, and Nora stared at Jack in amazement. What a surprising boy he was! However could they bring a cow and hens to the island?

"Hurry up and get the supper, girls," said Jack, smiling at their surprised faces. "I'm hungry. We'll think about things to-morrow. We'll have our meal now and a quiet read afterwards, then to bed early. To-morrow we'll go on with the house."

Soon they were munching bread and margarine, and eating lettuce. They saved the currants for another time. Then they took out books and papers and sprawled on the soft heather, reading whilst the daylight lasted. After that they had a dip in the lake, threw on their clothes again, and settled down for the night in their heathery beds.

"Good-night, everyone," said Mike. But nobody answered — they were all asleep!

The next day, after a meal of fish and lettuce, the children were ready to go on with the building of their house in the willow thicket. It was lucky that Jack had caught more fish on his line that morning, for stores were getting low. There were still plenty of potatoes, but not much else. Jack made up his mind that he would have to take the boat and see what he could bring back in it that night. There was no doubt that food was going to be their great difficulty.

All morning the four children worked hard at the house. Jack cut down enough young willows to make the walls. Mike dug the holes to drive in the willow stakes. He and Jack drove them deeply in, and the girls were delighted to see what fine straight walls of willow the boys were making.

The willow stakes were set a little way apart, and Jack showed the girls how to take thin, supple willow branches and weave them in and out of the stakes to hold the walls in place, and to fill up the gaps. It was quite easy to do this when they knew how, but it was very hard work.

Mike went up and down to the spring a dozen times that morning to fetch water! They all drank pints of it, and were glad of its coldness. The sun was really very hot, although it was nice and shady in the green willow thicket.

"It begins to look like a house now," said Jack, pleased. "Look, this front gap here is where we shall have the door. We can make that later of long stakes interwoven with willow strips, and swing it on some sort of a hinge so that it opens and shuts. But we don't need a door at present."

That day all the walls were finished, and the girls had worked hard at weaving the stakes together so that the walls stood firmly, and looked thick and strong.

"In the olden days people used to fill up the gaps with clay and let it dry hard," said Jack. "But I don't think there's any clay on this island, so we must stuff up the cracks with dried bracken and heather. That will do nicely. And the willow stakes we have rammed into the ground will grow, and throw out leaves later on, making the walls thicker still."

The four children worked hard at the house.

"How do you mean — the stakes we have cut will grow?" asked Mike in surprise. "Sticks don't grow, surely!"

Jack grinned. "Willow sticks do!" he said. "You can cut a willow branch off the tree, strip it of all buds and leaves, and stick it in the ground, and you'll find that, although it has no roots, and no shoots — it will put out both and grow into a willow-tree by itself! Willows are full of life, and you can't stamp it out of them!"

"Well — our house will be growing all the year round, then!" cried Nora. "How funny!"

"I think it's lovely!" said Peggy. "I like things to be as alive as that. I shall love to live in a house that's growing over me — putting out roots and shoots and buds and leaves! What shall we call our house, Jack?"

"Willow House!" said Jack. "That's the best name for it!"

"It's a good name," said Peggy. "I like it. I like everything here. It's glorious. Just us four — and our secret island. It's the loveliest adventure that ever was!"

"If only we had more to eat!" said Mike, who seemed to feel hungry every hour of the day. "That's the only thing I don't like about this adventure!"

"Yes," said Jack. "We'll have to put that right! Don't worry. We shall get over it somehow!"

That night there was nothing much to eat but potatoes. Jack said he would go off in the boat as soon as it was dark, to see what he could find at his old farm.

So he set off. He took with him a candle, set in the lantern, but he did not light it in case he should be seen.

"Wait up for me," he said to the others, "and keep a small fire going — not big, in case the glow could be seen."

The other three waited patiently for Jack to come back. He seemed a long, long time. Nora stretched herself out on the old rug and fell asleep.

But Mike and Peggy kept awake. They saw the moon come up and light everything. The secret island seemed mysterious again in the moonlight. Dark shadows stretched beneath the trees. The water lapped against the sand, black as night close by them, but silvered where the moon caught it beyond. It was a warm night, and the children were hot, even though they had no covering.

It seemed hours before they heard the splash of oars. Mike ran down to the edge of the water and waited. He saw the boat coming softly over the water in the moonlight. He called Jack.

"Hallo, there, Jack! Are you all right?"

"Yes," said Jack's voice. "I've plenty of news for you!"

The boat scraped on the sand and stones. Mike pulled it up the beach, and Jack jumped out.

"I've got something here for us!" said Jack, and they saw his white teeth in the moonlight,

Four of the hens had laid eggs.

as he grinned at them. "Put your hands down there in the boat, Nora."

Nora did — and squealed!

"There's something soft and warm and feathery there!" she said. "What is it?"

"Six of my hens!" said Jack. "I found them roosting in the hedges! I caught them and trussed them up so that they couldn't move! My word, they were heavy to carry! But we shall have plenty of eggs now! The hens can't escape from the island!"

"Hurrah!" cried Peggy. "We can have eggs for breakfast, dinner, and tea!"

"What else have you brought?" asked Mike.

"Corn for the hens," said Jack. "And packets of seeds of all kinds from the shed. And some tins of milk. And a loaf of bread, rather stale. And lots more vegetables!"

"And here are some cherries," said Nora, pulling out handfuls of red cherries from the boat. "Did you pick these, Jack?"

"Yes," said Jack. "They are from the tree in our garden. It's full of them now."

"Did you see your grandfather?" asked Mike.

"Yes," grinned Jack, "But he didn't see me! He's going away — to live with my aunt. The farm is to be shut up, and someone is to feed the animals until it's sold. So I think I shall try and get my own cow somehow and make her swim across the lake to the island!"

"Don't be silly, Jack," said Peggy. "You could never do that!"

"You don't know what I can do!" said Jack. "Well, listen — I heard my Grandad talking to two friends of his, and everyone is wondering where we've all gone! They've searched everywhere for us — in all the nearby towns and villages, and in all the country round about!"

"Oooh!" said the three children, feeling rather frightened. "Do you suppose they'll come here?"

"Well, they may," said Jack. "You never know. I've always been a bit afraid that the smoke from our fire will give the game away to someone. But don't let's worry about that till it happens."

"*We must finish Willow House,*" *said Jack.*

"Are the police looking for us, too?" asked Peggy.

"Oh yes," said Jack. "Everyone is, as far as I can make out. I heard Grandad tell how they've searched barns and stacks and ditches, and gone to every town for twenty miles round, thinking we might have run away on a lorry. They don't guess how near we are!"

"Is Aunt Harriet very upset?" asked Peggy.

"Very!" grinned Jack. "She's got no one to wash and scrub and cook for her now! But that's all she cares, I expect! Well, it's good news about my Grandad going to live with my aunt. I can slip to and fro and not be seen by him now. My word, I wished Mike was with me when I got these hens. They did peck and scratch and flap about. I was afraid someone would hear them."

"Where shall we put them?" said Mike, helping Jack to carry them up the beach.

"I vote we put them into Willow House till the morning," said Jack. "We can stop up the doorway with something."

So they bundled the squawking hens into Willow House, and stopped up the doorway with sticks and bracken. The hens fled to a corner and squatted there, terrified. They made no more noise.

"I'm jolly tired," said Jack. "Let's have a few cherries and go to bed."

They munched the ripe cherries, and then went to their green bedroom. The bracken which they had picked and put on the hillside to dry had been quite brown and withered by that afternoon, so the girls had added it to their beds and to-night they seemed even softer and sweeter-smelling than usual. They were all tired. Mike and Jack talked for a little while, but the girls went to sleep quickly.

They slept late the next morning. Peggy woke first, and sat up, wondering what the unusual noise was that she heard. It was a loud cackling

"Of course! The hens!" she thought. She slipped off her bracken-and-heather bed, jumped lightly over the two sleeping boys and ran to Willow House. She pulled aside the doorway and squeezed inside. The hens fled to a corner when they saw her, and Peggy saw a welcome sight!

Four of the hens had laid eggs! Goody! Now they could have a fine breakfast! The little girl gathered them up quickly, then, stopping up the doorway again, she ran out. She soon had a fire going, and, when the others sat up, rubbing their eyes, Peggy called them.

"Come on! Breakfast! The hens have laid us an egg each!"

They ran to breakfast. "We'll have a dip afterwards," said Mike. "I feel so hungry."

"We must finish Willow House properly today," said Jack. "And we must decide what to do with the hens, too. They can't run loose till they know us and their new home. We must put up some sort of enclosure for them."

After breakfast the four of them set to work to make a tiny yard for the hens. They used willow stakes again and quickly built a fine little fence, too high for the hens to jump over. Jack made them nesting-places of bracken, and hoped they would lay their eggs there. He scattered some seed for them, and they pecked at it eagerly. Peggy gave them a dish of water.

"They will soon know this is their home and lay their eggs here," said Jack. "Now, come on, let's get on with Willow House! You two girls stuff up the cracks with heather and bracken, and Mike and I will make the door."

Everyone worked hard. The girls found it rather a nice job to stuff the soft heather and bracken into the cracks and make the house rain-and-windproof. They were so happy in their job that they did not notice what a fine door Jack and Mike had made of woven willow twigs. The boys called the girls, and proudly showed them what they had done.

The door had even been fixed on some sort of a hinge, so that it swung open and shut! It looked fine! It did not quite fit at the top, but nobody minded that. It was a door — and could be shut or opened, just as they pleased. Willow House was very dark inside when the door was shut — but that made it all the more exciting!

"I'm so hungry and thirsty now that I believe I could eat all the food we've got!" said Mike at last.

"Yes, we really must have something to eat," said Jack. "We've plenty of bread and potatoes and vegetables. Let's cook some broad beans. They are jolly good. Go and look at my fishing-line, Mike, and see if there are any fish on it."

There was a fine trout, and Mike brought it back to cook. Soon the smell of frying rose on the air, and the children sniffed hungrily. Fish, potatoes, bread, beans, cherries, and cocoa with milk from one of Jack's tins. What a meal!

"I'll think about getting Daisy the cow across next," said Jack, drinking his cocoa. "We simply must have milk."

"And, Jack, we could store some of our things now, couldn't we?" said Peggy. "The ants get into some of the things in the cave-larder. It's a good place for things like hammers and nails, but it would be better to keep our food in Willow House. Are we going to live there, Jack?"

"Well, we'll live in the open air mostly, I expect," said Jack, "But it will be a good place to sleep in when the nights are cold and rainy, and a fine shelter on bad days. It's our sort of home."

"It's a lovely home," said Nora; "the nicest there ever was! What fun it is to live like this!"

Jack had a candle set in a lantern.

3. Miss Hannah's Roundabout

MISS Hannah came into the playroom to look for the children. They were all there, gazing mournfully out of the window. They turned round when she came in.

"Miss Hannah! Isn't it maddening? We were going to sail boats on the stream and now the rain is absolutely *pouring* down."

"Yes, it's very tiresome," said Miss Hannah. "I felt sorry for you so I've come up to see if you'd like to make something this afternoon."

"Oh, *yes*! Something really exciting. Can you make absolutely *anything*, Miss Hannah?"

"Well," said Miss Hannah, "I think I can make most things. What do you want to make?"

"Er — let's think — oh, *I* know, a *roundabout*!" said Jack suddenly. "One that will really go round, a toy one. Can we make that, Miss Hannah?"

"Oh yes, I think so," said Miss Hannah. "We shall want some round pieces of cardboard, some cotton reels, and some wooden skewers. Go and ask Cook if she can let you have some skewers, Lucy. If not, we must make do with pieces of cane from the garden shed."

Lucy soon came back with a bunch of wooden meat skewers from the kitchen. Jane had found some small and large cotton reels. Jack had been sent to the odds-and-ends cupboard to see if he could find some round cardboard boxes. If not, they would have to cut circles from sheets of cardboard.

He found some old round chocolate boxes which Miss Hannah said would be "just the thing".

"Now," she said, "you can all do what I do. We will make a roundabout each. Take a large cotton reel — put your wooden skewer firmly into the hole in the reel. Now that's the middle post of our roundabout." *(See Fig. I.)*

Next she gave each child a round cardboard box. "Cut out a nice round platform about twelve inches in diameter," she said. "A platform for your roundabout, I mean. You can make it from the bottom of the box. Perhaps the bottom will do as it is, once you have taken the sides from it."

Soon they each had circles of cardboard in front of them. "Now make a hole exactly in the middle of your circle," said Miss Hannah. "And slip it over the wooden skewer, till it fits on to the reel. That's right. Does it turn easily? No, yours is a little tight, Lucy. Make your hole a bit bigger."

Soon all the platforms were turning easily on the skewers. "Now take off your platforms

again," said Miss Hannah, "because we must put animals on them to make the roundabout look real. We'll cut some out of books and paste them round the edge."

So they spent twenty minutes cutting out coloured animals from old books, and pasting them neatly round the edge of their "platforms".

"Now put your platforms back again on your skewers, right down to the reel," said Miss Hannah. "Aren't they beginning to look gay? Now take a smaller cotton reel and slip it down the skewer so that it holds and steadies the platform." *(See Fig. 2.)*

Soon all the "platforms" with their gay little roundabout animals were placed into position, with a second cotton reel above. "Now for the roundabout top," said Miss Hannah. "We can use the lid of a round chocolate box for that, but we must make it as gay as possible. Let's cut out a pretty edge to it and bend it downwards."

They decorated their roundabout tops as gaily as they could, and then cut out a pretty edging. "Now put your top on to the skewer," said Miss Hannah. "Make a hole first, of course. If it doesn't fit tightly we'll put a spot of glue to hold it fast."

Soon all the roundabout tops were on, and the roundabouts were finished. They looked really lovely! "Now make them go round," said Miss Hannah, and gave her platform a twirl with her fingers. Round and round it went, with the little animals spinning in a circle just like a real roundabout.

Jack, Jane and Lucy spun theirs, too. Then Jane fetched her little musical box and set it going whilst the roundabouts went gaily round.

"They look so *real*!" she said. "Oh, Miss Hannah, this is one of the nicest things we've made. Whoever would have thought it was so easy to make a roundabout!"

Loony the Spaniel

Another extract from a Barney Books seaside story, The Rub a dub Mystery.

AFTER the first few days the holidays began to slip away fast, as holidays always do.

A week had gone by before any of the children realised it. It had been a good week — bathing, boating, paddling, walking, and messing about with Barney the spaniel and Miranda. Loony had enjoyed himself too.

He dug violently each morning, covering every one with sand. He then ran into the sea and got thoroughly wet. Then he came back and shook himself really vigorously, showering every one with drops of sea water.

He had also developed a new and most irritating habit. Having been smacked hard for attempting to bring brushes, towels and mats on to the beach, he cast about for something that nobody could possibly object to.

He brought along a strange dog each day to play with him! The first time he brought a peculiar-looking mongrel with very short legs and a large head.

"Look at that," said Snubby. "Poor creature. If its legs were much shorter they wouldn't touch the ground!"

"Ha ha — very old joke," said Diana. "All the same, it *is* a peculiar dog."

"It's a bit of a smelly dog," said Roger, as the dog sat down heavily on his legs. "Get off, Smelly! Go away!"

But Smelly had no intention of leaving his good friend Loony. They went crazy together and nearly drove Miss Pepper mad as they tore round and round her deck-chair. They had to put up with Smelly all day, and were amazed to see Loony sharing all his tit-bits with him.

The next day Loony trotted off the beach and returned with a second friend — a bulldog with a face a bit like Mr. Tubby's. He wasn't as bad as Smelly, and he liked to sit as near everyone as possible.

"I wish you wouldn't *dribble* all over me,"

Snubby said to the bulldog. "You want a bib or something. Miss Pepper, do bulldogs always dribble or is this one just doing it on purpose?"

"He's dribbled over me too," said Diana. "I remember a teacher at school who had a bulldog and he dribbled as well. Loony, next time you bring a friend, bring one who doesn't smell *or* dribble!"

The bulldog was very sweet-tempered until he took a fancy to a bone that Loony was gnawing. Then he gave out such blood-curdling growls that even Snubby drew back. Miranda was with them at the time and she leapt to the top of Barney's head in fright.

"Go away," said Miss Pepper firmly to the bulldog. "That's Loony's bone. Go away!"

The bulldog calmly picked up the bone and waddled off. Snubby gave Loony a poke with his foot.

"Coward dog! Couldn't keep his own bone!"

Loony hung his head. He crept off the beach when no one was looking. He returned looking quite a different dog, bright and cheerful, accompanied by three small dogs of the terrier type, all very alert and inquisitive.

"Oh, stop it, Loony! Have you gone potty?" said Snubby, surveying the four dogs in disgust. "What do you want to go and pick up half the town for? Shoo! Clear off, all of you. No, not you, Loony. You're going to be tied up to Miss Pepper's deck-chair for the rest of the day."

"Oh no, *indeed* he's not," said Miss Pepper at once. "You did that two days ago and he got up much too suddenly and made my chair collapse. If he's going to be tied to anything, you can tie him to your foot, Snubby!"

FIVE GO OFF IN A CARAVAN

An extract from the book of the same name, which tells how the Famous Five go off in their caravans pulled by Trotter and Dobby, the horses, and meet the Circus and the gang!

The common sloped right down to the edge of an enormous lake that lay glittering in the sunshine.

THE next three or four days were absolutely perfect, the children thought. Blue skies, blazing sun, wayside streams to paddle or bathe in, and two houses on wheels that went rumbling for miles down roads and lanes quite new to them — what could be lovelier for four children all on their own?

Timmy the dog seemed to enjoy everything thoroughly, too, and had made firm friends with Trotter, the little black horse. Trotter was always looking for Timmy to run beside him, and he whinnied to Timmy whenever he wanted him. The two horses were friends, too, and when they were set free at night they made for the stream together, and stood in the water side by side, nuzzling one another happily.

"I like this holiday better than any we've ever had," said Anne, busily cooking something in a pan. "It's exciting without being adventurous. And although Julian thinks he's in charge of us, *I* am really! You'd never get your bunks made, or your meals cooked, or the caravans kept clean if it wasn't for me!"

"Don't boast!" said George, feeling rather guilty because she let Anne do so much.

"I'm not boasting!" said Anne, indignantly. "I'm just telling the truth. Why, you've never even made your own bunk once, George. Not that I mind doing it. I love having two houses on wheels to look after."

"You're a very good little housekeeper," said Julian. "We couldn't possibly do without you!"

Anne blushed with pride. She took the pan off the camp-fire and put the contents on to four plates. "Come along!" she called, in a voice just like her mother's. "Have your meal while it's hot."

"I'd rather have mine when it's cold, thank you," said George. "The day doesn't seem to have turned any cooler, even though it's evening-time."

They had been on the road four days now, and Anne had given up looking for the hills where they hoped to find the circus folk camping. In fact she secretly hoped they wouldn't find them, because she was so much enjoying the daily wanderings over the lovely countryside.

Timmy came to lick the plates. The children always let him do that now because it made them so much easier to wash. Anne and George took the things down to a little brown brook to rinse, and Julian took out his map.

He and Dick pored over it. "We're just about here," said Julian, pointing. "And if so, it looks as if to-morrow we ought to come to those hills above the lake. Then we should see the circus."

"Good!" said Dick. "I hope Nobby will be there. He would love to show us round, I'm sure. He would know a good place for us to camp, too, perhaps."

"Oh, we can find that ourselves," said Julian, who now rather prided himself on picking excellent camping-sites. "Anyway, I don't want to be *too* near the circus. It might be a bit smelly. I'd rather be up in the hills some way above it. We'll get a place with a lovely view."

"Right," said Dick, and Julian folded up the map.

The two girls came back with the clean crockery, and Anne put it neatly back on the shelves in the red caravan. Trotter the horse came to look for Timmy, who was lying panting under George's caravan.

Timmy wouldn't budge, so Trotter tried to get under the caravan too. But he couldn't possibly, of course, for he was much too big. So he lay down on the shady side, as near to Timmy as he could get.

"Trotter's really a comic horse," said Dick. "He'd be quite good in a circus, I should think! Did you see him chasing Timmy yesterday — just as if they were playing 'He'!"

The word "circus" reminded them of Nobby and his circus, and they began to talk eagerly of all the animals there.

"I liked the look of the elephant," said George. "I wonder what his name is. And wouldn't I like to hold a monkey!"

"I bet that chimpanzee's clever," said Dick. "Whatever will Timmy think of him? I hope he'll get on all right with all the animals, especially the other dogs."

"I don't want to see much of Nobby's uncle," said Anne. "He looked as if he'd like to box anybody's ears if they so much as answered him back."

"Well, he won't box *mine*," said Julian. "We'll keep out of his way. He doesn't look a very pleasant chap, I must say. Perhaps he won't be there."

"Timmy, come out from under the caravan!" called George. "It's quite cool and shady where we are. Come on!"

He came, panting. Trotter immediately got up and came with him. The little horse lay down beside Timmy and nuzzled him. Timmy gave his nose a lick and then turned away, looking bored.

"Isn't Trotter funny?" said Anne. "Timmy, what *will* you think of all the circus animals, I wonder! I do hope we see the circus to-morrow. Shall we get as far as the hills, Julian? Though really I shan't mind a bit if we don't; it's so nice being on our own like this."

They all looked out for the hills the next day as the caravans rumbled slowly down the lanes, pulled by Trotter and Dobby. And, in the afternoon, they saw them, blue in the distance.

"There they are!" said Julian. "Those must be the Merran Hills — and Merran Lake must lie at the foot. I say, I hope the two horses are strong enough to pull the caravans a good way up the hills. There should be an absolutely marvellous view over the lake if we get up high enough."

The hills came nearer and nearer. They were high ones, and looked lovely in the evening light. Julian looked at his watch.

"We shan't have time to climb them and find

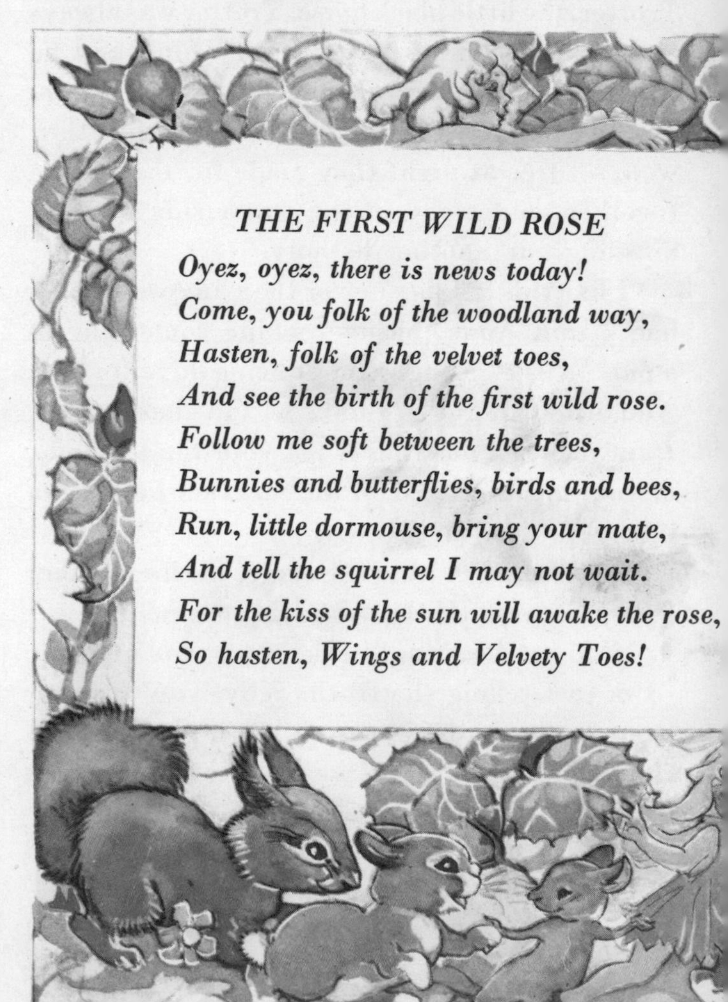

a camping-site there tonight, I'm afraid," he said. "We'd better camp a little way further on this evening, and then make our way up into the hills to-morrow morning."

"All right," said Dick. "Anything you say, Captain! There should be a farm about two miles on, according to the map. We'll camp there."

They came to the farm, which was set by a wide stream that ran swiftly along. Julian went as usual to ask permission to camp, and Dick went with him, leaving the two girls to prepare a meal.

Julian easily got permission, and the farmer's daughter, a plump jolly girl, sold the boys eggs, bacon, milk and butter, besides a little crock of yellow cream. She also offered them raspberries from the garden if they liked to pick them and have them with the cream.

"Oh, I say, thanks awfully," said Julian.

Low on the hedge she lies asleep,
Come, you bunnies, and softly peep!
Fly, you butterflies hovering near,
And kiss the sweetest rose of the year.
Palest pink will her petals be
When from the bud they are shaken free,
And sweet as honey her scent will come,
(Hush, little bees, too loud you hum!)

. . . .

And hush now, folk of the velvet toes,
For the sun is waking the first wild rose!

"Could you tell me if there's a circus camping in those hills? Somewhere by the lake."

"Yes, it went by about a week ago," said the girl. "It goes camping there every year, for a rest. I always watch the caravans go by — quite a treat in a quiet place like this! One year they had lions, and at nights I could hear them roaring away. That fair frizzled my spine!"

The boys said good-bye and went off, chuckling to think of the farm-girl's spine being "fair frizzled" by the roars of the distant lions.

"Well, it looks as if we'll pass the circus camp to-morrow all right," said Julian. "I shall enjoy camping up in the hills, won't you, Dick? It will be cooler up there, I expect — usually there's a breeze on the hills."

"I hope we shan't get our spines fair frizzled by the noise of the circus animals at night," grinned Dick. "I feel fair frizzled up by the sun today, I must say!"

The next morning the caravans set off again on what the children hoped would be the last lap of their journey. They would find a lovely camping-place and stay there till they had to go home.

Julian had remembered to send a post card each day to his parents, telling them where he was, and that everything was fine. He had found out from the farm-girl the right address for that district, and he planned to arrange with the nearest post office to take in any letters for them that came. They had not been able to receive any post, of course, when they were wandering about in their caravans.

Dobby and Trotter walked sedately down the narrow country lane that led towards the hills. Suddenly George caught sight of something flashing blue between the trees.

"Look! There's the lake! Merran Lake!" she shouted. "Make Dobby go more quickly, Ju. I'm longing to come out into the open and see the lake."

Soon the lane ended in a broad cart-track that led over a heathery common. The common sloped right down to the edge of an enormous blue lake that lay glittering in the August sunshine.

"I say! Isn't it magnificent?" said Dick, stopping Dobby with a pull. "Come on, let's get down and go to the edge, Julian. Come along, girls!"

"It's lovely!" said Anne, jumping down from the driving-seat of the red caravan. "Oh, do let's bathe straight away!"

"Yes, let's," said Julian, and they all dived into their caravans, stripped off shorts and shirts and pulled on bathing-things. Then, without even a towel to dry themselves, they tore down to the lake-side, eager to plunge into its blue coolness.

It was very warm at the edge of the water, but further in, where it was deep, the lake was deliciously cold. All the children could swim strongly, and they splashed and yelled in delight. The bottom of the lake was sandy, so the water was as clear as crystal.

When they were tired they all came out and lay on the warm sandy bank of the lake. They dried at once in the sun.

Then, as soon as they felt too hot, in they went again, squealing with joy at the cold water.

"What gorgeous fun to come down here every day and bathe!" said Dick. "Get away, Timmy, when I'm swimming on my back. Timmy's enjoying the bathe just as much as we are, George."

"Yes, and old Trotter wants to come in, too," shouted Julian. "Look at him — he's brought the red caravan right down to the edge of the lake. He'll be in the water with it if we don't stop him!"

They decided to have a picnic by the lake, and to set the horses free to have a bathe if they wanted one. But all that Dobby and Trotter wanted was to drink and to stand knee-high in the water, swishing their tails to keep away the flies that worried them all day long.

"Where's the circus camp?" said George suddenly as they sat munching ham and tomato sandwiches. "I can't see it."

George walked up and held out her hand.

The children looked all round the edge of the lake, which stretched as far as they could see. At last George's sharp eyes saw a small spire of smoke rising in the air about a mile or so round the lake.

"The camp must be in that hollow at the foot of the hills over there," she said. "I expect the road leads round to it. We'll go that way, shall we, and then go up into the hills behind?"

"Yes," agreed Julian. "We shall have plenty of time to have a word with Nobby, and to find a good camping-place before night comes — and to find a farm, too, that will let us have food. Won't Nobby be surprised to see us?"

They cleared up, put the horses into their harness again and set off for the circus camp. Now for a bit of excitement!

It did not take the caravans very long to come in sight of the circus camp. As George had said, it was in a comfortable hollow, set at the foot of the hills — a quiet spot, well away from any dwelling-places, where the circus animals could enjoy a certain amount of freedom and be exercised in peace.

The caravans were set round in a wide circle. Tents had been put up here and there. The big elephant was tied by a thick rope to a stout tree. Dogs ran about everywhere, and a string of shining horses was being paraded round a large field nearby.

"There they all are!" said Anne, excitedly, standing up on the driving-seat to see better. "I say — the chimpanzee is loose, isn't he? No, he isn't — someone is with him. Is it Nobby with him?"

"Yes, it is. I say, fancy walking about with a live chimp like that!" said Julian. "And look, the chimpanzee is wearing little white football shorts. I bet they dress him up properly when he's in the circus ring."

The children looked at everything with the greatest interest as their caravans came nearer to the circus camp. Few people seemed to be about that hot afternoon. Nobby was there with the chimpanzee, and some women were stirring pots over small fires — but that seemed to be all.

"Who are these kids?" said Lou.

The circus dogs set up a great barking as the red and green caravans drew nearer. One or two men came out of the tents and looked up the track that led to the camp. They pointed to the children's caravans and seemed astonished.

Nobby, with the chimpanzee held firmly by the paw, came out of the camp, curious to meet the strange caravans. Julian hailed him.

"Hie, Nobby! You didn't think you'd see *us* here, did you?"

Nobby was amazed to hear his name called. At first he did not remember the children at all. Then he gave a yell.

"Jumping Jiminy, it's you kids I saw away back on the road! What are *you* doing here?"

Timmy growled ominously and George called to Nobby. "He's never seen a chimpanzee before. Do you think they'll be friends?"

"Don't know," said Nobby doubtfully. "Old Pongo likes the circus dogs all right. Anyway, don't you let your dog fly at Pongo, or he'll be eaten alive! A chimp is very strong, you know."

"Could *I* make friends with Pongo, do you think?" asked George. "If he would shake hands with me or something, Timmy would know I was friends with him and he'd be all right. Would Pongo make friends with me?"

"Course he will!" said Nobby. "He's the sweetest-tempered chimp alive — ain't you, Pongo? Now, shake hands with the lady."

Anne didn't feel at all inclined to go near the chimpanzee, but George was quite fearless. She walked up to the big animal and held out her hand. The chimpanzee took it at once, raised it to his mouth and pretended to nibble it, making friendly noises all the time.

George laughed. "He's nice, isn't he?" she said. "Timmy, this is Pongo, a friend. Nice Pongo, good Pongo!"

She patted Pongo on the shoulder to show Timmy that she liked the chimpanzee, and Pongo at once patted her on the shoulder, too, grinning amiably. He then patted her on the head and pulled one of her curls.

Timmy wagged his tail a little. He looked

very doubtful indeed. What was this strange creature that his mistress appeared to like so much? He took a step towards Pongo.

"Come on, Timmy, say how do you do to Pongo," said George. "Like this." And she shook hands with the chimpanzee again. This time he wouldn't let her hand go, but went on shaking it up and down as if he was pumping water with a pump-handle!

"He won't let go," said George, trying to take her hand away.

"Don't be naughty, Pongo," said Nobby in a stern voice. Pongo at once dropped George's hand and covered his face with a hairy paw as if he was ashamed. But the children saw that he was peeping through his fingers with wicked eyes that twinkled with fun.

"He's a real monkey!" said George, laughing.

"You're wrong — he's an *ape*!" said Nobby. "Ah, here comes Timmy to make friends. Jumping Jiminy, they're shaking paws!"

So they were. Timmy, having once made up his mind that Pongo was to be a friend, remembered his manners and held out his right paw as he had been taught. Pongo seized it and shook it vigorously. Then he walked round to the back of Timmy and shook hands with his tail. Timmy didn't know what to make of it at all.

The children yelled with laughter, and Timmy sat down firmly on his tail. Then he stood up again, his tail wagging, for Barker and Growler, two of the circus dogs, had come rushing up. Timmy remembered them, and they remembered him.

"Well, *they're* making friends all right," said Nobby, pleased. "Now they'll introduce Timmy to all the other dogs, and there'll be no trouble. Hey, look out for Pongo, there!"

The chimpanzee had stolen round behind Julian and was slipping his hand into the boy's pocket. Nobby went to him and slapped the chimpanzee's paw hard.

"Naughty! Bad boy! Pickpocket!"

The children laughed again when the chimpanzee covered his face with his paws, pretending to be ashamed.

"You'll have to watch out when Pongo's about," said Nobby. "He loves to take things out of people's pockets. I say — do tell me — are those your caravans? Aren't they posh?"

"They've been lent to us," said Dick. "As a matter of fact, it was seeing your circus go by, with all its gay caravans, that made us think of borrowing caravans, too, and coming away for a holiday."

"And as you'd told us where you were going we thought we'd follow you and find you out, and get you to show us round the camp," said Julian. "Hope you don't mind."

"I'm proud," said Nobby, going a bright red. "'Tisn't often folks want to make friends with a circus fellow like me — not gentlefolk like you, I mean. I'll be proud to show you round — and you can make friends with every blessed monkey, dog, and horse on the place!"

"Oh, thanks!" said all four at once.

"Jolly decent of you," said Dick. "Gosh, look at that chimp — he's trying to shake hands with Timmy's tail again. I bet he's funny in the circus ring, isn't he, Nobby?"

"He's a scream," said Nobby. "Brings the house down. You should see him act with my Uncle Dan. He's the chief clown, you know. Pongo is just as big a clown as my uncle is — it's a fair scream to see them act the fool together."

"I wish we *could* see them," said Anne. "Acting in the ring, I mean. Will your uncle mind you showing us all the animals and everything?"

"Why should he?" said Nobby. "Shan't ask him! But you'll act polite to him, won't you? He's worse than a tiger when he's in a temper. They call him Tiger Dan because of his rages."

Anne didn't like the sound of that at all — Tiger Dan! It sounded very fierce and savage.

"I hope he isn't about anywhere now," she said nervously, looking round.

"No. He's gone off somewhere," said Nobby. "He's a lonesome sort of chap — got no friends much in the circus, except Lou, the acrobat. That's Lou over there."

Lou was a long-limbed, loose-jointed fellow with an ugly face, and a crop of black shining hair that curled tightly. He sat on the steps of a caravan, smoking a pipe and reading a paper. The children thought that he and Tiger Dan would make a good pair — bad tempered, scowling and unfriendly. They all made up their minds that they would have as little as possible to do with Lou the acrobat and Tiger Dan the clown.

"Is he a very good acrobat?" said Anne in a low voice, though Lou was much too far away to hear her.

"Fine. First class," said Nobby with admiration in his voice. "He can climb anything anywhere — he could go up that tree there like a monkey — and I've seen him climb a drainpipe straight up the side of a tall building just like a cat. He's a marvel. You should see him on the tight-rope, too. He can *dance* on it!"

The children gazed at Lou with awe. He felt their glances, looked up and scowled. "Well," thought Julian, "He may be the finest acrobat that ever lived — but he's a jolly nasty-looking fellow. I shouldn't think there's much to chose between him and Tiger Dan!"

Lou got up, uncurling his long body like a cat. He moved easily and softly. He loped over to Nobby, still with the ugly scowl on his face.

"Who are these kids?" he said. "What are they doing messing about here?"

"We're not messing about," said Julian politely. "We came to see Nobby. We've seen him before."

Lou looked at Julian as if he was something that smelt nasty. "Them your caravans?" he asked, jerking his head towards them.

"Yes," said Julian.

"Posh, aren't you?" said Lou sneeringly.

"Not particularly," said Julian, still polite.

"Any grown-ups with you?" asked Lou.

"No. I'm in charge," said Julian, "and we've a dog that flies at people he doesn't like."

Timmy clearly didn't like Lou. He stood near him, growling in his throat. Lou kicked out at him.

George caught hold of Timmy's collar just in time. "Down, Tim, down!" she cried. Then she turned on Lou, her eyes blazing.

"Don't you dare kick my dog!" she shouted. "He'll have you down on the ground if you do. You keep out of his way, or he'll go for you now."

Lou spat on the ground in contempt and turned to go. "You clear out," he said. "We don't want no kids messing about here. And I ain't afraid of no dog. I got ways of dealing with bad dogs."

"What do you mean by that?" yelled George, still in a furious temper. But Lou did not bother to reply. He went up the steps of his caravan and slammed the door shut. Timmy barked angrily and tugged at his collar, which George was still holding firmly.

"*Now* you've torn it!" said Nobby dismally. "If Lou catches you about anywhere he'll hoof you out. And you be careful of that dog of yours, or he'll disappear."

George was angry and alarmed. "*Disappear!* What do you mean? If you think Timmy would let anyone steal him, you're wrong."

"All right, all right. I'm only telling you. Don't fly at me like that!" said Nobby. "Jumping Jiminy, look at that chimp. He's gone inside one of your caravans!"

The sudden storm was forgotten as everyone rushed to the green caravan.

Pongo was inside, helping himself liberally from a tin of sweets. As soon as he saw the children he groaned and covered his face with his paws — but he sucked hard at the sweets all the time.

"Pongo! Bad boy! Come here!" scolded Nobby. "Shall I whip you?"

"Oh, no, don't," begged Anne. "He's a scamp, but I do like him. We've plenty of sweets to spare. You have some, too, Nobby."

"Well, thank you," said Nobby, and helped himself. He grinned round at everyone. "Nice to have friends like you," he said. "Ain't it, Pongo?"

Goofy isn't very clever

"Now, Goofy, if you lose your handkerchief again I shall whip you," his mother said crossly. "It's only Wednesday — and you've lost four hankies already this week."

"Sorry, Ma," said Goofy.

"It's no good being sorry if you keep on doing the same thing," said his mother. "If you're really sorry you won't lose a single hanky again this week!"

"Ma, I won't," said Goofy earnestly. "I really won't, Ma. If I do you can whip me, and take all the money out of my money-box to buy new hankies, and you can send me to bed with nothing to eat but bread. There now — surely that will make you believe I'm really sorry and I mean what I say about not losing any more hankies!"

His mother looked at him. "All right, I believe you, Goofy," she said. "But that's a dreadful lot of punishment you're laying up for yourself! You'd better be very, very careful. Look at your hanky now!"

She gave Goofy an enormous pin.

Goofy looked. It was hanging half out of his pocket, just ready to drop. He stuffed it back, but changed his mind and pulled it right out.

"I'm going to pin it on me, Ma," he said. "Then I can't possibly lose it."

"Well, here's my very biggest safety-pin," said Ma, and she gave Goofy an enormous one. "Now, let me see you pin your hanky on your front."

Goofy solemnly pinned it there. He smacked himself on the chest.

"Now I'm safe! The hanky can't possibly be lost, so don't worry any more, Ma!" And off he went to get the basket to do the shopping.

His mother called after him: "Goofy! Don't forget to put your sun-hat on, now — the sun is blazing down to-day, and you'll get sunstroke again if you go without your hat."

"Right, Ma!" called Goofy, and went to the cupboard for the shopping basket. He came out with it, and carefully put the shopping-list in the bottom of the basket. Oh, Goofy was going to be very, very careful about everything now! He'd show Ma he could be trusted.

He went off down the street. He quite forgot to fetch his sun-hat before he started out! The sun blazed down, tremendously hot. Goofy toiled along, panting.

He met Dame Slow. She called out to him.

He did all the shopping quite well.

"Goofy! What's your mother thinking of to send you out without your sun-hat? You'll get sunstroke again as sure as eggs are eggs!"

Goofy put his hand up to his head. His hair was burning hot! Goodness gracious, he'd forgotten his sun-hat after all! Now he would get sunstroke and feel sick again, and have a dreadful headache!

"I can't go all the way home again to fetch my hat," groaned Goofy. "What can I do?" Then he thought of a splendid idea. "Of course! I'll knot my big hanky at the corners and wear it like a cap! Then I'll be quite all right."

He unpinned the big safety-pin, and took his hanky off his chest. He carefully pinned the safety-pin back again, so that he wouldn't lose it. Then he knotted his hanky at the corners, and made a very nice little cap for himself.

He slipped it over his hot head. Ah — that was better. Now he'd be all right! He went off happily to the shops, feeling very, very clever.

He did all the shopping quite well. Then he set off home again, thinking how pleased his mother would be with him. She might even give him a slice of the new fruit cake!

Now, just as he was going in at the front gate he sneezed.

Whooooosh-oo! He felt for his hanky at once — but, dear me, it wasn't on his chest. Goofy stared down at himself in dismay.

"Now I've gone and lost my hanky again!" he groaned. "How could it have gone? The big safety-pin is still there on my chest — but the hanky isn't. It isn't in my pockets, either. Oh dear, oh dear, it's gone!"

His mother was out. Goofy felt very, very sad. He remembered the punishment he had told his mother she could give him if he lost his hanky.

He put the shopping on the table. He went to the larder and cut himself two slices of dry bread. He took his money box and emptied it out on the kitchen-table and wrote a little ticket beside it. "To buy a new hanky."

Then he climbed slowly upstairs, undressed himself, and put himself to bed.

His mother was most astonished to see him there, with the dry bread beside him, when she came home.

"Oh, Ma!" wept Goofy, "I lost that hanky, I did, I did! Though it was pinned on me too! So I've emptied my money-box, and cut myself some dry bread, and put myself to bed. Now you've got to whip me."

"But, Goofy," said his mother, puzzled. "What's that on your head?"

Goofy put up his hand to his head. He had quite forgotten that he had made himself a sun-hat out of his hanky! He pulled it off, and looked at it joyfully, very red in the face.

"Oh, Ma! I *didn't* lose it! I can get up! I can have my money back! I made a sun-hat of my hanky and then forgot all about it! My, I've been very, very silly."

"I could have told you that long ago," said his mother, laughing. "Get up quickly, Goofy — there's the biggest slice of fruit cake that ever you saw waiting on the kitchen-table for you!"

Well, well, well — some people do peculiar things, don't they?

Goofy put up his hand to his head.

"WHO wants to go twigging?" said Uncle Nat.

"What's twigging?" asked Mary.

"Finding out how many twigs you know," said Uncle Nat. "We'll bring a whole lot home and see if you can name them. Anyone who knows them can have sixpence. Anyone knowing less than six can give *me* sixpence!"

"Well, I'm sure I don't know six," said Mary. "Still, I'll try. We'll collect the twigs from trees and bring them home to name them."

So they all set off. They broke little twigs, set with buds, from most of the trees they came to. Mary looked at them. She thought she only knew about two.

"Twigs look much the same on the trees, but they are different when you look at them closely, in a bunch like this," she said. "There are black buds and red buds, brown ones, sharp ones and blunt ones, and even sticky ones."

"I believe I know quite a lot," said Peter. "Haven't we enough, Uncle Nat? Do you know them all?"

"Of course," said Uncle Nat. "But then I've had many more years to use my eyes than you have."

"I know lots of people older than you who have seen trees every single day of their lives and don't know which is an oak and which is an ash; I mean to know them all soon," said Mary.

The twigs were arranged in a vase. "Now," said Uncle Nat, "as long as you know six common ones I shall be pleased. That is a good beginning. You can add others as the days go on."

"We *both* know this one," said Mary, and took from the vase a fat, brown twig with very sticky buds. "It's the horse-chestnut. Its buds are always sticky."

"One," said Uncle Nat. "Next, please,"

"We know this one too," said Peter, and pulled out a slender twig, set with long thin buds so sharp that they pricked. "It's a beech twig. The buds are always very long and sharp and pointed."

"Two," said Uncle Nat. "Next one?"

"Well, we know this one because it has a green catkin on it," said Mary. "It's a hazel twig."

"Three," said Uncle Nat. "Another one?"

"We know this one, because it has hard, very black buds," said Peter, and he pulled a grey, sturdy twig from the vase. "It's an ash twig. Its buds are always black."

"Good," said Uncle Nat. "Four. Which is the fifth?"

"We know the oak," said Mary, and she took out an untidy-looking twig, set with clusters of buds of all sizes. "The oak buds are always set higgledy-piggledy anywhere on the twig."

"And the sixth?" said Uncle Nat, rattling the money in his pocket.

That was a puzzler. The children stared at the twigs. Did they know any more?

"Yes," said Peter. "Look — a lime-tree twig, Mary. Don't you remember, it has red buds. We can tell it by that."

"Well done," said Uncle Nat. "Sixpence for each of you. You've begun your twigging quite well!"

(Do you know six common twigs? See if you can find the ones in this story.)

"Mam'zelle's Treek"

An extract from another of Enid Blyton's "Malory Towers" school stories, IN THE FIFTH AT MALORY TOWERS. Mam'zelle is very gullible and the girls often play tricks on her, and take her in beautifully. They have dared her to play one on them, but this she didn't dream of doing until one day —

MAM'ZELLE sat down at her desk in Miss Potts' room, and announced her intention of turning it out.

"About time too," said Miss Potts, drily. I never saw such a collection of rubbish in anyone's desk in my life."

"Ha, Miss Potts! You wish to be funny?" said Mam'zelle, huffily.

"No," said Miss Potts. "Merely truthful."

Mam'zelle snorted, and took hold of about a hundred loose papers in her desk. She lifted them out and they immediately fell apart and slithered all over the floor. One leaflet floated to Miss Potts' feet. She looked at it with interest, for there was a brightly coloured picture on the cover, showing a conjurer doing tricks. "New tricks. Old tricks. Tricks to play on your enemies. Tricks to play on your friends," she read out loud.

She glanced at Mam'zelle in astonishment. "Since when did you think of taking up tricks to play?" she inquired.

"I do not think of it," said Mam'zelle, depositing another hundred papers on the floor. "*Tiens!* Here is the programme of the play the third-formers gave six years ago!"

"What did I tell you?" said Miss Potts. "You'll probably find the Speeches made at the Opening of the First Term at Malory Towers if you look a little further into your desk."

"Do not tizz me," said Mam'zelle. "I do not like being tizzed."

"I'm not teasing," said Miss Potts. "I'm quite serious. I say — *where* did you get these trick and conjuring lists from? Look at this one — I'm sure it has in it all the tricks that Alicia and Betty ever played on you!"

Mam'zelle took the booklets. She was soon completely absorbed in them. She chuckled. She laughed. She said "*Tiens!*" and "Oh, *là là!*" a dozen times. Miss Potts went on with her work. She was used to Mam'zelle's little ways.

Mam'zelle had never read anything so enthralling in all her life as these booklets that described tricks of all sorts and kinds. She was completely lost in them. She read of machines that could apparently saw people's fingers in half without hurting them — cigarettes with glowing ends that were not really alight — ink spots and jam-clots that could be placed on tablecloths to deceive annoyed mothers or teachers into thinking they were real.

Mam'zelle was absolutely fascinated. She came to one trick that made her laugh out loud. "Ah, now listen, Miss Potts," she began.

"*No*, Mam'zelle," said Miss Potts, sternly. "I've twenty-three *disgraceful* maths papers to mark that the first form have had the nerve to give in today — and I do NOT want to listen to your recital of childish tricks."

Mam'zelle sighed and went back to the booklets. She read over again the pages that had so intrigued her. There were two photographs with the description of the trick. One showed a smiling man with ordinary teeth — the other showed the same man — with trick teeth! He looked horrible.

Mam'zelle read the description over again. "These trick teeth are cleverly made of celluloid, and are shaped to fit neatly over the wearer's own teeth — but project forwards and downwards, and so alter the expression of the wearer's face considerably as soon as he smiles, giving a really terrifying and strange appearance."

Mam'zelle studied the photographs. She tried to imagine herself wearing teeth like that — and suddenly flashing them at the girls with a smile. Ha! They had dared her to do a trick on them!

Mam'zelle had a very very good mind to write for this teeth trick.

Mam'zelle shook with laughter. Ha ha — so many "treeks" had those bad girls played on her, it was time their poor old Mam'zelle played a "treek" on them too.

Mam'zelle scuffled about among her untidy papers and found her writing-pad. In her slanting French handwriting she wrote for the "teeth trick" and sent a cheque with the letter. She was delighted. She would not tell even Miss Potts.

"No, I will not tell her. I will suddenly smile at her — like this," said Mam'zelle to herself — and gave a sudden fierce grin — "and I shall look so strange that she will start back in fright at my horrible teeth."

(Mam'zelle had no chance of playing her trick for a week — but the teeth finally arrived by post on the day of the House Match. Mam'zelle went temporarily mad, and played her trick all too successfully!)

Ah, those teeth! Mam'zelle had tried them on. They might have been made for her! They fitted over her own teeth, but were longer, and projected slightly forward. They were not noticeable at all, of course, when she had her mouth shut — but when she smiled — ah, how sinister she looked, how strange, how fierce!

Mam'zelle had shocked even herself when she had put in the extraordinary teeth and smiled at herself in the glass. "*Tiens!*" she said, and clutched her dressing-table. "I am a monster! I am truly terrible with these teeth . . ."

That afternoon she put them in carefully over her own teeth and went downstairs to the playing-fields, wrapping herself up warmly in coat, scarf and turban. Darrell saw her first, and made room for her on the form she was on.

"Thank you," said Mam'zelle, and smiled at Darrell. Darrell had a tremendous shock. Mam'zelle had suddenly looked altogether different — quite terrifying. Darrell stared at her — but Mam'zelle had quickly shut her mouth.

The next one to get the Smile was little Felicity who came up with Susan.

"Oh!" said Felicity in sudden horror, and Susan stared in alarm. Mam'zelle shut her mouth. A desire to laugh was suddenly working up inside her. No, no — she must not laugh. Laughing spoilt tricks.

She did not smile for some time, trying to conquer her urge to laugh. Miss Linnie, the sewing-mistress, passed by and nodded at Mam'zelle. Mam'zelle could not resist showing her the teeth. She smiled.

Miss Linnie looked amazed and horrified. She walked on quickly. "Was that really Mam'zelle?" she wondered. "No, it must have been someone else. What awful teeth!"

Mam'zelle felt that she must get up and walk about. It was too cold to sit — and besides she so badly wanted to laugh again. Ah, now she understood why the girls laughed so much and so helplessly when they played their mischievous tricks on her.

She walked along the field and met Bill and Clarissa. They smiled at her and she smiled back. Bill stood still, thunderstruck. Clarissa hadn't really noticed.

"Clarissa!" said Bill, when Mam'zelle had gone. "What's the matter with Mam'zelle this afternoon? She looks *horrible!*"

"Horrible? How?" asked Clarissa.

"Well, her *teeth!* Didn't you see her teeth?" asked Bill. "They seem to have changed or something. Simply awful teeth she had — long and sticking-out."

Clarissa was astonished. "Let's walk back and smile at her again," she said. So back they went. But Mam'zelle saw their inquisitive looks, and was struggling against a fit of laughter. She would not open her mouth to smile.

Matron came up. "Oh, Mam'zelle — do you know where Gwen is? She's darned her navy gym pants with grey wool again. I want her indoors this afternoon!"

Mam'zelle simply could not resist smiling at Matron. Matron stared as if she couldn't believe her eyes. Mam'zelle shut her mouth. Matron backed away a little, looking rather alarmed.

"Gwen's over there," said Mam'zelle, her extra teeth making her words sound rather thick. Matron looked even more alarmed at the thick voice and disappeared in a hurry. Mam'zelle saw her address a few words to Miss Potts.

"Aha!" thought Mam'zelle, "Matron has told her I look terrible! Now Miss Potts will come to look at my smile. I shall laugh. I know I shall. Soon I shall laugh without stopping!"

Miss Potts came up, eyeing Mam'zelle carefully. She was given a quick glimpse of the famous teeth. Then Mam'zelle clamped her mouth shut. She would explode if she didn't keep her mouth closed! She pulled her scarf across her face, trying to hide her desire to laugh.

"Do you feel the cold today, Mam'zelle?" asked Miss Potts anxiously. "You — er — you haven't got toothache, have you?"

A peculiar wild sound came from Mam'zelle. It startled Miss Potts considerably, but actually it was only Mam'zelle trying to stifle a squeal of laughter. She rushed away hurriedly and Miss Potts stared after her uncomfortably.

Mam'zelle strolled down the field by herself, trying to recover. She gave a few loud gulps that made two second-formers wonder if she was going to be ill.

Poor Mam'zelle felt she couldn't flash her teeth at anyone for a long time, for if she did she would explode like Irene! She decided to go in. She turned her steps towards the school — and then, to her utter horror, she saw Miss Grayling bearing down on her with two parents!

"Oh — there's Mam'zelle," said Miss Grayling's pleasant voice. "Mam'zelle, will you meet Mrs. Jennings and Mrs. Petton?"

Mam'zelle was forced to go to them. She lost all desire for laughter at once. The trick teeth suddenly stopped being funny, and became monstrosities to be got rid of at once. But how? She couldn't spit them into her handkerchief when people were just about to shake hands with her!

Mrs. Jennings held out her hand. "I've heard so much about you, Mam'zelle Dupont," she said, "and what tricks the naughty girls play on you, too!"

Mam'zelle smiled. The fifth-formers got a shock.

Mam'zelle tried to smile without opening her mouth at all, and the effect was rather peculiar — a sort of suppressed snarl. Mrs. Jennings looked surprised. Mam'zelle tried to make up for her lack of smile by shaking Mrs. Jennings' hand very vigorously indeed.

She did the same with Mrs. Petton, who turned out to be a talkative mother who wanted to know *exactly* how her daughter Teresa was getting on in French. She smiled gaily at Mam'zelle while she talked, and Mam'zelle found it agony not to smile back. She had to produce the suppressed snarl again, smiling with her mouth shut and her lips firmly over her teeth.

Miss Grayling was startled by this peculiar

smile. She examined Mam'zelle closely. Mam'-zelle's voice was not quite as usual either — it sounded thick. "As if her mouth is too full of teeth," thought Miss Grayling, little knowing that she had hit on the exact truth.

At last the mothers went. Mam'zelle shook hands with them most vigorously once more, and was so relieved at parting from them that she forgot herself and gave them a broad smile.

They received a full view of the terrible teeth, Miss Grayling too. The head stared in the utmost horror — *what* had happened to Mam'zelle's teeth? Had she had her old ones out — were these a new, false set? But how TERRIBLE they were! They made her look like the wolf in the tale of little Red Riding Hood.

The two mothers turned their heads away quickly at the sight of the teeth. They hurried off with Miss Grayling who hardly heard a word they said, because she was so concerned about Mam'zelle's teeth. She determined to send for Mam'zelle that evening and ask her about them.

Mam'zelle was so thankful to see the last of the mothers that she walked straight into a little company of fifth-formers going back to the school, some to do their piano practice and some to have a lesson in elocution.

"Hallo, Mam'zelle!" said Mavis. "Are you coming back to school?"

Mam'zelle smiled. The fifth-formers got a dreadful shock. They stared in silent horror. The teeth had slipped a little, and now looked rather like fangs. They gave Mam'zelle a most sinister, big-bad-wolf look. Mam'zelle saw their alarm and astonishment. Laughter surged back into her. She felt it swelling up and up. She gasped. She gulped. She roared.

She sank on to a bench and cried with helpless laughter. She remembered Matron's face — and Miss Grayling's — and the faces of the two mothers. The more she thought of them the more helplessly she laughed. The girls stood round, more alarmed than ever. What was the matter with Mam'zelle? What was this enormous joke?

Mam'zelle's teeth slipped out altogether, fell on to her lap, and then to the ground. The girls stared at them in the utmost amazement, and then looked at Mam'zelle. She now looked completely normal, with just her own small teeth showing in her laughing face.

"It is a treek," she squeaked at last, wiping her eyes with her handkerchief. "Did you not give me a dare? Did you not tell me to do a treek on you? I have done one with the teeth. They are treek teeth. Oh, *là là* — I must laugh again. Oh my sides, oh my back!"

She swayed to and fro, laughing. The girls began to laugh, too. Mam'zelle Rougier came up, astonished to see the other French mistress laughing so much.

"What is the matter?" she asked, without a smile on her face.

Irene exploded into laughter. She pointed to the teeth on the ground. "Mam'zelle wore them for a trick — and they've fallen out and given the game away!"

She went off into squeals of laughter again, and the other girls joined in. Mam'zelle Rougier looked cold and disapproving.

"I see no joke," she said. "It is not funny, teeth on the grass. It is time to see the lentist when such things happen."

She walked off, and her speech and disapproving face sent everyone into fits of laughter again. It was altogether a most successful afternoon for Mam'zelle, and the "treek" story flew all through the school immediately.

Mam'zelle suddenly found herself extremely popular, except with the staff. "A little *undignified*, don't you think?" said Miss Williams.

"Not a thing to do *too* often, Mam'zelle," said Miss Potts, making up her mind to remove the trick booklets from Mam'zelle's desk at the first opportunity.

But the girls loved Mam'zelle for her "treek", and every class in the school, from top to bottom, worked twice as hard (or so Mam'zelle declared) after she had played her truly astonishing "treek"!

A Bunch of Flowers

IT was a dull November day. The four children were gathered round the fire. They had been playing games and reading, and now they felt rather bored.

"What about a quiz?" said Richard. "Would your mother come and give us another, Jack?"

"We'll see," said Jack, and he went to find his mother. She soon came along with her knitting, and sat down close to them.

"So you want another quiz?" she said. "Well let's do it differently this time. We'll have a Common Flower quiz, shall we — but we'll *each* take it in turn to describe one, instead of only me."

"Oh yes — we'll do it that way," said Joan. "But don't let's have *very*, very common flowers, Mrs. Robins — they'll be too easy. Let's choose some that everybody *ought* to know."

"Right. We'll leave out buttercups, daisies, violets, primroses, thistles and dandelions," said Mrs. Robins. "Everyone knows those, I should think. Now — I'll begin, shall I? You can find this flower in February or March, growing in big patches. It has eight glossy golden petals and . . ."

"Buttercup," said Richard, without thinking.

"*Eight* petals — and early spring — and anyway we've ruled out buttercups," said Mrs. Robins. "Do *listen*, Richard. Eight glossy golden petals, and heart-shaped leaves."

"Celandine, of course!" said Alice at once. "Now my turn, as I guessed. *I'm* thinking of another yellow flower, a little like a tiny dandelion. It has scaly stalks, a bit woolly."

"What are its leaves like?" asked Joan.

"Hasn't got any," said Alice, promptly.

"But it *must* have," said Jack. "Don't be silly."

"I'm not. I've never found any when I picked the flower," said Alice.

"Ah, I know!" said Mrs. Robins. "You mean the little yellow coltsfoot, Alice. It has no leaves when the flowers are out. They come later. That was a good flower to choose."

"Now you again, Mother," said Joan.

"Well, now here's a flower with no *petals*,"

TANSY
GERMANDER SPEEDWELL
GARLIC MUSTARD
WILD ARUM
IVY
F
DOG'S MERCURY
M
COLT'S-FOOT

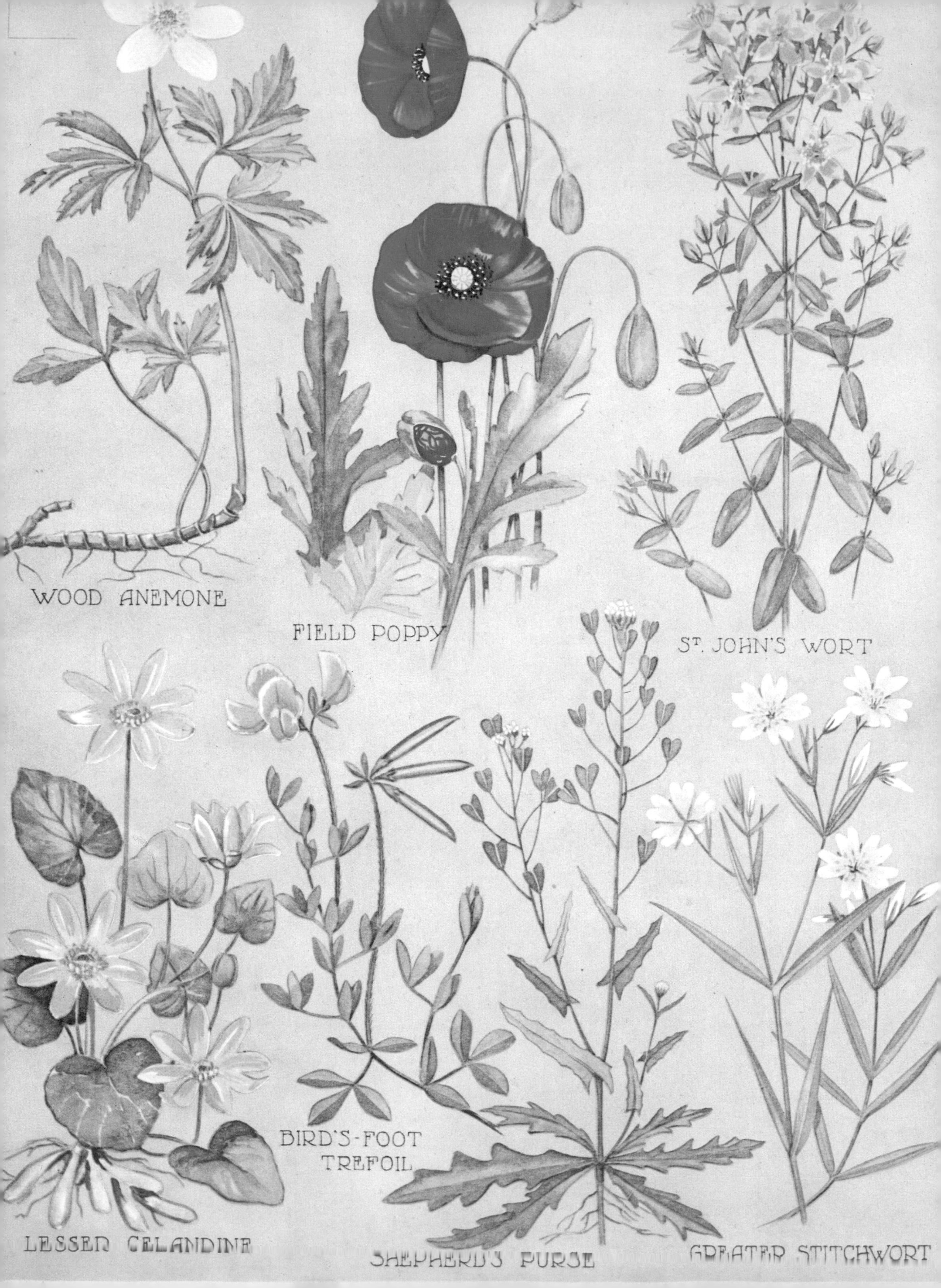
WOOD ANEMONE
FIELD POPPY
ST. JOHN'S WORT
BIRD'S-FOOT TREFOIL
LESSER CELANDINE
SHEPHERD'S PURSE
GREATER STITCHWORT

said Mother. "And yet it looks exactly as if it had six lovely white petals, tinged with pink or purple. It dances in the April woods."

"Funny!" said Richard. "A flower without petals that looks as if it had some. What does it have then?"

"It has taken its sepals and turned them into petals," said Mrs. Robins. "And it dances so beautifully in the wind."

"*Wind*-flower!" cried the girls.

"Wood anemone!" yelled Jack.

"Both of you are right," said his mother. "You can have a turn, Alice."

"My flower is very common," said Alice, beaming. "It grows all the year round. It has tiny white flowers at the top of a spike, but you'll see its seed-vessels better than its flowers, because they're set all the way down the stalk."

"Gracious — what can it be?" wondered Jack. "What shape are the seed-vessels?"

"Like little purses, or wallets," said Alice, and that made Jack call out the name.

"Shepherd's Purse, of course! Now it's my turn. My flower is a very common one too. It has green flowers in strings, and you can find it in February or March."

"*Green* flowers? Do you mean the nettle?" asked Alice.

"Wrong," said Jack. "The nettle doesn't flower in February or March, silly."

"Oh, I know — what is it now — it's Dog's Mercury!" cried Joan, and everyone clapped.

"Good," said Mrs. Robins. "It's certainly a very common flower, but not one that people notice very much. Your turn, Joan."

"A brilliant blue flower, with four small petals and a tiny middle like a white eye," said Joan. Richard gave a shout.

"Speedwell, speedwell."

"Which one?" asked Joan.

"Germander," said Richard, feeling very clever. "Now my turn. I'm thinking of a queer plant with a title, and . . ."

"With a *title* — what do you mean, silly?" said Jack.

"With a title, and a tongue in the middle of a green hood," said Richard. "The leaves are arrow-shaped and have purple blotches on them."

"Oh — I know — the Common Arum," said Mrs. Robins. "But what do you mean — a plant with a *title*?"

"Well, it's called Lords and Ladies, isn't it?" said Richard, triumphantly. "Very titled!"

"Idiot," said everyone. "Your turn, Mother."

"Well, here's a pretty little flower for you to guess. It's found all along the hedge-side in spring. It has five notched petals, and a dainty head hanging from a thread-like stalk. Its stem is very weak indeed."

Silence. What could it be? Nobody could guess.

"It gets its name from the thread-like stalk its head hangs on," said Mrs. Robins, "as thin as a stitch of cotton."

"Oh — Stitchwort!" cried Alice. "Of course. Hurrah — my turn now! My flower has clusters of tiny white four-petalled blossoms at the top of its tall stalk."

"Shepherd's purse," said Richard at once.

"We've *had* that," said Alice.

"Well, you might give us a bit more help," said Richard. "You haven't told us much."

"All right. It has large heart-shaped leaves — and when you crush them in your hand they smell of garlic," said Alice.

"Garlic-Mustard!" cried Jack.

"Jack-by-the-Hedge!" cried the rest.

"Quite right," said Alice. "Jack, you said the most correct name. You choose now."

"Well, I'm thinking of a frothy, lacy plant that fills the hedges in June," said Jack. "It has very tiny white flowers growing on thin green spokes like the ribs of an umbrella."

"Goodness!" said Alice, "do you mean Hedge Parsley by any chance?"

"I do," said Jack. "Jolly good, Alice."

"My turn," said Alice, thinking hard. "Well, what's *this* flower? It wears a green hat before it's out, but it throws it off. It has four

silky petals and lots of black-headed stamens."

"What colour is it?" asked Jack.

"Scarlet," said Alice.

"Poppy!" shouted Richard, deafening everyone. "Good — my turn. I'll give you a teaser! What has clusters of sweet-pea-shaped flowers with red streaks, and leaflets in fives?"

"Fives? Then it can't be one of the trefoils," said Alice, "because *their* leaflets are in threes. And yet it *sounds* like one."

"What are its seed-pods like?" asked Mrs. Robins, suddenly.

"Well — they're rather like a bird's foot," said Richard, grinning.

"Oh, Richard — it's Bird's-foot Trefoil, of course," said Mrs. Robins. "And you're perfectly right, the leaflets *are* in fives not threes. How clever of you to have noticed that. You nearly beat us there."

"Your turn, Mother," said Alice.

"Well — I'm thinking of a plant that is just like a collection of little yellow buttons," said Mrs. Robins. "In fact it looks as if someone had pulled all its petals off, leaving just the round yellow middles. Its leaves look rather ferny."

"Do you mean the Tansy?" asked Joan, thinking hard. "That's the only flower I can think of that seems to have no petals and is button-shaped."

"Quite right, Joan," said Mrs. Robins. "Now you think of one."

"Mine's a yellow flower too," said Joan, "rather showy and handsome. Its petals are pale yellow and open into a starry-shaped flower."

"That's *really* not enough description, is it Mother?" said Jack. "We can't guess it from that. There are so many yellow flowers."

"Well — I'll give you a bit more help then," said Joan. "If you hold up the leaves to the light you will see there are little clear dots all over them."

"Oh, now I know," said Mrs. Robins, though nobody else did. "St. John's Wort, Joan. You can always tell it by holding up the leaves."

"Good, Mrs. Robins," said Joan. "We just can't beat *you*."

"A very pretty flower comes to my mind," said Mrs. Robins. "You'll find it in summer-time. It has bright blue flowers, really vivid, with a ring of strap-shaped petals. Its stem is very, very tough."

"Bluebell," said Richard. The others booed him. "How *can* it be, silly? Mother said strap-shaped petals and a *tough* stem!"

"Chicory, chicory, chicory!" chanted Joan, and chicory it was. "Now I've got a good one for you. It flowers as the winter comes on, in big clusters of greeny-yellow."

Nobody could think what it was. "Flowers as the *winter* comes on — no plant does that, surely," said Richard. "What shape are its leaves?"

"Ivy-shaped," said Joan, without thinking, and then everyone roared with laughter, and yelled out the name. "Ivy, of course!"

"Whose turn now?" said Richard. "We all shouted together."

"I think we'll stop," said Mrs. Robins. "It's tea-time. Come along and sit down at the table and I'll give you a little tea-time quiz. I'm thinking of something white and greasy, that wants spreading with something yellow and sticky, and . . ."

"Bread and butter and honey!" shouted the children and sat down at the table. "Lovely!"

"I'm thinking of something pretty and nice and good enough to eat," said Richard, suddenly. "It's got eyes rather like speedwell's and it makes very nice noises. And its name makes you think it belongs to the bird family. What is it?"

"Sounds quite mad to me," said Joan, putting honey on her bread. "Pretty and nice and good enough to eat — and has blue eyes — and a nice voice . . ."

"And its name makes you think it belongs to the *bird* family! Richard, what is it?"

"Do you give it up?" said Richard, and everyone said "Yes." "Though it's the first quiz we *have* given up," said Joan. "And mind you, Richard, if it's a silly make-up we'll jolly well kick you out."

"Well, I'll tell you what's pretty and nice and good enough to eat and all the rest of it," said Richard, with his wide grin. "It's *Mrs. Robins* and I bet you won't kick me out for *that* quiz!"

And they didn't of course. In fact, Mrs. Robins said it was quite the nicest one she had heard!

MR. GOON IS ASTOUNDED

From THE MYSTERY OF THE STRANGE BUNDLE, which is the tenth adventure of the Five Find-Outers and Dog. Fatty and the other Find-Outers have come to a house called "The Cedars" to see if they can discover something about a burglary there — and while they are at the house, Mr. Goon the village policeman also arrives, discovers the children there, and is very angry. Fatty decides to try his powers of ventriloquism on the policeman.

"Now then, you kids! What are you doing here? Clear orf!"

ALMOST before Fatty had had time to get downstairs there came the sound of Goon's angry voice.

"Now then, you kids! What are you doing here? Clear off!"

Then came the sound of Buster's barking. Fatty grinned. How many, many times had this same scene been acted — the Find-Outers snooping round — Goon finding them — ordering them off — and Buster objecting loudly! Well — Buster could certainly look after not only himself but all the children too!

Fatty wondered whether he could slip out of the front door. He could hear that Mr. Goon was round at the back.

"Interfering with the Law!" he heard, in the policeman's angry voice. "Poking your noses in! What's it to do with you, I'd like to know. Clear off!"

"Well, we live just close by," said Larry. "It's naturally interesting to us — to Daisy and me I mean. If burglars are in the district I want to get some information in case they come to rob our house too, next door but one."

"Gah!" said Goon disbelievingly. "Tommy-rot! Just an excuse for interfering. This here job's a potty little job — no mystery in it at all. Not worth your notice, see? And take that dog away before I lose my temper with him. Nasty yappy little mongrel!"

Fatty longed to be out there with the others. Calling Buster a *mongrel*! Why, the little Scottie had a pedigree a yard long, and all his grand-parents had been champions. Fatty boiled with rage. He tiptoed to the front door. He didn't want Mr. Goon to catch him in the house, even though he had the perfectly good excuse to offer of rescuing the kitten.

"Where's that fat boy?" demanded Mr. Goon, suddenly realising that Fatty was absent. "Still in bed with the 'flu', I hope. Best place for him, too. Hope he gets a relapse! WILL you call this dog off?"

Larry called Buster. "Buster, come here. I can find some better ankles for you if you want some."

Mr. Goon snorted. That was one of the things he did remarkably well. "Go on out of this garden, all of you," he said. "Any more messing about here and I'll report you. Yes, and I'll go round to your parents again, too — specially yours, Master Philip Hilton!"

Pip hastily removed himself from the garden of the little house, taking Bets with him. He didn't want Goon to make any more complaints to his parents. They had a habit of taking Mr. Goon seriously! Larry and Daisy followed, Larry holding Buster by the collar. They stood outside the front gate, wondering what Fatty was going to do.

Fatty was most unfortunate. He opened the front door from inside at exactly the same moment that Mr. Goon unlocked it from the outside. Mr. Goon stared at Fatty as if a thunderbolt had hit him. His mouth fell open and he went a familiar purple colour. He swallowed hard.

"Good morning, Mr. Goon," said Fatty, smoothly. "Do come in. I'll shut the door for you."

Mr. Goon stepped in, still wordless. Then he exploded into speech.

"What are you doing here? HERE, in this house that's under police supervision. You want to get locked up, I suppose — Being Found on Enclosed Premises, and up to no good, I'll be bound! HO!"

Fatty stepped back out of range of Mr. Goon's explosions. "I heard a kitten mewing here," he said, still politely. "And being a subscriber to the R.S.P.C.A. — if you know what that means, Mr. Goon — I naturally had to come into the house to find it."

"Pah!" said Mr. Goon disbelievingly. "This here house is habsolutely hempty! I've been through it meself with a tooth-comb already!"

"This 'ere 'ouse hisn't habsolutely hempty," said Fatty. "Dear me, I seem to be getting muddled. Hark, Mr. Goon — can't you hear the kitten mewing now?"

"Miaow!" said the kitten, and obligingly crept out from under the hall-stand. It went to Fatty and rubbed affectionately against his legs. Then it looked at Mr. Goon, hissed at him and spat.

"Most intelligent behaviour," observed Fatty. "I hope you believe in the kitten now, Mr. Goon."

Mr. Goon did. He had to. "Take it away and take yourself off too," he said to Fatty. "I've work to do here. And Keep Out of This, see?"

"You'll be careful of the dog here, won't you, Mr. Goon," said Fatty. "I'm not quite sure where it is — you may possibly hear it growling somewhere, and trace it by that."

"There's no dog here," said Mr. Goon, stalking past Fatty. "A kitten I might have missed, being so small-like, but not a dog. What do you take me for?"

"It would be better not to tell you," murmured Fatty. "Not here, anyway."

He was just behind the policeman, and it was as well for Mr. Goon that he couldn't see the innocent expression on Fatty's face — a look that all his form-masters knew only too well.

A blood-curdling growl suddenly came from somewhere in the house. Mr. Goon stopped as if he had been shot. "What's that?" he said.

"Sounded like the dog," said Fatty. "What a horrible animal it must be. I think I'll go, Mr. Goon, and leave you to tackle him."

Another growl came from somewhere, and the policeman took two hurried steps backwards, treading heavily on Fatty's foot.

"Ouch!" said Fatty. "Look out where you're going if you want to walk backwards, Mr. Goon! Well — good-bye — I'll leave you now."

"You come and help me find that dog," said Mr. Goon, changing his mind completely about wanting Fatty to clear off. "It might want two of us to get him. Funny I didn't see him or hear him when I was here before this morning."

Fatty grinned behind Mr. Goon's broad back. He debated whether to produce another animal-noise. This ventriloquism was Most Useful!

"All right, Mr. Goon," he said. "If you think it's my duty to stay and help you, I will. I'm always around when Duty Calls, you know."

Mr. Goon was very thankful. He began to tiptoe forward into the little dining-room. Fatty followed a few paces behind. He suddenly gave a shout that made Mr. Goon nearly fall over backwards.

"Look, look — what's that — over there! LOOK OUT!"

Mr. Goon was so anxious to get out as well as to look out that he almost fell over Fatty, as he tried to rush out of the room. Fatty clutched him as he went.

"It's all right! It's all right! I just caught sight of you in that mirror over there, Mr. Goon, and it was such a dreadful sight I thought it must be someone lying in wait for us. Gosh, thank goodness it was only your reflection!"

Mr. Goon was very angry and very relieved. He glared at Fatty. "Any more of this funny business," he began, and then stopped suddenly.

From somewhere behind came the sound of heavy grunting. Mr. Goon swung round at once. "Did you hear that?" he asked Fatty, breathlessly. "That grunting noise. What was it? It sounded out there in the hall."

"Yes, it did," said Fatty, clutching at Mr. Goon's arm and making him jump again. "You go first, Mr. Goon. I'm scared."

So was Mr. Goon. He tiptoed into the hall and promptly fell over the kitten which made a dart at him as soon as he appeared. He retreated into the dining-room again, bumping into Fatty. The grunting noise was heard once more, this time sounding farther off.

"It's a pig!" said Mr. Goon, hardly able to believe his ears. "Sounded upstairs that time. Did you think it was a pig, Master Frederick?"

The more frightened and puzzled Mr. Goon became, the more polite he was. At this rate, thought Fatty, he'll soon be bowing to me every time he speaks! He badly wanted to laugh, but he firmly thrust down the ever-mounting guffaw that wanted to rise up and explode.

"What sort of a fellow was it who lived here, Mr. Goon?" asked Fatty innocently. "Was he fond of animals? He seems to have kept kittens, and dogs, and pigs, anyway."

"How was it I didn't see the pig when I was here this morning," marvelled Mr. Goon. "I turned everything over and looked everywhere for clues. And yet I didn't see the dog or the pig. Shall we go upstairs to find the pig?"

"Yes. But be careful the dog doesn't rush out at you," said Fatty. "You go first, Mr. Goon."

Mr. Goon didn't want to go first. He pushed Fatty in front of him, and then immediately wished he hadn't because a deep and ferocious growl came from somewhere behind him. Fatty was certainly practising his new talent well!

And then a new sound came to worry poor Mr. Goon. A voice came from somewhere, a groaning voice that said:

"I never did it, I never! Ooooooh! I never did it! Where's my auntie?"

Goon listened, petrified. He began to feel as if he was in a nightmare. He whispered to Fatty.

Fatty opened the front door at exactly the same moment.

Goon stumbled to the telephone and dialled a number.

"There's a man here somewhere! This beats all! We'd better get help. I'm not going to snoop round here with dogs, and pigs, and a man groaning. What's been happening since I was here this morning?"

"Look, you stay here, Mr. Goon, and I'll go and get help," said Fatty, and moved firmly into the hall. But Mr. Goon clutched at him.

"No, don't leave me here alone. Can't *you* stay while I get help?"

"Remember your duty, Mr. Goon," said Fatty, solemnly. "There is Something Queer here, and it's your duty to examine it. But it's not *my* duty. I'll go and get help. Good-bye!"

Goon held on to him tightly, and then the Voice began again. "I never did it, I never! Ooooooh! I never did it! Where's my auntie?"

Goon began to shake. "What's he mean, talking about his auntie?" he whispered. "Come on, let's go! This is a mad-house, this is."

"Mr. Goon — why not telephone for help!" said Fatty, suddenly catching sight of the telephone in the hall. "You'd get someone here in a trice then."

Mr. Goon was so relieved at this bright idea of Fatty's that he almost embraced him. He stumbled to the telephone and dialled a number.

Fatty heard him telephoning to another constable. He tiptoed silently out of the front door, grinning as he heard Goon's agonised voice.

"Send someone up here at once. There's a fierce dog in the house — and a pig — yes, I said a pig — P-I-G. Yes, PIG, you ass. And a groaning man who wants his auntie. AUNTIE! Yes, I did say Auntie. Are you deaf, or something? Well, how do *I* know why he wants his Auntie? No, I'm not daft, but I soon shall be if you don't send someone to this address at once. Yes, I do want help — YES, there IS a dog here — and a pig — and an Auntie — no, not an Auntie, but a man who wants one. Oh, and there's a kitten. I forgot to mention that."

There was a pause as Goon listened to a few remarks from the other end of the telephone. He spluttered into it again.

"Any more sauce from you, Kenton, and I'll report you. I'm NOT having a joke with you. You come up here at once. AT ONCE, do you hear?"

Fatty heard all this, and felt that he really must go somewhere and laugh. He tiptoed round to the back of the house where there was a shed he could go into and laugh in peace. He saw the broken casement window, hanging open, as he passed. He thrust his head inside, and sent a terrible growl into the house.

Mr. Goon heard it. He looked round, and found that Fatty had gone. He was alone — alone in the house with a host of terrifying things. It was too much for Goon. He fled at top speed out of the front door, and didn't stop running till he came to the bottom of the road.

Fatty heard him go. And then he laughed. How he laughed! It really was the best laugh Fatty had ever had in all his life!

FOXGLOVE Fairies

Some fairies came half-running, half-flying round by the foxgloves in the wood. The foxgloves were much taller than they were, and the fairies stopped to look at them.

"See!" said Winks, bending down to pick up a fallen foxglove bell. "Wouldn't this do beautifully for a glove-finger! We could sew five together and make some lovely gloves for the little folk, couldn't we? Do let's."

"The foxgloves might not want us to take their fallen flowers," said Pippi.

"Well, we'll ask them," said Chatter. So she called up to the dreaming foxgloves.

"Foxgloves, are you awake? Listen! Can we take your fallen flower-bells to make gloves with?"

"What will you give us in return?" asked the foxgloves.

"What would you like?" said Winks.

"Well, I suppose you couldn't tell us how to stop the tiny insects and small flies from climbing into our bells and stealing our honey, could you?" asked the foxgloves. "You see, the only visitors we want are the bumble-bees, but so many smaller insects come and steal what we store for the big bumbles."

"We'll think about it," said the fairies. So they did, and, of course, they knew what to do at once.

"Can you grow a little mat of hairs at the entrance to your bells?" said Winks. "That would keep out the tiny flies, wouldn't it, for the hairs would seem like a great forest to them!"

"A good idea!" said the foxgloves. "We will do that. But then the bumble-bees might not see the way up our bells!"

"Well, grow some nice bright coloured spots all the way up to the honey," said the fairies. "Then the bees will see them and follow them like a path. We'll tell the bumbles you put them there."

"Thank you!" said the foxgloves, and they grew mats of hair at the entrance of their bells, and put a coloured pathway of spots leading to their honey.

"We'll measure you and see if you are exactly the right size to take a bumble-bee's body," said Winks, and she whipped out her little tape-measure. First she measured a foxglove bell, and then she measured a fat bumble-bee, who was one of her friends.

"Your bells need to be just a tiny bit bigger!" she cried, and the foxgloves nodded in reply.

"Thank you," they said. "Now we shall keep our honey safely! The hairs will keep out the smaller insects, the spots will guide the bumbles, and they will be able to squeeze in nicely, for our bells will be made to fit them! Take as many of the fallen bells as you like, fairies, and make gloves for the little folk from them!"

That's how the foxglove got its name; it is really called folk's glove, not foxglove. Did you know that? And would you like to see the mat of hairs and the pretty pathway of spots put there for the bumble-bees? Well, you go and see!

BIRDS AND FLOWERS IN APRIL

A chapter from Enid Blyton's NATURE LOVER'S BOOK, which tells of one of the walks that Uncle Merry took John, Pat and Janet.

ONE morning Uncle Merry saw three excited children rushing through his garden gate. He leaned out of his window and waved.

"Uncle Merry! We've heard the cuckoo! We've heard the cuckoo! We've heard the cuckoo!" called Pat in excitement.

"We all heard him at the same time," said John. "Oh, it was lovely to hear him again!"

"I heard him too," shouted down Uncle Merry. A loud barking from below the window inside the room told the children that Fergus had evidently heard the cuckoo as well!

COWSLIP

BLACKCAP

"It's Saturday. Are you going to take us for a walk?" asked Janet. "This morning or this afternoon?"

Uncle Merry looked up at the cloud-swept April-blue sky. "This morning," he said, "I meant to do some work — but how can I sit indoors on a day when three excited children come and tell me that the cuckoo is back? I feel I want a day off. Ten minutes — and I'll be with you!"

So, with Fergus scampering madly round on his short legs, his tail wagging so fast that it could hardly be seen, the five soon set off down the familiar lanes, now green with hawthorn hedges on each side, the dainty stitchwort embroidering the banks, and the golden celandines turning polished stars to the sun. John couldn't walk. He skipped, he ran, he trotted, he capered. He said it was too happy a day for walking.

"There's the cuckoo again!" said Pat, as the lovely double-note sounded on the wind. "Oh, it does seem like summer-time to hear that! I love the cuckoo, don't you, Uncle Merry?"

"Well, no, I can't say I do," said Uncle Merry. "He's not really a favourite of mine, except that I, like you, love to hear his call in the spring-time. But, you see, the cuckoo leads a lazy life — he leaves all the work of building a nest and of bringing up and feeding young ones, to *other* birds."

"Doesn't he make a nest then?" asked John, in surprise. "I thought all birds built nests."

"Not the cuckoo," said Uncle Merry. "The hen cuckoo puts her egg in another bird's nest, first taking out the egg from the nest to make room for it. The bird who owns the nest doesn't seem to notice that it is a strange egg, and when it hatches into a bare, black, ugly nestling, the bird cares for it and brings it up as if it were her own."

"How queer!" said Pat. "It doesn't seem to be fair, does it?"

"No," said Uncle Merry. "The funny thing is that when the cuckoo nestling grows, it becomes much bigger than its little stepmother, and she has to sit on the baby cuckoo's shoulder to feed it!"

"Cuckoo! Cuckoo!" called a voice, and over their heads flew a big grey bird, with a barred chest. "There goes the cuckoo!" said Uncle Merry. "Probably she has only just returned to this country. She has spent the winter far away in warmer lands, feeding on the insects there."

"What other birds will be back soon?" asked John. "I know the swallows go away, don't they?"

"Yes — and the martins and swifts, the nightingales, the whitethroats, the chiffchaffs, and others," said Uncle Merry. "Listen — I do believe I can hear the chiff-chaff now!"

They all stood still and listened. They had come to a little copse of trees in which many birds were singing. "What's his song like?" whispered John.

"Oh, he says his name over and over again," said Uncle Merry. "There it is — listen — chiff, chaff, chiff, chaff, chiff, chaff!"

They all heard it in delight. "Now I will always know the chiff-chaff's voice," said John, pleased.

They left the trees and went on, Fergus putting his head down every hole they came to. Suddenly Uncle Merry stopped and looked upwards, intense pleasure on his face. The children looked up too. They saw a steel-blue, long-tailed bird sweeping through the air, and a few more on the telegraph wires, making a musical twittering sound. "Feet-a-feetit, feet-a-feetit!" they said.

HEDGE SPARROW

"The swallows!" said Uncle Merry. "Bless them, they're back again! How I love them!"

The children loved them too, as they watched them flying swiftly through the air, forked tails streaming behind them. With them flew birds rather like them, but with a good deal of white about them, both underneath and on the back. Their tails were not so long.

"Are those shorter-tailed birds swallows too?" asked John.

"They belong to the Swallow Family," said Uncle Merry. "They are house-martins. They build their nests of mud, under the eaves of houses. You must have seen them. The swallows put their nests on rafters or beams in barns and sheds, and that is why we call them barn-swallows. The martin up there is called the house-martin because he likes to build near our houses. There is another little martin too, brown and white, the sand-martin. He builds his nest in a hole in a bank or quarry."

"I shall never know them all," sighed Janet, looking at the swallows and martins. "Isn't there another bird like the swallows, Uncle — the swift?"

"Ah yes," said Uncle Merry, "but he doesn't come until a bit later. He isn't a swallow. He is rather like them to look at simply because he leads the same aerial life, and therefore needs the same kind of wings and long tail. He is sooty-black, not blue. I'll point him out to you when he arrives."

"There is such a lot to learn," said Janet. How do you remember everything, Uncle?.'

"It's because I love the countryside and am always looking around and noticing things; and then, of course, because I love them I read about them in my books," said Uncle Merry. "You can do the same — and perhaps when you are my age you will know ten times more than I do!"

Janet thought that was quite impossible. She slipped her hand into Uncle Merry's and thought how lovely it would be to know so much and love so much. She was already beginning to understand the deep delight and intense joy he showed and felt in the host of things that made up the countryside. It was something only those could know who felt it themselves too — and Janet was beginning to feel it. She felt it when she looked at the sheet of golden celandines; she felt it when she saw a tangle of white stitchworts, starry against the green bank. She squeezed her Uncle's hand.

"When I scc things like that, I feel sometimes as if I'd like to write a poem about them, and keep them for ever!" she half-whispered.

Uncle Merry looked down at her, a wise smile in his brown eyes. "You feel as artists do when they long to paint something," he said. "They want to catch the beautiful thing their eyes see and keep it prisoner for ever on their canvas. Poets want to capture it and hold it imprisoned in words. Musicians entangle it in music. Janet, it is a precious gift to be able to feel like that. Let it grow!"

HOUSE SPARROW

"Well, I may be silly sometimes," thought Janet to herself, "but Uncle Merry wouldn't talk to me like this if I was really and truly stupid!"

The birds were singing madly that morning, though many of them were busy with nest-making. The children saw them carrying dead leaves and bits of moss in their beaks. They heard the many songs — and they heard a new one, most delicious and sweet.

THE THRUSH'S NEST

"The blackcap!" said Uncle Merry, listening. "What rich clear notes it has! Almost as fine as the blackbird — so mellow and full. How lucky we are in this country to have so many singing birds!"

"Uncle Merry, what is the little bird over there — like a sparrow?" asked Pat, pointing to a small bird looking for insects in the ditch.

"It's not like a sparrow," said John at once, "except that it's brown! Look at its thin beak, Pat — sparrows have a big clumsy beak. That bird looks more like a robin."

"John, sometimes I think you are the sharpest of all you three children," said Uncle Merry. "You really do notice things. That bird is a hedge-sparrow — but, as you say, it *isn't* really a sparrow. You have only to see its beak to know that it is an insect-eater, not a seed-eater like the real sparrow."

They all watched the sober-brown bird. It made some funny little movements with its wings.

"It shuffles them!" said John.

"Its other name is Shufflewing," said Uncle Merry. "You can see why!"

"Uncle — it's flown up into that hedge there," said Pat, as the bird flew into a green hawthorn nearby. "Has it built its nest do you think?"

The bird flew out again. Uncle Merry went quietly to the hedge and parted a few twigs. He saw a nest there, with a sitting bird. The bird flew off in fright. Uncle Merry beckoned.

"I hate frightening a sitting bird," he said, "but you must really see one of the prettiest sights in the bird kingdom. Look!"

The children looked — and there in the nest were four hedge-sparrow eggs as blue as the sky above — the purest, brightest blue imaginable, gleaming against the brown of the nest-cup.

"Oh, lovely!" said Janet, her eyes starry with delight. "Quite, quite perfect!"

They left the nest of eggs for the mother to come back to, and went on their way. A big bumble bee sailed past and Janet nearly squealed, but not quite. Fergus jumped up at it in indignation, for it went very near his nose.

"Zooooom!" said the bee, and sailed away.

"He spent the winter sleeping in a hole in a bank," said Uncle Merry. "Lovely thing, isn't he, with his velvet coat of thick fur?"

"Uncle Merry, we haven't found a single new flower," said Pat. "Isn't that queer?"

"Not very," said Uncle Merry with a laugh. "We've been looking up into the sky most of the time, haven't we, and seeing the birds? We can't look down at the ground as well. But now we will. Come along — who will see a new flower first?"

John did, of course. His eyes never seemed to miss anything. Janet was a bit of a dreamer, and sometimes seemed to look at things without seeing them. Pat was full of eagerness and saw plenty of things, but because he didn't look carefully, like John, he made many mistakes.

"Here's a pretty little flower!" cried John, and he picked a stem from the bank. The flowers were small and rosy-purple, and each of the petals was notched in the centre of its broadest edge. The leaves were almost round, and downy with hairs, deeply cut at the edges.

"It's the dove's foot crane's-bill," said Uncle Merry, "one of our many pretty little wild geraniums."

"Why is it called crane's-bill?" asked John.

SONG THRUSH

"I can't see anything like a crane's beak in the flower."

"No — you must wait for the seeds to form before you see that," said Uncle Merry. "Then you will see a long beak growing out from the middle of the flower, just like a crane's long bill."

"Is this another dove's foot crane's-bill?" asked Pat, picking another flower.

John gave it a glance. "Of course it isn't!" he said. "The flower may be purple-pink, but look at the leaves, silly! They are quite different!"

So they were, all cut up into fingers, not a bit rounded as were the soft leaves of the dove's foot. "I've seen these leaves in the autumn — they go a bright red, don't they?" said John, remembering.

"Quite right," said Uncle Merry. "This flower, that Pat has found, is the Herb Robert, another wild geranium. Look at the two closely and see the differences — you especially, Pat. See how the petals of the dove's foot are notched, and its leaves rounded — and notice the larger flowers of the Herb Robert, and its cut-up leaves. Later on, when these plants go to seed, we will see how they each grow beak-like seed-vessels."

The children found more flowers after that — one that Pat called a yellow dead-nettle, because it looked rather like it.

"It is the yellow archangel," said Uncle Merry, "and it belongs to the Lip Family of course. You can see its resemblance to the other members we know, though its leaves are not so nettle-like as those of the white dead-nettle. See the lower lip — a platform for the bee to alight on — and look into the upper lip, where you will find the stamens and pistil. They are carefully placed there, so that when the bee seeks for nectar his back will brush against the pollen and he will fly off covered with it, to rub it against the pistil of the next archangel flower he visits."

"I really do think the flowers are clever, the way they work with the insects to get their pollen sent about," said Janet. "It's wonderful! They haven't brains to think with, as we have, and yet all these ideas are there, worked out to perfection. It's mysterious."

"It is certainly most mysterious," said Uncle Merry. "Look — there's the first cowslip! I really must mention it, because I feel *I* would like to claim a new flower, too, this morning!"

The cowslip nodded its head in the wind as it grew in the grass nearby.

"I know it belongs to the Primrose Family," said Janet, picking it. "Oh — it does smell sweet! There will be thousands of these out here next month, Uncle. We must gather a big bunch then to take home to Mother."

The ramblers had walked in a big circle, and were now almost home. Fergus scampered ahead, and stopped at the usual rabbit-hole. His head disappeared, and a shower of earth came up from behind him.

Pat went to pull him out, for once Fergus really got going, nothing would make him come along home. As he bent down to get hold of the dog, he saw some big leaves growing nearby. He stared at them. He tried to remember something. "Big cobwebby leaves — the shape of a young horse's foot — coltsfoot leaves!" thought Pat, using his brain well. He gave a shout. "Look! Coltsfoot leaves! I've found *those* first, anyway!"

"Bright boy!" said Uncle Merry, looking really pleased. "Yes — they are. Do you remember the coltsfoot flowers growing here earlier? See — there are some seeding now. Aren't the leaves big, and do you see how cobwebby they seem to be? I am glad you found them, Pat. I had forgotten all about them."

Pat felt really proud. Now *he* had had a word of praise from Uncle Merry too. They all went home in a very good temper, and just got in before an April shower swept over the countryside, drenching everything in a few minutes.

"Our next walk is in May," said Uncle Merry. "We shall wish we had a hundred eyes then, there will be so much to see!"

HOUSE MARTIN

A little Aquarium

JOHN could not keep a proper aquarium because he hadn't enough money to buy one. So Uncle Merry gave him a very big glass pickle-jar, wide for its height.

"Here you are," he said. "You can make a dear little aquarium with this, John. We'll go and get some things for it this afternoon, shall we?"

"Oh yes," said John. "I want a real little pond in my jar, Uncle — with sand at the bottom and pebbles, and pond weed and snails and beetles and everything — oh, and tadpoles, of course!"

"You can't have *everything*," said Uncle Merry. "For two reasons. One is that your jar would be too crowded and the creatures would die. The other is that you must only keep creatures that do not eat one another. If you have one of the fierce water-beetles, for instance, it would gobble up your tadpoles!"

"Oh dear!" said John. "I shouldn't like that. What could I have in my little pickle-jar pond, Uncle?"

"Well, tadpoles and snails would be all right," said Uncle Merry. "And one or two caddis-grubs if we can find them. I'll put some string around the neck of the pickle-jar and we'll take it with us to fill it with pond-water. Pond creatures do not thrive very well in tap-water."

Off they went together to the pond. John had a net with him and caught at least twenty tadpoles, which he wanted to put into his jar. But Uncle Merry said "no" very firmly.

"Six or seven is quite enough. That's right — look at them swimming round the jar, John! Now for some water-snails."

They found three beauties, and Uncle Merry managed to get two caddis-grubs too, in their funny hard cases. He pulled up some water-weed, and put that into the jar as well.

"Now back home we go!" he said. "You will have a dear little pickle-jar pond now, John!"

When they reached home, Uncle Merry carefully emptied everything out of the jar into a pail for a while. Then he and John put a layer of clean, washed sand at the bottom of the jar. Then John went to hunt for some tiny pebbles, which he washed under the running tap. Those went on top of the sand. Then Uncle Merry tied stones on to the bottom of the water-weed stems, to keep them upright in the water.

"Now for the water," he said. "We must pour it carefully back into the jar. John, put a piece of brown paper over the sand, will you — cut it into a rough circle — that's right — then the water will not disturb the sand and make the jar cloudy as I pour it in."

The water was poured gently into the jar, and all the little creatures went with it. The water-weed arose upright when the circle of wet paper was fished out of the jar. The tadpoles wriggled madly, and the snails began to crawl up the side. The caddis-grubs explored the bottom of their funny little pond.

"Oh, isn't it lovely!" said John. "Pat! Janet! Look at my pond! Isn't it fine?"

Janet and Pat at once wanted ponds like John.

"I'll show you how to make your ponds," said John proudly. "I know exactly how to, don't I, Uncle Merry?"

"I hope so," said Uncle Merry. "Remember to put a cupful of pond-water, or water from your greenhouse tank or rain-barrel into your 'pond' every week."

BOM

Bom is a little drummer, who goes about the world with his drum and his little dog, Wuffy. This incident is taken from one of the books about him, "Bom goes to Ho-Ho Village". He has just been to see his Aunt Twinkle, and she has asked him to go to the market and sell a great bunch of gay balloons for her. So off he goes, carrying the balloons and wearing his drum.

AWAY went Bom to the corner of the market, and there he found Aunt Twinkle's stool, just as she had said. He sat down on it, his drum in front of him, holding the bobbing balloons by their long strings. Wuffy sat down beside him, and Bom began to sing:

Balloons for sale,
Do come and buy,
Watch them bobbing,
See them fly!

Blue, red and green,
So light and gay
Balloons for sale,
Buy one to-day!

The wind blew a little, and the balloons bobbed up and down like a lot of gay bubbles! They looked so pretty that the folk of Ho-Ho Village came up at once to buy them.

"One balloon, please, a red one," said a small toy monkey — and do look, he has tied it to his tail, and away he goes, with the balloon hanging on to his tail, bobbing about in the breeze!

Then Mrs. Golliwog came along and bought a balloon for each of the four baby gollies — dear me, how pleased they were!

Two teddy-bears walked up, arm in arm, and spent a penny each on a balloon, and after them came a pretty little doll.

And then a toy horse galloped up and stared hard at the bobbing balloons. "They look good enough to eat!" he said. "May I nibble one?"

"Certainly NOT!" said Bom. But oh dear, the little horse gave one a very small nibble — and it went POP! Goodness me, how he galloped away in fright!

"You owe me a penny!" shouted Bom, but the little horse was much too scared to come back.

And now who is THIS coming? No — it can't be, it really can't be — but it is! It's Skipper Heave-Ho — Bom's good friend, old Skipper Heave-Ho. What a surprise!

The Skipper didn't see Bom at first, because he was almost hidden by balloons, and he was very startled to hear his name being shouted.

"Skipper Heave-Ho! Hey! Skipper!"

"Who wants me? Who's calling?" shouted back the Skipper, in his loud voice.

"It's me. Bom the little drummer!" cried Bom, and then the balloons swung aside in the wind and the old sailor-man suddenly saw Bom's smiling face under his red helmet.

"BOM! What are you doing here?" he shouted. "And if it isn't the Wuffy-dog too! Well, well, well!" And he hugged Bom and Wuffy and the balloons too! It's a wonder they didn't all burst!

"Bom! Come and have an ice-cream with me and tell me your news," said Heave-Ho, trying to untangle himself from the balloons. "Come, along, do!"

"I'd love to," said Bom. "But what shall I do with my balloons, Skipper? I can't take them into a shop."

"Leave them here, then," said Heave-Ho. "Look, take off your drum, set it on the stool, and tie your balloon strings to it. The balloons will look after your drum for you, and the drum will take care of your balloons!"

"That's a very good idea," said Bom, and he tied all the balloon-strings to his big drum. How they bob about in the wind, wishing they could fly away!

Then off went Heave-Ho, Wuffy and Bom to the ice-cream shop for a good long talk. You should have seen the enormous ice-creams that Heave-Ho ordered, and the big plate of biscuits too. Even the Wuffy-dog had an ice-cream to himself, and as many biscuits as he could eat. He wagged his tail without stopping.

"How's your dear little boat-house?" asked Bom. "I often think of it — just a boat turned upside down with chimneys and doors and windows! You are lucky to live in a house made from a boat, Skipper."

"Well, you know, it's a bit lonely living by myself," said Skipper Heave-Ho. "That's why I often set off to visit people. I'm on my way back from a visit now — and wasn't I surprised to see you sitting on a stool in the middle of a cloud of balloons, Bom! Tell me why you're here."

So, over two more ice-creams, Bom told Heave-Ho about his kind Aunt Twinkle, and how he was selling her balloons while she made him a meat-pie. "I do hope my balloons are all right," he said. "It's a bit windy now!"

So it was! The balloons were having a fine time! They bobbed and jigged and bumped into one another, and two little clockwork mice were standing and watching them in delight.

Then suddenly there came a very BIG wind indeed. Whoo-hoo! Whoooooosh! It came whirling down the street, and found the balloons bobbing to and fro above the big drum on the stool.

It began to blow them about, and they tugged hard at their strings. The wind sang a merry song as it blew.

Who-hoo-hoo-hoo,
I'll play with you,
I'll blow you here,
I'll blow you there,
I'll blow you high up in the air!
WHOO-HOO, WHOO-HOOOOOOOO!

But the wind couldn't get the balloons away from the drum, because Bom had tied their strings to it so tightly. It was cross, and blew harder, singing its song again.

Whoo-hoo-hoo-hoo,
I'm BLOWING you.
Hear what I say,
Now fly away
Up in the sky
So high, so high!
WHOO-HOO, WHOO-HOO!

The balloons bobbed wildly, and their strings tugged hard at the drum on the stool. It began to jerk and jiggle. Then it gave a little hop in the air and fell back. It gave a bigger hop — and then away it went, high in the air, with all the balloons pulling it!

The folk around were astonished! "Look — the balloons are flying away in the wind — and taking the drum with it!" they cried.

The little toy monkey pointed up into the sky and shouted loudly. "Come down, balloons; come down, drum!"

The toy horse galloped up and shouted "Come down!" too, and so did a teddy-bear. "Come down, come down!"

But the drum couldn't come down, and neither could the balloons. They just flew higher and higher. Bom, come out and get your drum before it's gone for ever!

Bom heard the shouts and came to see what was the matter, old Skipper Heave-Ho and Wuffy behind him.

"Look, look!" shouted everyone. "Your drum has gone — the balloons have taken it away, and the wind is blowing them off to the moon!"

Bom stared up into the sky in surprise and fright. His drum! His precious drum — and Aunt Twinkle's balloons!

"Oh, look at my drum! It'll go to the moon, it will never come back!" cried Bom, very much upset.

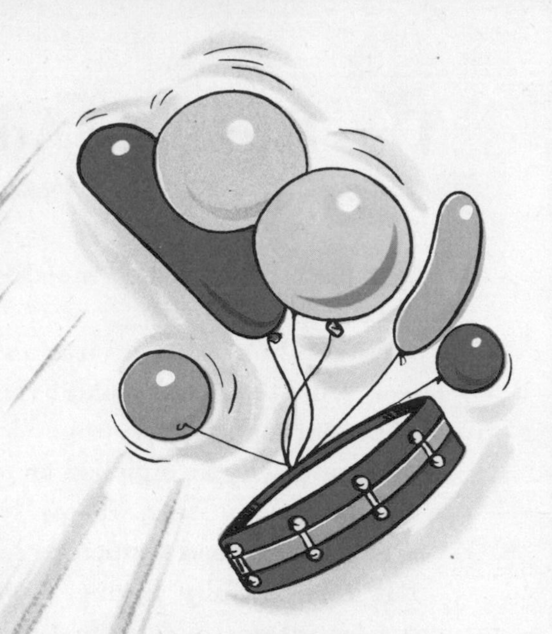

Oh drum, oh drum,
Come back to me,
I'll miss your diddy-bom-bom!
Don't fly to the moon
But come back soon
With your bom-diddy-bom-diddy-bom!

Bom sang his song as loudly as he could, but his drum grew smaller and smaller in the sky and the balloons looked like tiny coloured dots.

Bom looked so sad and Wuffy-dog whined so miserably that Skipper Heave-Ho couldn't bear it. He took Bom's hand.

"Now, now, young fellow-me-lad!" he said, in his great big voice. "Don't look so upset. We'll follow that drum of yours. We'll run fast below it, and watch where it comes down, for come down it will! Run, now, run!"

And then began such a chase! The drum and the balloons bobbed up and down in the sky, rushing away with the chuckling wind, and Bom, Wuffy and the Skipper raced after them — running, running, running — down lanes and round corners, and up hills, and over fields, and down hills, and through little towns, and past cows and horses — really, there never was such a chase before!

Keep it up, Bom; run, Skipper Heave-Ho: bark, little Wuffy, quick, quick, never give up!

(You'll want to know where the drum and the balloons flew to — well they landed on the top of a chimney — what a to-do for little Bom!)

The Humbug Adventure

Another tale of the Secret Seven

THE Secret Seven had a meeting one day after morning school.

"What about this invitation from old Professor Wills to go and look at the planet Jupiter tonight through his telescope?" asked Peter. "I don't know why he's picked on *us* to ask!"

"I've already seen it on television," said Colin. "There wasn't much to see either!"

"It'll be awfully boring," said Jack. "He's not a bit interesting. He just drones on and on. Let's not go."

"Well — wouldn't it be rude if we all left messages to say we weren't coming?" asked Janet. "After all — he means it kindly."

"It's going to rain," said Pam, looking up at the sky. "I bet it is. So we shan't see a thing if we do go!"

"If it rains, we won't go," said Peter. "So we'll just hope that it pours and pours!"

It didn't. The sky was certainly cloudy, but no rain came at all. The Seven sighed as they ate their tea in their different homes.

"Uthing ooing," he said.

She showed Peter how to train the telescope.

So they went, waiting for each other outside Professor Wills's house, which was called "Night Skies". That made them laugh.

The maid showed them into a study, and then went to fetch the old professor. She came back looking sorry.

"It's such a cloudy night that the professor didn't expect you," she said. "So he's gone out. But his wife says that if you are very, very careful, she will show you how to work the telescope and you can see if you can spy Jupiter for yourselves. Ah — here she comes."

Mrs. Wills was very nice. To begin with she produced a tin of most enormous humbugs to suck. Then she showed Peter and the others how to train the big telescope on to different points of the sky. "I know just about where the planet Jupiter is," she said, "and if you like I'll leave the telescope pointed at the place it should be, behind the clouds. Then when the clouds move on you may catch a glimpse of it now and then."

None of the Secret Seven could speak a word because of the big humbugs they were sucking. Peter made some polite noises, and hoped that Mrs. Wills understood. When she had gone out of the room, the Seven looked at each other in relief.

"Ooogle, eles-copy, oogle, urble, oopiter," said Peter. Nobody understood. He put his eye to the end of the great tube and looked up.

"Uthing ooing," he said, which the others correctly understood as "Nothing doing." Jack worked his humbug round to the other side of his mouth.

"Urgle, onky, ooky ky," he said, meaning "Let's not look at the sky," but nobody understood a word! So he took his humbug out of his mouth and explained:

"Let's not bother about looking at the cloudy sky," he said clearly. "Let's bend the telescope down a bit and look at the village and the hills beyond and the farm — things like that. It would be fun to stand here, far away from them, and see them almost as if we could touch them!"

"Yes, let's," said Peter. "We know how to move the telescope. But for goodness sake be careful, it's jolly valuable."

The telescope had a curious window of its own to look through — a great window that reached from ceiling almost to ground, and had no glass in it at all. The telescope itself could be swung to almost any angle at a touch of the finger once a screw had been loosened.

"Let's look at the Village Hall," said Janet. "There's a dance on and it's all lit up."

She had taken her humbug out of her mouth to speak, and put it back again when she had finished. Peter was afraid of sticky fingermarks on the telescope, and he handed Colin a clean hanky to wipe where anyone touched.

The Village Hall looked so near that it might have been in the garden. Barbara took her sweet out of her mouth and giggled. "There's Mrs. Dickson, look, standing at the door. And do look, there's that silly boy Harry selling programmes or something."

This was a marvellous game! They moved the telescope into another direction, and saw where a Fair was, in the farmer's field about a quarter of a mile away.

"Goodness — it looks so near that I'm sure I heard that roundabout man sneeze!" said Janet. "And I can even see Dickie and Danny, paying their pennies to go on the roundabout!"

They spent a long time looking at the Fair, and began to wish they were there. "Urgle, ooble, oo," said Peter, forgetting to take out his humbug, but the others knew what he meant, because he was swinging the telescope slowly in a different direction. It was now pointing towards the dark farm. One window was brilliantly lighted and no curtains were drawn.

"There's nice Mrs. Wingfield knitting in her chair," said Barbara, taking her turn.

"And old Mr. Wingfield filling his pipe," said Colin. "I can even see what tobacco he's using!"

Little flames sprang up . . .

"You *can't*," said everyone, mumbling through their humbugs. Then it was Jack's turn. He bent and looked through the great tube, seeing the farm itself and the barn nearby and a haystack. He suddenly gave a loud exclamation, and most unexpectedly swallowed his humbug. He gasped and choked, tried to call out something and pointed to the telescope. In astonishment, Peter looked through it. What was Jack fussing about?

He soon saw! Someone was moving near the haystack. Someone was striking matches! Little flames sprang up in the dry stack, and soon there were many more. Peter gasped, not taking

A minute later the police came up in a car.

any notice of poor, choking Jack. His eye was glued to the big telescope.

He squashed his humbug into his cheek in order to speak clearly. "Fire! There's a tramp firing Farmer Winfield's stack — and it's jolly near the old barn. Gosh, that's a big flame! Colin, go and ring up the farmer — at once! And, after that, the police. The stack will soon be burnt down, then the barn will catch!"

Colin ran to find the telephone in the hall. Peter had his eye glued to the telescope, watching everything. There was the man again, coming from behind the stack. He had probably fired the other side too! Peter could see him clearly — a small man — with a limp — and a beard that showed up well when he turned sideways to the flames. Janet tried to pull her brother away so that she could have a turn herself, but he wouldn't budge.

Colin telephoned to the farm and gave them a warning. Then he got on to the police. He ran back into the telescope room. "Peter, I've 'phoned! What's happening now?"

Peter was having a wonderful view of all the sudden excitement at the farm. The farm-door was flung open, and out ran the farmer and his son. His wife followed with buckets. A minute later the police came up in a car. The firemen, called by the police, arrived too. What a to-do! Peter gasped and exclaimed, and the others could hardly contain themselves!

"Let's have a look, Peter! Peter, you selfish thing, let *us* have a turn. What's happening?"

Peter told them. "Everyone's arrived — the stack's blazing, but the barn is safe. The firemen are drenching the stack now — and goodness, they've caught the man. No it's not him. The man who fired the stack was small and had a beard and a limp. They've got the wrong man — no wonder he's struggling!"

This was too much for the others. They raced

Miss Na

Miss
Nan
Nockabout
Wouldn't wash her face,
And everybody said it was
A real
Dis-
Grace!

Mud,
Soot,
And marmalade,
Smeared her cheeks and chin,
And nobody would guess she had
A pretty
White
Skin.

But one
Day
The chimney-sweep
Knocked at Nancy's door,

out of the room together. "We're going to the farm! It's too thrilling for words!"

So along to the farm they went, and managed to see the end of the excitement. Half the stack was saved — the barn was not touched — and a man was trying to get away from two stout policemen.

"I didn't fire it, I tell you!" he was shouting. Jack went up to the Sergeant.

"Sir — I don't think that man did do it," he

They managed to see the end of the excitement.

said. "The man you want has a limp — he's small — and has a beard."

"Why — that would be Jamey!" cried the farmer's wife. "We sent him off last week for stealing."

The police let the other man go. The Sergeant ordered them to go to Jamey's cottage, not far off. Then he turned to Jack.

"Now perhaps you'll tell us how you know all this, you kids?" he said with his large smile. "You warned the farmer — called the police — and even know who the man is who fired the stack! You're the Secret Seven, aren't you?

"We saw it all through Professor Wills's telescope," said Jack. "Peter's still back there, watching."

But he wasn't. As soon as he saw the others through the telescope, appearing in the midst of the excitement, he wanted to be with them — and he ran at top speed, sucking the very last of his humbug!

"Good work," said the Sergeant, when Peter told the whole of the story. "You saw something more exciting than the planet Jupiter, didn't you? Ah — you never know what you're going to see through telescopes."

"It was a jolly good adventure, but a very sudden and short one," said Colin.

"Yes," said Peter. "It only lasted as long as my humbug. An adventure *couldn't* very well be shorter than that!"

"Short and sweet — like the humbug," said Janet with a giggle. "Let's call it the Humbug Adventure — it's a jolly good name for it!"

So it is — don't you agree?

ockabout

And said, "Oh, little maid, you are
The one
I
Adore!"

"PLEASE
Say
You'll marry me,
Your face is just like mine,
We'll be a pair of chimney-sweeps,
I think
T'would
Be fine!"

But Miss
Nan
Nockabout,
Screamed and ran away,
And ordered twenty pounds of soap
That very
Same
Day!

You're Too Smart, Brer Rabbit!

Now one day when Brer Hare was lying in a warm cornfield, sunning himself, he saw three heads peering over the top of the nearby hedge.

"Ha! Brer Wolf — Brer Fox — and Brer Bear," said Brer Hare to himself, digging himself in a bit deeper, so that not even his long ears could be seen. The half-grown corn waved above him, and he felt quite safe.

Brer Wolf, Brer Fox and Brer Bear came a little way into the cornfield and sat down together, hidden, like Brer Hare. How angry the farmer would have been if he had seen them!

Brer Hare listened with both his ears. What were those three saying? Ah — they were talking about that rascal of a Brer Rabbit!

"I'm *tired* of Brer Rabbit!" said Brer Wolf. "He bumped into me the other day when I was carrying a full basket of carrots, and I spilt them all over the road. He was very polite, of course, and picked them up — but what happened to six of those carrots, I don't know! I only had *half* a basket of carrots when he said goodbye and ran off!"

"You just can't take your eyes off him for a minute," said Brer Fox. "He told me that my tail looked as if it was getting loose, and I'd better see to it. He even offered me a safety pin! The saucy rascal!"

"And he told *me* that I was so fat I'd go down the hill faster if I *rolled* down, instead of walking!" growled Brer Bear. Brer Fox gave a sudden giggle at the thought of Brer Bear rolling all down the hill.

Brer Bear glared at him, and Brer Fox stopped laughing at once. "Sorry," he said. "But — that's quite funny. I can *see* you rolling d . . ."

"That's enough, Brer Fox," said Brer Wolf. "We're meeting this morning to settle how to catch Brer Rabbit once and for all — not to laugh at his silly jokes."

"Yes. Yes, of course," said Brer Fox, humbly. "What's your plan, Brer Wolf?"

"We'll tell him that old Mister Lion is hunting for him," said Brer Wolf. "We'll tell him that Mister Lion is half-starved, and gone to skin and bone, and he's longing for a good fat rabbit to eat, and is looking everywhere for Brer Rabbit."

"What's the point of that?" asked Brer Bear.

"We'll tell Brer Rabbit that whatever he does he must NOT take his usual path through the woods," said Brer Wolf, "because Mister Lion is planning to catch him as he goes by with all his shopping. He must go the other way — through the hazel trees, along the track there."

"I still don't see what you're driving at," said Brer Bear. "I . . ."

"LISTEN!" said Brer Wolf, so fiercely that Brer Bear stared in fright. "We three are going to go to that track between the hazel trees — and we're going to dig a deep pit — and we're going to cover it with leafy twigs — and wait for him to step on it — and go down headlong..."

"Ah — now there's an idea for you!" said Brer Fox, in great admiration. "And I suppose we'll be hiding behind the bushes, ready to pounce on him?"

"No. *We'll* be down in the pit too!" said Brer Wolf, "ready to grab him the moment he falls in! If we don't, he'll be in and out of that pit, and be gone before we're even round the bushes. We must GRAB him as he falls into the pit."

"Yes. Yes, a very good idea," said Brer Fox. "I like the sound of that. Well, shall Brer Bear and I go and warn Brer Rabbit about Mister Lion, while you dig the pit, Brer Wolf?"

"*No,*" said Brer Wolf. "*I'll* go and tell him — and you two can dig the pit. You can begin right away now — and make it deep enough for all of us! Come along — it will take quite a time, so you'd better begin at once. I'll show you where to dig."

Well, while Brer Wolf took the others to the hazel-wood track, Brer Hare, who had been lying low in the corn listening hard with both his ears, hopped off to find Brer Rabbit. Ha — he would have something to tell him that would put Brer Rabbit on his guard at once!

Brer Rabbit was at home when Brer Hare called, and he listened to all that Brer Hare said. Then he laughed.

"Thanks, Cousin Hare!" he said. "You come with me to Mister Lion now, and back me up when I tell him what Brer Wolf has said about him."

"No! No — *I'm* not going to Mister Lion's den!" said Brer Hare, in fright. "You must be mad."

"No — not mad — just tricky!" said Brer Rabbit. "I'm friendly with Mister Lion just now, Brer Hare — didn't you know?"

"No, I didn't. And I don't believe you," said Brer Hare.

"Well, it's true," said Brer Rabbit. "Someone tied his tail to a tree while he was asleep — and I happened to come along and notice it. So I woke him and told him, and untied it for him. He was very, very pleased. And now he's quite a friend of mine."

Brer Hare looked hard at Brer Rabbit. "I suppose it wasn't *you* who tied up his tail, Brer Rabbit, was it?" he said. "As well as untied it?"

"Don't ask awkward questions," said Brer Rabbit, getting up. "I'm going to see Mister Lion this very minute — and you're coming too!"

So, very scared indeed, Brer Hare went with Brer Rabbit to Mister Lion's den. On the way, Brer Rabbit leapt up on to the broad branch of a dead tree, and dipped a mug he had brought with him into a hole there. Wild bees flew all round him angrily, for their nest was in that hole. Brer Rabbit scooped with his mug — and brought it up full of honey!

"A present for Mister Lion!" he said. "He likes honey as much as Brer Bear does. Come along."

Mister Lion was lying outside his den in the sun, and Brer Hare kept quite a way behind Brer Rabbit as they came near. Mister Lion greeted Brer Rabbit in a most friendly manner, especially when he sniffed the honey.

"Mister Lion, how's your tail?" asked Brer Rabbit. "And how are *you*? I heard you were half-starved, so I've brought you some honey to help you along. Honey's good for half-starved people who've gone to skin and bone."

"WHO SAID THAT?" roared Mister Lion, getting up and swishing his tail angrily. "Skin and bone! Do I LOOK like skin and bone?"

"No. Not at all," said Brer Rabbit, truthfully. "Brer Hare — you come near and tell Mister Lion what you heard Brer Wolf and Brer Bear and Brer Fox saying about him."

"They s-s-s-said that you'd gone to skin and b-b-b-bone," stammered Brer Hare, trembling all over, "and that you were l-l-looking for Brer Rabbit to eat him, and . . ."

"Brer Rabbit is a good friend of mine," bellowed Mister Lion. "What else did they say?"

"Well," said Brer Rabbit, "I suppose if they think you're half-starved, and gone to skin and bone, they reckon you're no good any more. I guess they think you're slinking about like a coward, Mister Lion, looking for nuts and

THE BONFIRE AT NIGHT

Bonfire, you're a merry fellow
With your flames of red and yellow,
And your cheery cracks and pops —
You gobble up the old bean-props,
The pea-sticks, withered plants, and all
The leaves blown down beside the wall.
Your never-ending spires of smoke
(The colour of a pixie's cloak)
Go mounting to the starry sky,
And when the wind comes bustling by
Oh, what a merry game you play,
And how you pop and roar away!
Your heart is red, your smoke is thick,
Oh, pile on leaves and branches, quick!
Let's dance around and shout and sing,
Oh, Bonfire, you're a LOVELY thing!

berries to eat, not able to hunt any more, a poor old . . ."

Mister Lion was so angry to hear all this that his tail swished about like a lash, cutting leaves off the bushes behind him, and making quite a wind. He sent a roar through the wood that made every creature tremble and run to hide. "What else did Brer Wolf say?" he shouted to Brer Hare.

"Now don't you tell him the other dreadful things they said," called Brer Rabbit to Brer Hare. "Poor Mister Lion is angry enough already. He'll be off to find the three rogues in a minute."

"I'm going at once!" said Mister Lion, just as Brer Rabbit hoped he would. "Where are they?"

"Brer Hare — go and see where they are," ordered Brer Rabbit. "Then come back here and tell us, and I'll guide Mister Lion to them." Brer Hare went off like a puff of wind, glad to be away from the fierce Mister Lion. He soon found where Brer Bear and Brer Fox were digging away at a pit, which was already very deep. Brer Wolf came up to them at that moment, looking cross.

"There's no one in at Brer Rabbit's house," he said. "Hallo, Brer Hare — what are you doing here? Is Brer Rabbit anywhere about?"

"Yes! He's coming along here soon, with a friend," said Brer Hare. "Mind you shout to warn him of that pit when he comes along, or he'll fall in."

"Dear, dear — we wouldn't like *that* to happen!" said Brer Wolf, with a grin that showed all his sharp white teeth, and laughed as Brer Hare ran off.

"So Brer Rabbit's coming this way — with a friend!" he said. "Let me get down into the pit quickly, you two. Make room!"

But there wasn't room for all three, so Brer Wolf pushed out Brer Bear. "Hide behind that bush and tell us when Brer Rabbit is coming," he said. "Pull a few leafy twigs across the pit, quickly."

Brer Bear clambered out, and placed some leafy twigs across the top of the hole, while Brer Wolf and Brer Fox crouched below. Now to get that rascally, annoying, exasperating rabbit. WHAT a bit of luck that he was coming that way, instead of the way he usually went!

Now Brer Hare had already run back to Brer Rabbit and Mister Lion. He winked at Brer Rabbit. "I've found them," he said. "I'll lead the way."

So he went first, Brer Rabbit next, and Mister Lion last. They hadn't gone far before Brer Rabbit gave a yell, and began to limp badly. "Oh, my foot!" he said. "Oh, my poor foot. Mister Lion, could I ride on your back till it gets right again?"

"Certainly," said Mister Lion graciously, thinking of the honey that Brer Rabbit had so kindly brought him. So up hopped Brer Rabbit on to Mister Lion's back, and away they lumbered, with Brer Hare running in front.

Brer Rabbit began to sing a little song. "Lippitty-clippitty, here we go, bumpity, bumpity, to and fro . . ."

Brer Bear, who was waiting behind a bush, heard the song, and called in a low voice to the others. "He's coming! I can hear him singing. Watch out!"

"Who's with him?" called Brer Wolf from the pit, and was extremely surprised to hear the answer.

"Oh, Brer Wolf — he's with MISTER LION!"

"Don't make silly jokes," said Brer Wolf crossly.

"He's riding on Mister Lion's BACK!" shouted Brer Bear, amazed and scared. "He's holding on to his *mane* — he's playing with Mister Lion's *ears*!"

Brer Wolf didn't believe Brer Bear at all. Angrily he poked his head through the twigs that covered his hole — and there, sure enough, ambling down the track, he saw Mister Lion — with Brer Rabbit riding on his back, singing at the top of his voice! He simply couldn't believe his eyes!

"Gee-up, Mister Lion!" cried Brer Rabbit, spotting Brer Wolf's ears sticking out of the pit. "Gee-up, then. You'll soon catch Brer Wolf and the others!"

And at that very moment Mister Lion walked straight on to the leafy twigs that covered the hole, and found himself falling on top of a mighty scared Brer Wolf and Brer Fox!

What a to-do there was! Brer Wolf and Brer Fox tried to get out, and Mister Lion, just as surprised as they were, began to roar and struck out with his paws all over the place.

"Plonk! That was one for Brer Wolf! Ker-PLONK! That was one for Brer Fox — and then Mister Lion spotted Brer Bear, stiff with fright by a nearby bush, and leapt out at him too. Ker-plonkity-PLONK! Brer Bear fell down flat on his back, rolled over and made off at top speed.

"You're a very *brave* lion to take on three enemies at once!" called Brer Rabbit admiringly from the rabbit hole in which he and Brer Hare had gone to shelter while the fight lasted.

Mister Lion roared so loudly that Brer Rabbit and Brer Hare disappeared down the hole at top speed. "I'll have all of them!" bellowed Mister Lion, and set off through the wood with a mighty crashing noise. Brer Rabbit's ears popped out of the hole and he watched Mister Lion disappear like a streak of tawny lightning.

He climbed out and began to wash his ears with his paws, but Brer Hare was too scared to join him. "Well, well," said Rabbit, setting off home, "I hope those three have learnt a lesson — digging a pit to catch me, indeed!"

And next time he met Brer Bear, Brer Wolf and Brer Fox, he looked at them hard. "Whatever *have* you been doing to yourselves?" he said. "You've lost half an ear, Brer Bear — and you're limping badly, Brer Wolf - and what *has* happened to your tail, Brer Fox? It looks most peculiar. I do hope my good friend, Mister Lion, hasn't been unkind to you!"

Then away he went, lippitty-clippitty through the woods, singing a most exasperating song.

"Brer Wolf's limping, isn't it queer?
And WHAT has happened to Brer Bear's ear?
And, oh, Brer Fox, I feel quite pale
When I look at your TERRIBLE chewed-up tail!
Take the advice of a wise old rabbit —
Don't fight with lions — it's SUCH a bad habit!"

I'd rather fight with a lion than with *you*, Brer Rabbit — you're too artful for words!

On Dorset Hills

A dozen larks sweep upward from my feet
As I come by,
And in the hazy sky
They soar on wings that with their quivering beat
Keep tremulous time to sibilant sweet song
That downward spills
Like rainfall on the hills,
Cascading round me, wild and sweet and strong.

And I and every living thing are held
In sheer delight;
The daisy, petalled white,
With golden eye upturned, is magic-spelled,
And primroses that nestle cheek to cheek
As children do,
Are still with listening too.
Bewitched the blackbird sits with silent beak,

Dumb is the strident wren, the yaffle stays
His laughing cry,
And rabbits running by
Are sudden all enchanted with amaze.
Oh voice of Spring, of Youth, heart's mad delight,
Sing on, sing on,
And when the sun is gone
I'll warm me with your echoes through the night.

Enid Blyton's Four Clubs for Children

As I have already told you in my foreword, children, there are four Clubs run by me for those readers of my books who feel that they would like to be a friend of mine, and help me in my work for sick, blind, or spastic children, and with sick or injured animals. A great many of you think as I do about these matters, and I am very glad to have you at my side.

Now about the Four Clubs, and how to join one or more of them.

First, *The Famous Five Club*, which, as I have already told you, helps me with the Children's Home in Beaconsfield, where we take 30 small children. To join, and get our badge with the heads of the Five on it, send a shilling postal order, and an envelope addressed to yourself, inside an envelope addressed to FAMOUS FIVE CLUB; 20, Warwick Square, London E.C. 4.

You will be interested to know that we have a Famous Five Ward at this little Home, which has a plaque on the door, showing our well-known badge.

The Sunbeam Society. This is the Youth Section of the great R.N.I.B. —The Royal National Institute for the Blind. Children belonging to this club help me with the Sunshine Homes for Blind Babies. Here we take babies and young blind children, and have well over 22,000 members. Our badge is a yellow one, showing the head of a blind child turning towards the sun. To join, send a shilling postal order for the badge, and a 3d stamp for postage, to The Sunbeam Society, R.N.I.B., 224, Great Portland Street, London W.1.

The Spastic Club. You may perhaps have heard me broadcasting now and again for the Spastic Centre in Cheyne Walk, Chelsea, London S. W. 3, where we take some of the most pathetic little children in the land. Your mother will be able to tell you about them. We have to teach them the very simplest things — how to walk, to eat, to speak — some of them can do hardly anything when they come to us. We now have about 126,000 members, and I would be glad to welcome you as one, too! Send a shilling postal order and a 3d stamp for a badge, to Miss White, Evans Bros. Ltd, Montague House, Russell Square, London W.C.1.

The Busy Bees. This is the oldest and largest of the four clubs, and has about 300,000 members. All are animal lovers, and our badge is yellow, with a bee on it. We help to raise funds for our animal dispensaries, and have our own Busy Bees Van which goes about the countryside, healing and helping animals of any kind, free. If you love animals, do join. We have our own magazine each month, called "The Busy Bees News". To join the Club send a sixpenny postal order to Enid Blyton Hive Headquarters, 44, Palace Road, Bromley, Kent. If you would like to have the *magazine* for a year, send an extra 5/-. I hope you will have it, as I can keep in touch with you through it.

A Night on Thunder Rock

"Daddy, we've something to ask you," said Robert. "We do hope you'll say 'yes'!"

"Well, I'm not promising till I know what it is," said Daddy, cautiously.

"It's something quite simple," said Rita.

"Yes, something you'd love to do yourself," said Fred. "It's this — *may* we spend a night on Thunder Rock!"

Thunder Rock was a tiny rocky island not far out from the coast. The three children had a small boat of their own, and were used to rowing about by themselves. They had often rowed to Thunder Rock and had a picnic there.

"So now you want to spend a *night* there," said their father. "Well, what does your mother say?"

"She says we must ask *you*," said Robert. "Say 'yes', Daddy. Only just one night. It would be such fun to camp out there all by ourselves."

"We'd take rugs and things," said Rita. "We'd choose a very fine warm night. It would be heavenly to go off to sleep at night with the waves beating on the rocks round us, and the stars blinking above us."

"And waking up in the morning with the sun, and slipping into the water first thing for a bathe," said Fred. "Come on, Dad — say 'yes'."

"Well, what about that old boat of yours?" said father. "I heard it was leaking. Is it safe?"

"Pretty safe, because we can always bale out the water," said Rita. "We don't mind. Anyway we can all swim. But I don't think the poor old boat will last much longer, Daddy. Are new boats very expensive?"

"Very," said her father. "No hope of getting one, so don't make plans! You'll have to make the leaky old tub do for some time — but mind, if it gets too bad we'll have to scrap it. No good running into danger, and you never know."

"Well — may we go to Thunder Rock for the night?" asked Fred. "You haven't said yet."

His father smiled. "All right — you can go. Take your food with you, and rugs and things. You'll be all right. It *is* fun to camp out on a little island like that."

"Oh, *thanks*, Daddy! We never thought you'd say 'yes'!"

In delight the three children rushed off to their mother to tell her. "Well, I do hope you'll all be all right," she said. "You're old enough to look after yourselves now — Robert is fourteen and very strong. Don't get up to any silly tricks though. And be sure that old tub of yours doesn't leak too much."

The children said nothing about their boat. She really was leaking very badly, and needed a lot of baling to keep her from sinking lower and lower! But if only she would last till they had had their night on Thunder Rock!

They made all their plans. Rita fetched a pile of old rugs and old coats. Fred went to ask Cook for a few tins of meat and fruit to take with them, and some ginger beer. Robert went to get the boat ready. They planned to set off that evening, have a picnic supper on the island, a swim in the sun-warmed water, and then a lovely talk lying on the rugs, looking up to the starry sky.

"It will be gorgeous hearing the waves lapping round all the time," said Robert. "Fancy being all by ourselves like that, too! Nobody to send us here and there, nobody to ask what we're up to, nobody to say we're making too much noise!"

They said goodbye and set off in the boat. Everything had been piled in. Had they forgotten anything? No, they didn't think so. Robert and Fred pulled at the oars and Rita baled hard. "Blow this leak! It's getting worse. I honestly don't think the poor old tub will last much longer."

"Well, Ted, the fisherman, says she's too old to mend," said Robert, pulling hard. "Say when you're tired of baling, Rita, and I'll have a turn and you can row."

Gulls cried loudly all round them. The sea was very calm, and only a slight swell lifted the boat now and again. The sun shone from the western sky, and the water gleamed blue and purple and green. Lovely!

They came to Thunder Rock at last. They pulled the boat into a tiny cove, out of reach of the waves. Rita took out the rugs and old coats and spread them on a sandy place between some high rocks.

"We'll be well sheltered here," she said. "And the sand is warm and soft. Won't it be gorgeous sleeping out here? Now what about supper?"

Supper was lovely. Tinned salmon, tinned pineapple, new bread and butter, chocolate and ginger beer. "Better than any meal on a table!" said Fred. "Now let's have a look round Thunder Rock and then have a bathe when our supper's settled a bit."

Thunder Rock was a queer little island. It was nothing but rocks and coves. Little but seaweed grew on it and there was plenty of that! The sea-birds came to it, and liked to stand on the highest rocks, gazing out to sea.

"Lovely things!" said Rita, watching a big gull alight. "I wouldn't mind being a gull — swimming, flying, paddling, gliding, diving — what a fine life!"

They had their bathe and then lay on their rugs in the twilight, warm and glowing. They put on pyjamas, and then Fred yawned. "Golly, are you sleepy already?" said Rita. "I'm not. I want to enjoy every minute of this exciting evening. Don't let's go to sleep for a while."

"Of course we won't," said Robert, nibbling a bar of chocolate. "The sun's quite gone now. There's not a single bit of pink cloud left in the sky. But it's still very warm."

"The waves sound nice, splashing all around Thunder Rock," said Rita, looking sleepy. They went on talking for a while, and then Fred gave another yawn, a most enormous one this time.

"I really don't believe I can keep awake," he

Gulls cried loudly all round them.

said. "I do want to, but my eyes keep closing. I bet we'll sleep well tonight — with nothing whatever to disturb us except the sound of the sea!"

"All right. We'll say goodnight then," said Rita. "I feel sleepy, too. I'm going to fix my eyes on that bright star over there and see how long I can keep awake. It's so lovely out here all alone on Thunder Rock."

It was not long before they were all asleep. The stars shone in the sky, and the sea splashed quietly on the rocks. There was no other sound to be heard.

But wait a minute — *was* there no other sound? Robert suddenly woke up with a jump. He lay there for a moment, wondering where he was. How queer to see the sky above him instead of the ceiling of his bedroom! Then he remembered — of course — he was on Thunder Rock.

He was just about to go to sleep again when he again heard the sound that had awakened him. It was an extra loud splash — and then another and another. Regular splashes.

Robert sat up. It sounded like a boat being rowed along, not far from Thunder Rock!

Then he heard low voices. That made him stiffen to attention even more. A boat near Thunder Rock — and voices in the middle of the night! What did it mean?

Cautiously Robert awoke Fred and whispered in his ear. "Don't make a row! There's a boat being rowed to Thunder Rock."

The boys sat and listened, but the boat did not come to Thunder Rock after all. It went right round it and the voices died away. The splash of the oars could no longer be heard.

The boys sat and listened.

"The boat's on the landward side of the rock now," whispered Robert. "Let's go round and see if we can spot it. There's only star-light to see by but we might just make it out."

They walked cautiously over the rocks, and round to the other side of the little island. They could see a dark mass some way off — that must be the boat! But who was in it — and why come rowing over the sea at this time of night?

"It's all jolly mysterious," said Robert. "Now let's think. Where is that boat heading for?"

"It's going towards the rocky cliffs of the mainland," said Fred. "I should think towards the part that is always washed by the sea — the part we've never been able to explore properly because you can't get round to it."

"There might be caves there," said Robert. "I wonder where the boat came from, though. It seemed to come from out at sea — and yet it was only rowed."

"Do you know — I bet that boat came from a motor launch some way out," said Fred, suddenly. "They wouldn't dare to bring it right in, if they were doing anything they shouldn't, because the motor would be heard. I bet the boat left the launch right out to sea — and was rowed in quietly, with some kind of goods. Probably they've come from France."

"Do you mean *smuggled* goods?" said Robert in sudden excitement. "My word — smugglers!"

"Well, you know there are plenty of smugglers today, now that things are expensive and difficult to get," said Fred. "We've heard Mother talking about it with Daddy, I bet you anything you like we've just heard a boat-load of smugglers passing, with smuggled goods in the boat — and they're heading for the cliffs, where they've either got a hiding-place or friends to take the goods from them!"

Robert whistled. He gazed towards the dark land, which could be faintly seen as a black blur in the starlit night. "Yes. You may be right. Smugglers! I say, what are we going to do about it?"

"Let's go and wake Rita," said Fred. "We can talk about it then, all together.

Rita was very excited when she heard the boys' news. "You might have wakened me before," she said indignantly. "Do you suppose the smugglers' boat will come back?"

"Well — yes — I suppose it may," said Robert. "We'd better keep a look-out."

They all went round to the other side of the little island, and strained their eyes towards the distant cliffs. Then Robert gave an exclamation.

"Look — I'm sure I can see a light — it must be at the bottom of the cliffs, I should think."

They all stared hard, and soon Rita and Fred could see a faint light, too.

"I bet that's where the smugglers are, with their goods!" said Robert.

They sat and watched and talked for a long time. The light disappeared. Then suddenly Robert's sharp ears heard something and he clutched Rita and Fred, making them jump.

"They're coming back! Sh!"

And then there came the sound of oars again, and a murmur of voices. The boat passed in the darkness, a blur against the water. The children hardly dared to breathe. They began to whisper when the boat was out of hearing.

"They must have put the goods in a cave! Let's go tomorrow and find out!"

"Sh! Listen! I believe I can hear a motor starting up a good way out. I bet the smugglers are off back to France!"

"I wish daylight would come. I want to go off and hunt for the smuggled goods!"

But day was nowhere near! It was still only the middle of the night and the children fell asleep again and could hardly believe, in the morning, that anything had happened in the night.

"But it must have, because we all know about it!" said Rita. "So it can't have been a dream. Let's have breakfast and then go and explore those cliffs. We can row quite near to them."

So after a meal they set off in their leaky old

They strained their eyes towards the cliffs.

boat. They rowed towards the towering, rocky cliffs, round whose base the sea washed continually. They came nearer and nearer, and then, when they were afraid of going on to the rocks, they rowed round the cliffs, examining every foot of them as carefully as they could.

And they found what they were looking for! They came suddenly to a cleft in the cliff, and guided their boat carefully towards it. A wave took them into the curious crack and they found themselves in an enclosed channel, walled in by steep cliffs, with not much more room than the boat needed for itself.

On one side of the channel was a cave, running into the cliff, quite hidden from the sea outside. "You hold the boat steady by hanging on to this rock, Fred, and I'll have a look into the cave," said Robert. He leapt from the boat on to a rock and then peered into the cave.

"I *say!* Stacks of things! Boxes and packages of all kinds. This is where those smugglers put their goods. I bet someone on the mainland collects them when it's safe to do so — probably by boat."

He went back to the boat and jumped in. "I'd like to undo some of those boxes," he said. "But I suppose I'd better not. It's a matter for the police now."

"Is it really?" said Rita, looking rather scared. "Well, come on, then. Let's get back home."

They shoved the boat down through the cleft of the cliff back to the open sea again. Robert and Fred took the oars. Fred gave a sudden shout of dismay.

"I say! You'll have to bale like fury, Rita, the boat's awfully full of water. We'll be swimming soon! Get the baler, quick."

Certainly the boat was leaking worse than ever. Rita began to bale quickly. The boys rowed hard. But the boat was heavy now with water, and it was difficult going. In the end the boys had to stop rowing and help Rita with the baling.

They rowed towards the towering cliffs.

When they had made the boat a good bit lighter, they took the oars again.

"You'll have to buck up," said Rita, anxiously. "It'll fill again directly. It must have sprung another leak."

The boat began to fill quickly again. The boys rowed hard. Just before they came to shore the boat quietly began to sink beneath them!

They had to get out and wade to shore, carrying what they could of their goods. "That's very bad luck," said Robert, sadly. "I liked that old boat. I'm afraid she's done for now. Come on, let's go home and tell Mother what's happened. Then she can ring up the police."

Mother was amazed at all they had to tell. She was horrified about the boat, and very glad they had arrived home safely.

"I can hardly believe this tale of smugglers," she said. "But I suppose I'd better ring up the police. I'll do it now, whilst you go and put on dry things."

It wasn't long before an Inspector of Police came round in his car. He listened with the greatest interest to all that the children told him.

"I expect they've really hit on something," he told their mother. "We know smuggling is going on all round the coast. But it's difficult to trace. I'll get a boat and go round to this cave. Perhaps I could take the children's boat and they could direct me to the place."

"It's sunk," said Fred, sorrowfully. "We haven't a boat now! We feel very upset about it. Ted, the fisherman, will lend you his. We'll come too."

The Inspector found that the goods in the cave were most certainly smuggled. "Silk stockings! Bottles of brandy! Perfume of all kinds! My word, this is a haul!" he said in delight. "Well, we'll remove all these goods tonight when nobody is likely to see us, and then we'll set a watch for the smugglers' friends, whoever they are. They are sure to come for the goods soon. And we will also put somebody on Thunder Rock, lying in wait for the smugglers when they come again, as they are sure to do."

It all sounded very exciting indeed. The children wanted to go to Thunder Rock with the watchers, but the Inspector said no. "There may be danger — shooting, for instance," he said. "You're better out of things like that. I'll let you know what happens, never fear!"

He kept his word, and brought them a very exciting story the next week. "We've caught the men who receive the goods," he began. "We spotted them rowing round to the cave to fetch them. And now we've got the smugglers too! Three of them!"

"Did you catch them in their boat?" asked Rita.

"We followed their boat when it went back to the open sea," said the Inspector. "And there, sure enough was a smart little motor launch waiting for them. We caught the whole lot — so *that* spot of smuggling is stopped for a little while at any rate."

"What a good thing we went to spend the night on Thunder Rock!" said Fred. "Jolly bad luck our boat is gone, though."

"Oh, I wouldn't worry about that," said the Inspector in an airy voice. "We want to give you a reward for your help — you'll find it in Ted the fisherman's charge if you care to go and look!"

The children tore down to the beach at once and found Ted there, grinning. Beside his boat lay another one, newly-painted and very smart.

"Good morning to you," said Ted. "Come to have a look at your new boat? Smart, isn't she? My word, you're lucky children, aren't you?"

"We *are!*" said Rita, in delight. "Bags I row her first! Oh, what a beauty. Come on, boys — haul her down the beach. Off we go!"

And off they went, bobbing lightly up and down on the waves. They rowed to Thunder Rock, pulled the boat up on the sand and lay down in the sun.

"Good old Thunder Rock!" said Fred, banging the sand below him with his open hand. "If it hadn't been for you we'd never have got that marvellous — wonderful — new boat!"

THE MYSTERY OF THE VANISHED PRINCE

This is an exciting little incident from THE MYSTERY OF THE VANISHED PRINCE. A small prince has been kidnapped, and Fatty thinks that he is hidden in an old farmhouse. So off he and his friends go to find out — and suddenly they are captured and locked up by two men. But Fatty knows how to go through a locked door!

In silence the two men hurried the children along. Bets was frightened and kept close to Fatty. Ern was scared too, and forgot all about slapping at the flies. And all the time the helicopter hovered about overhead, evidently waiting for some signal to land.

Round a corner they came into a big farmyard. Pigs were in a sty, and hens wandered about. It looked very homely and countrified all of a sudden. Ducks quacked in a pond, and a horse lifted its head from a trough where it had been drinking, and stared at the little company.

A very big farmhouse lay back from the yard. Its tall chimneys showed that it was old — probably built in Elizabethan times. There was a small door in the wall of the farmhouse not far from them. The men hurried the children over to it, opened it, and shoved them all in, giving them a push if they thought anyone was not quick enough.

Down a long passage — up some narrow, curving stairs, along another passage, with wooden boards that were very old and uneven. The passage was dark, and Bets didn't like it at all. She slipped her hand into Fatty's and he squeezed it hard.

They came to a door. The man in front opened it. "In here," he said, and in they all went. Fatty put his foot in the doorway just as the man was about to shut them in.

"What are you doing this for?" he asked. "You know you'll get into trouble, don't you? We're only kids out on a walk. What's the mystery?"

"You'll be kept here for a day or two," said the man. "There are reasons. You came at an unfortunate time for yourselves. Be sensible and nothing will happen to you."

He kicked Fatty's foot away suddenly and slammed the door. The six children heard the key turning in the lock. Then they heard the footsteps of the two men as they hurried away down the passage.

Fatty looked desperately round the room. It was small and dark, lined with oak panels. There was one small window, with leaded panes. He ran to it and peered out. A sheer drop to the ground! Nobody could climb out there with safety.

"Fatty! What's all this about?" said Ern, in a frightened voice. "Sawful!"

"Shall I tell you what I think?" said Fatty, in a low voice. "I think the Prince Bongawah was taken here and hidden, when he was kidnapped from his car. And I think he's been kept prisoner here till arrangements could be made to spirit him away somehow — and that's what that helicopter is arriving for! It will land somewhere here, the Prince will be hurried aboard — and nobody will ever hear of him again!"

Bets shivered. "I don't like you saying that," she said. "Fatty, what are we going to do? Do you think they'll hurt us?"

"No," said Fatty. "I think we're a nuisance, but I think they really do believe we're only six kids out hiking. They've no idea we're hunting for old Goon, or that we know anything is going on here."

"But what are we going to *do?*" said Bets,

Two men suddenly rose up from the long grass and captured the children. In silence they hurried them along to the farmhouse.

again. "I don't like this place. I want to get out."

"I can hear the helicopter again," said Pip. "It sounds nearer. It must be coming down."

"Do you suppose Mr. Goon is a prisoner too?" said Larry. "We haven't seen or heard a sign of him. Perhaps he didn't come to Raylingham Marshes after all."

"Perhaps he didn't," said Fatty. He went over to the door and tried it. It was locked. He looked at the door. It was old but very stout and strong. Nobody could possibly break it down.

"Do your trick of getting out through a locked door, Fatty," said Daisy suddenly. "There's a good space under the door — I believe you could manage it beautifully."

"That's just what I was thinking," said Fatty. "The only thing is I need a newspaper – and I haven't brought a newspaper with me today. Very careless of me."

"I've got a comic," said Ern, unexpectedly. "Would that do? What are you going to do, Fatty?"

"Get through this locked door," said Fatty, much to Ern's amazement. Ern fished in his pocket and brought out a crumpled and messy comic, which he handed to Fatty.

"Good work," said Fatty, pleased. He took the comic and opened out the middle double sheet. He slid it carefully under the door, leaving only a small corner on his side. Ern watched, puzzled. How was that going to open a locked door?

Fatty took a small leather case from his pocket and opened it. In it were a number of curious small tools, and a little roll of wire. Fatty took out the wire and straightened it.

He inserted it into the keyhole and began delicately to work at the key. He prodded and pushed and jiggled it — until, suddenly, he gave a sharp push and the key slid out of the keyhole on the other side of the door, and fell with a thud down to the floor.

Ern stared open-mouthed. He couldn't for the life of him make out what Fatty was doing. But the others knew. They had seen Fatty doing his locked-door trick before!

"Hope it's fallen on to the comic," said Fatty, and bent down to draw the sheet of paper back under the bottom of the door. Carefully he pulled it, very carefully. More and more of the comic appeared, and oh joy, at last the key appeared too under the door, on the second half of the double sheet! There it was, on their side of the door. Fatty had managed to get it!

Ern gasped. His eyes almost fell out of his head. "Coo — you are a one!" he said to Fatty. "You're a genius, that's what you are."

"Be quiet, Ern," said Fatty. He slid the key into the lock on his side of the door and turned it. The door unlocked. Now they could all go free!

NEXT-DOOR JAMES

JIMMY had a fine bicycle, but next-door James hadn't. Sometimes his big sister let him ride hers, but he didn't like that much, because it wasn't a proper boy's bicycle. So he was always looking over the wall at Jimmy's bicycle, begging to have a little ride.

"No, you can't," said Jimmy. He didn't like sharing his things with anyone. "I'm not going to have it messed up by you."

"I wouldn't mess it up," said next-door James. "And anyway, I'd clean it after I'd had it."

"Well, you can't have it," said Jimmy.

"You're selfish," said James. "You never let anyone share. You've never even let me have a kick at your new football."

James was right. Jimmy was selfish. He kept his sweets to himself. He wouldn't run errands for his mother unless she paid him. He wouldn't do anything he didn't really want to do.

One Saturday, when his father was home, he called to Jimmy. "Jimmy, old man — bike down to the paper shop for me, will you, and tell them my paper hasn't come."

"Good morning, Mr. Brown. Is there anything you want me to do?"

"I'm busy, Dad," called back Jimmy. "I'll go in a minute." But he forgot, of course.

Then his mother called him. "Jimmy! Are you there? Will you go and give a message to Granny for me, dear? And fetch the meat? I'm so busy today."

"Oh, Mother — so am I!" said Jimmy. "I'm just in the middle of something. You make me into an errand boy, you and Daddy."

Mother didn't say anything to that. She was hurt and shocked. What a thing to say! But his father had heard it, and he frowned. He went next door and asked for James. James came at once.

"Good morning, Mr. Brown. Is there anything you want me to do? I'm just going down to the village for my mother."

Mr. Brown looked at James. He had a very big basket indeed. "How are you going? On foot?" he asked.

"Yes. I haven't a bike like Jimmy," said James. "I wish I had! It wouldn't take me any time then to get down to the village and back!"

"I was wondering if you'd go a few errands for me and Mrs. Brown," said Mr. Brown. "I was going to suggest that you rode Jimmy's bike.

He has a big basket on the front and a good carrier at the back."

"Oh, sir — can I really ride it?" said James. "It's such a beauty! My word, I shall feel grand riding that. I've never had a ride on it yet. Do you think Jimmy will mind?"

"It doesn't matter whether he does or not," said Mr. Brown. "I say you can take it, and I'm much obliged to you for being so ready to go. Look — here are the things we want done — there's a message for Jimmy's Granny — you know where she lives. And I want my newspaper, and here's Mrs. Brown's shopping list. Can you do all this?"

"Why, it's nothing!" said James. "I do much more for Mother. I can go to and fro several times to the village this morning, as I'm having Jimmy's bike. Thanks very much, sir."

Jimmy didn't see James come in and take his bike. He didn't see him ride away on it in the greatest delight. He didn't know that James was riding proudly down the village street, ringing the bell and feeling very grand indeed.

Now, it so happened that Jimmy suddenly remembered that he wanted to buy some sweets that day. He hadn't a single one left. He went

James rode away in the greatest delight.

"That's my bike! How dare you! I never said you could ride it. Get off at once!"

to fetch his bicycle — and it wasn't there! The shed was empty! Jimmy looked everywhere.

"Mother! My bike's gone!" shouted Jimmy. "And I wanted to go and fetch some sweets. Wherever can it be?"

Nobody answered. Jimmy ran to the front gate and looked out. Had he left his bicycle outside, by any chance?

And then he suddenly saw James sailing up the street on his bicycle, ringing the bell loudly. He could hardly believe his eyes! He rushed out at once.

"That's my bike! How dare you! I never said you could ride it. Get off at once! I'll tell my father."

"He knows," grinned James. "He told me I could take it. He wanted all kinds of errands done and so did your mother, so he came and asked if I'd do them for him — and he said I could use your bike. My, it's a fine one — I've been three times down to the village and back on it already."

Jimmy snatched at his bike in a rage.

"You give it to me!" he shouted. "And don't you dare ride it again. I don't believe a word you say."

"I want a nice, cheerful, willing boy like you, James."

Then a stern voice spoke behind him.

"Jimmy! I told James to take your bike. I asked you to go an errand for me and you didn't. Your mother asked you, and you were rude to her. The only errand you meant to do was to fetch sweets for yourself."

It was Jimmy's father. Jimmy was most alarmed.

"Do you remember what you promised us when we gave you your bicycle, Jimmy?" said his father. "You promised you would always do our errands cheerfully and quickly. You haven't kept your bargain."

Jimmy went very red. He hated next-door James to hear all this.

"Well, we don't want you to do things for us if you can't bear to," went on his father. "So I have decided to ask James here if he'll run our errands on your bicycle. He's very willing to do so, and I'm sure he'll take care of your bicycle. Won't you, James?"

"Of course, sir," said James. "But — er — suppose Jimmy wants to do your errands, Mr. Brown?"

"He won't want to," said Mr. Brown. "He hasn't gone any messages or errands for us for weeks. There's no reason to think he'll change. Besides, I want a nice, cheerful, willing boy like you, James. It's a pleasure to ask you anything."

"You might give me a chance, Dad," said Jimmy, in a low voice.

"Yes. Give him a chance, sir," said James. "It's his bike, after all. I know how he feels. I'll always do your errands for you if Jimmy won't. But I'd like him to have a chance."

"Very well. Put the bike away now, James, and come in and have some chocolate cake and a drink of lemonade," said Mr. Brown.

He didn't ask Jimmy to come, and Jimmy didn't go with them. He suddenly felt ashamed of himself. To think that his father and mother had lent his bike to next-door James to go the errands he should have gone. He didn't like another boy helping his mother and father. Let next-door James run his own mother's errands!

Jimmy was given his chance. You should see him sailing away on his bicycle immediately his mother wants anything fetched. It really makes her smile. But she's pleased about another thing, too — Jimmy always lends his bicycle to James whenever he wants it. Quite right, too — after all, it was James who gave him his chance!

Jimmy sails away on his bicycle immediately his mother wants anything fetched.

A LIST OF BOOKS BY ENID BLYTON

ADVENTURE AND MYSTERY

The Famous Five Series (all published by Hodder and Stoughton):

FIVE ON A TREASURE ISLAND
FIVE GO ADVENTURING AGAIN
FIVE RUN AWAY TOGETHER
FIVE GO TO SMUGGLER'S TOP
FIVE GO OFF IN A CARAVAN
You will find an extract on page 181.
FIVE ON KIRRIN ISLAND AGAIN
FIVE GO OFF TO CAMP
FIVE GET INTO TROUBLE
FIVE FALL INTO ADVENTURE
FIVE ON A HIKE TOGETHER
FIVE HAVE A WONDERFUL TIME
You will find an extract on page 165.
FIVE GO DOWN TO THE SEA
FIVE GO TO MYSTERY MOOR
FIVE HAVE PLENTY OF FUN
FIVE ON A SECRET TRAIL
FIVE GO TO BILLYCOCK HILL
FIVE GET INTO A FIX
FIVE ON FINNISTON FARM
FIVE GO TO DEMON'S ROCKS
THE FAMOUS FIVE SPECIAL
(An Omnibus volume containing FIVE GO OFF TO CAMP, FIVE GO OFF IN A CARAVAN, FIVE HAVE A WONDERFUL TIME)
You will find a complete Famous Five story on page 115, 'Five and a Half-Term Adventure.' This originally appeared in ENID BLYTON'S MAGAZINE ANNUAL NO. 3 (Evans), now out of print.

The Secret Seven Series (all published by Brockhampton Press):

THE SECRET SEVEN
SECRET SEVEN ADVENTURE
WELL DONE SECRET SEVEN
SECRET SEVEN ON THE TRAIl
GO AHEAD SECRET SEVEN
GOOD WORK SECRET SEVEN
SECRET SEVEN WIN THROUGH
THREE CHEERS SECRET SEVEN
SECRET SEVEN MYSTERY
PUZZLE FOR THE SECRET SEVEN
SECRET SEVEN FIREWORKS
GOOD OLD SECRET SEVEN
A SHOCK FOR THE SECRET SEVEN
You will find two stories of the Secret Seven on pages 14 and 218. 'The Humbug Adventure' originally appeared in ENID BLYTON'S MAGAZINE ANNUAL NO. 1, and 'Hurry, Secret Seven, Hurry!' appeared in ENID BLYTON'S MAGAZINE ANNUAL NO. 4. Both books published by Evans, now out of print.

The Barney Books (all published by Collins):

THE RILLOBY FAIR MYSTERY
THE RING O'BELLS MYSTERY
THE ROCKINGDOWN MYSTERY
THE RUBADUB MYSTERY
You will find extracts on pages 78 and 180
THE RAT-A-TAT MYSTERY
THE RAGAMUFFIN MYSTERY

The Mystery Series (Methuen):

THE MYSTERY OF THE BURNT COTTAGE, THE MYSTERY OF THE DISAPPEARING CAT, THE MYSTERY OF THE SECRET ROOM, THE MYSTERY OF THE SPITEFUL LETTERS, THE MYSTERY OF THE MISSING NECKLACE, THE MYSTERY OF THE HIDDEN HOUSE, THE MYSTERY OF THE PANTOMIME CAT, THE MYSTERY OF THE INVISIBLE THIEF, THE MYSTERY OF THE VANISHED PRINCE (You will find an extract on page 238), THE MYSTERY OF THE STRANGE BUNDLE (You will find an extract on page 202), THE MYSTERY OF HOLLY LANE, THE MYSTERY OF TALLY-HO COTTAGE, THE MYSTERY OF THE MISSING MAN, THE MYSTERY OF THE STRANGE MESSAGES
THE MYSTERY OF BANSHEE TOWERS

The Adventure Series (Macmillan):

THE ISLAND OF ADVENTURE
THE CASTLE OF ADVENTURE
THE VALLEY OF ADVENTURE
THE SEA OF ADVENTURE
THE MOUNTAIN OF ADVENTURE
You will find an extract on page 36.
THE SHIP OF ADVENTURE
THE CIRCUS OF ADVENTURE
You will find an extract on page 132.
THE RIVER OF ADVENTURE

Other Adventure Stories:

THE SECRET ISLAND (Blackwell):
You will find an extract on page 170.
THE SECRET OF SPIGGY HOLES (Blackwell)
THE SECRET MOUNTAIN (Blackwell)
THE SECRET OF KILLIMOOIN
THE SECRET OF MOON CASTLE (Blackwell)
THE BOY NEXT DOOR (Collins)
THE TREASURE HUNTERS (Collins)
ADVENTURE STORIES (Collins)
MYSTERY STORIES (Collins)
HOLIDAY HOUSE (Evans)
SIX COUSINS AT MISTLETOE FARM (Evans) SIX COUSINS AGAIN (Evans)
THE ADVENTUROUS FOUR (Newnes)
THE ADVENTUROUS FOUR AGAIN (Newnes)
THE ADVENTURE OF THE STRANGE RUBY (Brockhampton Press)
THE SECRET OF THE OLD MILL (Brockhampton): Temporarily out of print.

NATURE AND ANIMAL STORIES

DOG STORIES (Collins)
SHADOW THE SHEEPDOG (Collins)
THE LAUGHING KITTEN (Harvill Press): Temporarily out of print.
MISCHIEF AGAIN (Harvill Press)
ADVENTURES OF PIP and MORE ADVENTURES OF PIP (Sampson Low)
HEDGEROW TALES (Methuen):
You will find an extract on page 153.
ENID BLYTON'S NATURE LOVER'S BOOK (Evans): You will find extracts on pages 90, 207 and 213.
ENID BLYTON'S ANIMAL LOVER'S BOOK (Evans): You will find an extract on page 98.
ROUND THE YEAR WITH ENID BLYTON (Evans)
RAMBLES WITH UNCLE NAT (National Magazine Company): Temporarily out of print. You will find extracts on pages 48, 62, 88, 122, 156 and 190. The illustrations are by Nora S. Unwin.
BIRDS OF OUR GARDEN (Newnes):
You will find an extract on page 91.
THE ANIMAL BOOK (Newnes)
BIRDS OF THE WAYSIDE AND WOODLAND (Warne)

LITTLE NODDY BOOKS

(all published by Sampson Low)

Noddy Library:

NODDY GOES TO TOYLAND
HURRAH FOR LITTLE NODDY
NODDY AND HIS CAR
HERE COMES NODDY AGAIN!
WELL DONE, NODDY!
NODDY GOES TO SCHOOL
NODDY AT THE SEASIDE
NODDY GETS INTO TROUBLE
NODDY AND THE MAGIC RUBBER
YOU FUNNY LITTLE NODDY
NODDY MEETS FATHER CHRISTMAS
NODDY AND TESSIE BEAR
BE BRAVE, LITTLE NODDY!
NODDY AND THE BUMPY DOG
DO LOOK OUT, NODDY!
YOU'RE A GOOD FRIEND, NODDY
NODDY HAS AN ADVENTURE
NODDY GOES TO SEA
NODDY AND THE BUNKEY
CHEER UP, LITTLE NODDY!
NODDY GOES TO THE FAIR
NODDY AND THE TOOTLES
MR. PLOD AND LITTLE NODDY

Noddy Annuals:

THE FIRST BIG NODDY BOOK
THE SECOND, THIRD, FOURTH, FIFTH, SIXTH, SEVENTH and EIGHTH BIG NODDY BOOKS

You will find two complete Little Noddy stories on pages 67 and 140.

Cartons of Noddy Books:

NODDY HOUSE OF BOOKS, NODDY ARK OF BOOKS, NODDY GARAGE OF BOOKS, NODDY CASTLE OF BOOKS, NODDY STATION OF BOOKS, NODDY SHOP OF BOOKS

Little Strip Picture Books:

NODDY AND THE WITCH'S WAND
NODDY'S PENNY WHEEL CAR
NODDY'S CAR GETS A SQUEAK
NODDY AND THE CUCKOO'S NEST
NODDY GETS CAPTURED
NODDY IS VERY SILLY
NODDY GOES DANCING
NODDY AND THE SNOW HOUSE
NODDY THE CRY-BABY
NODDY AND THE TRICKY TEDDY
NODDY TRICKS MR. SLY
NODDY AND THE BEAR WHO LOST HIS GROWL
NODDY GETS INTO TROUBLE
NODDY AND THE RUNAWAY WHEEL
NODDY'S BAG OF MONEY

Colour Strip Picture Books:

NODDY COLOUR STRIP BOOK
NEW NODDY COLOUR STRIP BOOK
HOW FUNNY YOU ARE, NODDY
HELLO, LITTLE NODDY

Pop-Up Books:

NODDY GOES TO THE FAIR
NODDY AND HIS FRIENDS
NODDY IN TOY VILLAGE

Board Books:

NODDY BOARD BOOK
BIG-EARS BOARD BOOK

Nursery Series:

A DAY WITH NODDY
NODDY'S OWN NURSERY RHYMES

Miscellaneous Noddy Books:

NODDY AND BIG-EARS, NODDY IN TOYLAND (The book of the Noddy pantomime), ABC WITH NODDY, NODDY'S CAR PICTURE BOOK, 1-2-3 WITH NODDY, NODDY'S TRAIN PICTURE BOOK, NODDY'S TALL RED BOOK, NODDY'S TALL BLUE BOOK, NODDY'S TALL GREEN BOOK, NODDY'S TALL YELLOW BOOK, NODDY'S TALL ORANGE BOOK, NODDY'S TALL PINK BOOK

COLLECTIONS OF STORIES

Holiday Books (Sampson Low):

THE ENID BLYTON HOLIDAY BOOK
SECOND, THIRD, FOURTH, FIFTH, SIXTH, SEVENTH, EIGHTH, NINTH, TENTH, ELEVENTH and TWELFTH HOLIDAY BOOKS

Flower Story Books:

THE BUTTERCUP STORY BOOK (John Gifford), THE SNOWDROP STORY BOOK (John Gifford), THE POPPY STORY BOOK (John Gifford): Temporarily out of print. THE FOXGLOVE STORY BOOK (John Gifford), THE WATER-LILY STORY BOOK (John Gifford), THE MARIGOLD STORY BOOK (John Gifford), BLUEBELL STORY BOOK (Macdonald), DAFFODIL STORY BOOK (Macdonald)

Bedside Books (Arthur Barker):

MY ENID BLYTON BEDSIDE BOOK, ENID BLYTON'S SECOND BEDSIDE BOOK, ENID BLYTON'S THIRD BEDSIDE BOOK (You will find an extract on page 145), ENID BLYTON'S FOURTH BEDSIDE BOOK, ENID BLYTON'S FIFTH BEDSIDE BOOK (You will find an extract on page 18), ENID BLYTON'S SIXTH BEDSIDE BOOK (You will find extracts on pages 28 and 188), ENID BLYTON'S SEVENTH BEDSIDE BOOK (You will find extracts on pages 131 and 206), ENID BLYTON'S EIGHTH BEDSIDE BOOK (You will find extracts on pages 126 and 137), ENID BLYTON'S NINTH BEDSIDE BOOK (You will find extracts on pages 130 and 240), ENID BLYTON'S TENTH BEDSIDE BOOK, ENID BLYTON'S ELEVENTH BEDSIDE BOOK, ENID BLYTON'S TWELFTH BEDSIDE BOOK (You will find an extract on page 169)

Little Books (Brockhampton Press):

Temporarily out of print: TALES ABOUT TOYS, WHAT AN ADVENTURE, AT APPLETREE FARM, COME TO THE CIRCUS, TEDDY BEAR'S PARTY, THE PROUD GOLLIWOG, HELLO TWINS

Nursery Series (Brockhampton Press):

Temporarily out of print.
OH, WHAT A LOVELY TIME
DEAR OLD SNOWMAN

Little Bedtime Books (Sampson Low):

ABOUT THE GOLLIWOG AND THE WIRELESS, ABOUT SILLY SAMMY, ABOUT THE DOLL THAT FELL OUT OF THE PRAM, ABOUT THE SURPRISING BROOM, ABOUT AMANDA GOING AWAY ABOUT THE WIZARD WHO REALLY WAS A NUISANCE, ABOUT THE BALLOON PIPE, ABOUT THE CLOUD KITTEN

Pleasure Books Series (Pitkin):

THE LITTLE TOY FARM
THE CASTLE WITHOUT A DOOR
Temporarily out of print: CHUFF THE CHIMNEY SWEEP, THE ENCHANTED SEA, A CAT IN FAIRYLAND, THE LITTLE SPINNING HOUSE, TOOWISE THE WONDERFUL WIZARD, BENNY AND THE PRINCESS, THE RUNAWAY TEDDY BEAR, THE MAGIC SNOW-BIRD, THE FLYING GOAT, THE STRANGE UMBRELLA, PIPPY AND THE GNOME, BOODY THE GREAT GOBLIN, LET'S HAVE A STORY, WE WANT A STORY

Other Story Books:

MR. ICY-COLD (Blackwell)
FRIENDLY STORY BOOK (Brockhampton Press)
LUCKY STORY BOOK, SUNNY STORY BOOK, BRIGHT STORY BOOK, GAY STORY BOOK, JOLLY STORY BOOK, MERRY STORY BOOK, HAPPY STORY BOOK (Brockhampton Press), JINKY'S JOKE (Brockhampton Press): Temporarily out of print. THE RED-SPOTTED HANDKERCHIEF (Brockhampton): Temporarily out of print. TALES AFTER SUPPER, TALES AFTER TEA, TALES AT BEDTIME (Collins)
HUMPTY DUMPTY AND BELINDA (Collins): Out of print.
FATHER CHRISTMAS AND BELINDA (Collins): Out of print.
HAPPY DAY STORIES (Evans)
'Let's Have a Club of our own,' appears on pages 26 and 102 of this book.
ENID BLYTON'S BOOK OF THE YEAR (Evans)
RAINY DAY STORIES (Evans)
ENID BLYTON'S TREASURY (Evans): Out of print. 'Things to Make on a Rainy Afternoon,' the story on page 230 and the two Nature Quizzes on pages 32 and 196 originally appeared in this book.
A STORY PARTY AT GREEN HEDGES (Hodder and Stoughton)
A PICNIC PARTY WITH ENID BLYTON (Hodder and Stoughton)
TINY TALES (Littlebury)
CHIMNEY CORNER STORIES (Macdonald)
MORE CHIMNEY CORNER STORIES (Macdonald)
ENID BLYTON'S GAY STREET BOOK (Macdonald): Temporarily out of print.
MY FIRST, SECOND, AND THIRD ENID BLYTON BOOKS (Macdonald)
ROUND THE CLOCK STORIES (Macdonald)
TALES OF TOYLAND (Macdonald): Out of print
RUBBALONG TALES (Macmillan)
I'LL TELL YOU A STORY (Macmillan)
I'LL TELL YOU ANOTHER STORY (Macmillan)
THE CONJURING WIZARD AND OTHER STORIES (Macmillan), THE LITTLE WHITE DUCK AND OTHER STORIES (Macmillan)
TRICKY THE GOBLIN AND OTHER STORIES (Macmillan)
THE THREE NAUGHTY CHILDREN AND OTHER STORIES (Macmillan)
THE ASTONISHING LADDER AND OTHER STORIES (Macmillan)
THE MAGIC KNITTING NEEDLES AND OTHER STORIES (Macmillan)
JUST TIME FOR A STORY (Macmillan)
FIVE-MINUTE TALES (Methuen)
TEN-MINUTE TALES (Methuen)
FIFTEEN-MINUTE TALES (Methuen)
TWENTY-MINUTE TALES (Methuen)
FIVE O'CLOCK TALES (Methuen)
SIX O'CLOCK TALES (Methuen)
SEVEN O'CLOCK TALES (Methuen)
EIGHT O'CLOCK TALES (Methuen)
BILLY-BOB TALES (Methuen)
TALES OF BETSY-MAY (Methuen)
A BOOK OF NAUGHTY CHILDREN (Methuen)
A SECOND BOOK OF NAUGHTY CHILDREN (Methuen)
THE BLUE STORY BOOK (Methuen)
THE RED STORY BOOK (Methuen)
THE GREEN STORY BOOK (Methuen)
THE YELLOW STORY BOOK (Methuen)
THE FAMOUS JIMMY (Muller)
GOOD MORNING BOOK (National Magazine Company): Out of print.
TALES OF GREEN HEDGES (National Magazine Company): Out of print.

PLAYS

CAMEO PLAYS BOOK 4 (Arnold)
SIX PLAYS FOR SCHOOLS (Blackwell): There is a play from this book on page 69
SIX ENID BLYTON PLAYS (Methuen)
THE PLAY'S THE THING (Newnes)

RELIGIOUS BOOKS

THE GREATEST BOOK IN THE WORLD (British and Foreign Bible Society)
THE BOY WITH THE LOAVES AND FISHES (Lutterworth)
THE LITTLE GIRL AT CAPERNAUM (Lutterworth)
BEFORE I GO TO SLEEP (Macdonald)
A STORY BOOK OF JESUS (Macmillan)
THE CHRISTMAS BOOK (Macmillan)
You will find an extract from this book on page 158
THE LITTLE DAUGHTER OF JAIRUS (Macmillan): You will find an extract from this book on page 107
THE LAND OF FAR-BEYOND (Methuen): You will find an extract from this book on page 136
THE CHILDREN'S LIFE OF CHRIST (Methuen): You will find an extract from this book on page 25
TALES FROM THE BIBLE (Methuen)
CHILDREN'S BOOK OF PRAYERS (Muller)
BIBLE STORIES (Muller)
TALES FROM THE BIBLE (Muller)

BOM BOOKS

(all published by Brockhampton Press)

Bom Library:
BOM THE LITTLE TOY DRUMMER
BOM AND HIS MAGIC DRUMSTICK
BOM GOES ADVENTURING
BOM GOES TO HO HO VILLAGE
You will find an extract from this book on page 214
BOM AND THE RAINBOW
BOM AND THE CLOWN
BOM GOES TO MAGIC TOWN
BOM AT THE SEASIDE
Bom Strip Picture Books:
HALLO BOM AND WUFFY DOG
BOM GOES TO THE CIRCUS
HERE COMES BOM

FARM AND COUNTRYSIDE

THE CHILDREN OF CHERRY TREE FARM, THE CHILDREN OF WILLOW FARM, MORE ADVENTURES ON WILLOW FARM (Country Life)
DOWN AT THE FARM WITH ENID BLYTON (Sampson Low)
LET'S GARDEN (Macdonald)
SIX COUSINS AT MISTLETOE FARM (Evans)
SIX COUSINS AGAIN (Evans)

FAMILY AND HOME LIFE STORIES

THOSE DREADFUL CHILDREN, THE HOUSE-AT-THE-CORNER, THE PUT-EM-RIGHTS, THE FAMILY AT REDROOFS, HOLLOW TREE HOUSE (Lutterworth)
THE SIX BAD BOYS (Lutterworth):
You will find an extract from this book on page 142.
THE CHILDREN AT GREEN MEADOWS (Lutterworth):
You will find an extract from this book on page 64.
THE CARAVAN FAMILY (Lutterworth)
THE SAUCY JANE FAMILY, THE POLE STAR FAMILY, THE SEASIDE FAMILY, THE QUEEN ELIZABETH FAMILY, THE BUTTERCUP FARM FAMILY, THE VERY BIG SECRET, SNOWBALL THE PONY, THE ADVENTURE OF THE SECRET NECKLACE, RUN-ABOUT'S HOLIDAY, FOUR IN A FAMILY, THE BIRTHDAY KITTEN (Lutterworth)
THE CHILDREN AT HAPPY HOUSE (Macdonald): Out of print.
THE HAPPY HOUSE CHILDREN AGAIN (Macdonald)
BENJY AND THE OTHERS (Macdonald): Out of print.

SCHOOL STORIES

THE TWINS AT ST. CLARE'S, THE O'SULLIVAN TWINS AGAIN, SUMMER TERM AT ST. CLARE'S, SECOND FORM AT ST. CLARE'S, CLAUDINE AT ST. CLARE'S' FIFTH FORMERS OF ST. CLARE'S, FIRST FORMERS OF ST. CLARE'S, FIRST TERM AT MALORY TOWERS, SECOND FORM AT MALORY TOWERS, THIRD YEAR AT MALORY TOWERS (Methuen). You will find an extract from this book on page 93.
UPPER FOURTH AT MALORY TOWERS, IN THE FIFTH AT MALORY TOWERS. You will find an extract from this book on page 192.
LAST TERM AT MALORY TOWERS (Methuen)
THE NAUGHTIEST GIRL IN THE SCHOOL, THE NAUGHTIEST GIRL AGAIN, THE NAUGHTIEST GIRL IS A MONITOR (Newnes)

MARY MOUSE STRIP PICTURE BOOKS

MARY MOUSE HAS A WONDERFUL IDEA, MARY MOUSE GOES TO THE FAIR, A DAY WITH MARY MOUSE, MARY MOUSE IN NURSERY RHYME LAND, LITTLE MARY MOUSE AGAIN, WE DO LOVE MARY MOUSE, HOW DO YOU DO MARY MOUSE, MARY MOUSE AND HER FAMILY, HERE COMES MARY MOUSE AGAIN, HURRAH FOR MARY MOUSE, A PRIZE FOR MARY MOUSE, MARY MOUSE GOES TO SEA, WELCOME MARY MOUSE, MARY MOUSE AND THE DOLL'S HOUSE, MORE ADVENTURES OF MARY MOUSE, HELLO LITTLE MARY MOUSE: Temporarily out of print.

CLICKY STRIP PICTURE BOOKS

CLICKY GETS INTO TROUBLE
CLICKY AND THE FLYING HORSE
CLICKY AND TIPTOE

STRIP PICTURE BOOKS

JOSIE CLICK AND BUN AND LITTLE TREE-HOUSE, JOSIE CLICK AND BUN AGAIN, FURTHER ADVENTURES OF JOSIE CLICK AND BUN, MORE ABOUT JOSIE CLICK AND BUN, BUMPY AND HIS BUS, DAME SLAP AND HER SCHOOL, UP THE FARAWAY TREE (Newnes)
MR. TUMPY AND HIS CARAVAN (Sidgwick and Jackson): Temporarily out of print.
MR. TUMPY PLAYS A TRICK ON SAUCEPAN (Sampson Low)
MR. TUMPY IN THE LAND OF WISHES (Sampson Low)
MR. TUMPY IN THE LAND OF BOYS AND GIRLS (Sampson Low)
MANDY, MOPS AND CUBBY (Sampson Low)
MANDY, MOPS AND CUBBY AGAIN (Sampson Low)
MANDY MAKES CUBBY A HAT (Sampson Low)
MANDY, MOPS AND CUBBY AND THE WHITEWASH (Sampson Low)
GOBO AND MR. FIERCE (Sampson Low)
GOBO IN THE LAND OF DREAMS (Sampson Low)

BRER RABBIT BOOKS

(all published by Macdonald)

FIRST BRER RABBIT BOOK
SECOND BRER RABBIT BOOK
THIRD BRER RABBIT BOOK
FOURTH BRER RABBIT BOOK
FIFTH BRER RABBIT BOOK
SIXTH BRER RABBIT BOOK
SEVENTH BRER RABBIT BOOK
EIGHTH BRER RABBIT BOOK

RETOLD CLASSICS

(all published by Macdonald)

ROBIN HOOD BOOK
TALES FROM THE ARABIAN NIGHTS
TALES OF ANCIENT GREECE
KNIGHTS OF THE ROUND TABLE

VERSE

NODDY'S OWN NURSERY RHYMES (Sampson Low)
THE ENID BLYTON POETRY BOOK (Methuen)
You will find extracts from this book on pages 23, 124, 202 and 227
The poem 'On Dorset Hills' which appears on page 228 originally appeared in *The Sunday Times*. The 'Lullaby' on page 135 appeared in the *Sunday Dispatch*.

FAIRY TALES AND HUMOROUS STORIES

Faraway Tree Series (all published by Newnes):
THE ENCHANTED WOOD
THE MAGIC FARAWAY TREE
THE FOLK OF THE FARAWAY TREE
Other Fairy Tales and Humorous Stories:
THE ADVENTURES OF THE WISHING CHAIR (Newnes)
THE WISHING CHAIR AGAIN (Newnes)
NAUGHTY AMELIA JANE (Newnes)
AMELIA JANE AGAIN (Newnes)
MISTER MEDDLE'S MISCHIEF (Newnes)
MISTER MEDDLE'S MUDDLES (Newnes)
THE ADVENTURES OF MR. PINKWHISTLE (Newnes)
MR. PINKWHISTLE INTERFERES (Newnes)
MR. PINKWHISTLE'S PARTY (Newnes)
You will find a story from this book on page 20.
You will find another complete Mr. Pinkwhistle story on page 125, 'Please Help Me, Mr. Pinkwhistle.' This originally appeared in ENID BLYTON'S MAGAZINE ANNUAL NO. 2 (Evans), now out of print.
HALLO, MR. TWIDDLE (Newnes)
You will find a story from this book on page 162
DON'T BE SILLY, MR. TWIDDLE (Newnes)
THE THREE GOLLIWOGS (Newnes)
THE BOOK OF FAIRIES (Newnes)
THE BOOK OF BROWNIES (Newnes)
THE ADVENTURES OF BINKLE AND FLIP (Newnes)
HEYHO, TUPPENY AND JINKS (Staples)
THE QUEER ADVENTURE (Staples)

CIRCUS BOOKS

MR. GALLIANO'S CIRCUS (Newnes)
HURRAH FOR THE CIRCUS (Newnes)
CIRCUS DAYS AGAIN (Newnes)
COME TO THE CIRCUS (Newnes)
LET'S GO TO THE CIRCUS (Odhams)
THE CIRCUS OF ADVENTURE (Macmillan)

AUTOBIOGRAPHY

THE STORY OF MY LIFE (Pitkin): Temporarily out of print

Teas